Core Connections Geometry
Second Edition*, Version 5.0, Volume 2

Managing Editors / Authors

Leslie Dietiker, Ph.D., Director of Curriculum (First Edition)
Boston University
Boston, MA

Michael Kassarjian (2nd Edition)
CPM Educational Program
Kensington, CA

Contributing Authors

Elizabeth Coyner
Christian Brothers High School
Sacramento, CA

Scott Coyner
Christian Brothers High School
Sacramento, CA

Lew Douglas
The College Preparatory School
Oakland, CA

David Gulick
Phillips Exeter Academy
Exeter, NH

Judy Kysh
San Francisco State University
San Francisco, CA

Lara Lomac
Phillip and Sala Burton Academic
High School, San Francisco, CA

Sarah Maile
CPM Educational Program
Sacramento, CA

Damian Molinari
Phillip and Sala Burton Academic
High School, San Francisco, CA

Jason Murphy-Thomas
George Washington High School
San Francisco, CA

Chris Mikles
Post Falls Middle School
Post Falls, ID

Leslie Nielsen
Isaaquah High School
Issaquah, WA

Misty Nikula
Whatcom Day Academy
Bellingham, WA

Karen O'Connell
San Lorenzo High School
San Lorenzo, CA

Bob Petersen
Rosemont High School
Sacramento, CA

Ward Quincey
Gideon Hausner Jewish Day School
Palo Alto, CA

Tom Sallee
University of California, Davis
Davis, CA

Barbara Shreve
San Lorenzo High School
San Lorenzo, CA

Michael Titelbaum
University of California
Berkeley, CA

Technical Manager

Sarah Maile
Sacramento, CA

Program Directors

Leslie Dietiker, Ph.D.
Boston University
Boston, MA

Lori Hamada
CPM Educational Program
Fresno, CA

Brian Hoey
CPM Educational Program
Sacramento, CA

Judy Kysh, Ph.D.
Departments of Education and Mathematics
San Francisco State University, CA

Tom Sallee, Ph.D.
Department of Mathematics
University of California, Davis

*Based on *Geometry Connections*

e-book Manager
Carol Cho
Director of Technology
Martinez, CA

e-book Programmers
Rakesh Khanna
Daniel Kleinsinger
Kevin Stein

e-book Assistants
Stephanie Achondo
Debbie Dodd
Shirley Paulsen
Wendy Papciak
Anna Poehlmann

Assessment Manager
Karen Wootton
Director of Assessment
Odenton, MD

Assessment Contributors
John Cooper
Leslie Dietiker, Ph.D.
Damian Molinari

Laura Lomac
Barbara Shreve

Assessment Website
Elizabeth Fong
Michael Huang
Daniel Kleinsinger

Illustration
Kevin Coffey
San Francisco, CA

Homework Help Manager
Bob Petersen
CPM Educational Program

Homework Help Website
Carol Cho
Director of Technology

Parent Guide with Extra Practice
Karen Wootton
CPM Educational Program
Odenton, MD

Elizabeth Coyner
Christian Brothers High School
Sacramento, CA

Bob Petersen
CPM Educational Program
Sacramento, CA

Technical Manager
Rebecca Harlow

Technical Assistants
Stephanie Achondo
Carrie Cai
Elizabeth Fong
Thomas Leong
Marcos Rojas

Erica Andrews
Daniel Cohen
Rebecca Harlow
Aubrie Maize
Susan Ryan

Elizabeth Burke
Carmen de la Cruz
Michael Leong
Anna Poehlmann

2 3 4 5 6   18 17 16 15 14 13   Version 5.0
Printed in the United States of America   ISBN: 978-1-60328-107-2

A Note to Students:

Welcome to a new year of math! In this course, you will learn to use new models and methods to think about problems as well as solve them. You will be developing powerful mathematical tools and learning new ways of thinking about and investigating situations. You will be making connections, discovering relationships, figuring out what strategies can be used to solve problems, and explaining your thinking. Learning to think in these ways and communicate about your thinking is useful in mathematical contexts, other subjects in school, and situations outside the classroom. The mathematics you have learned in the past will be valuable for learning in this course. That work, and what you learn in this course, will prepare you for future courses.

In meeting the challenges of this course, you will not be learning alone. You will cooperate with other students as a member of a study team. Being a part of a team means speaking up and interacting with other people. You will explain your ideas, listen to what others have to say, and ask questions if there is something you do not understand. In this course, a single problem can often be solved several ways. You will see problems in different ways than your teammates do. Each of you has something to contribute while you work on the lessons in this course.

Together, your team will complete problems and activities that will help you discover mathematical ideas and develop solution methods. Your teacher will support you as you work, but will not take away your opportunity to think and investigate for yourself. Each topic will be revisited many times and will connect to other topics. If something is not clear to you the first time you work on it, you will have more chances to build your understanding as the course continues.

Learning math this way has an advantage: as long as you actively participate, make sure everyone in your study team is involved, and ask good questions, you will find yourself understanding mathematics at a deeper level than ever before. By the end of this course, you will have a powerful set of mathematical tools to use to solve new problems. With your teammates you will meet mathematical challenges you would not have known how to approach before.

In addition to the support provided by your teacher and your study team, CPM has also created online resources to help you, including help with homework, and a parent guide with extra practice. You will find these resources and more at www.cpm.org.

We wish you well and are confident that you will enjoy this next year of learning!

Sincerely,

The CPM Team

Core Connections Geometry
Student Edition

Volume 1

Chapter 3 Justification and Similarity

Chapter 4 Trigonometry and Probability   210

The chapter number "144" appears to the right of the Chapter 3 title.

Volume 2

CHAPTER 7   Proof and Quadrilaterals

This chapter opens with a set of explorations designed to introduce you to new geometric topics that you will explore further in Chapters 8 through 12. You will learn about the special properties of a circle, explore three-dimensional shapes, and use a hinged mirror to learn more about a rhombus.

Section 7.2 then builds on your work from Chapters 3 through 6. Using congruent triangles, you will explore the relationships of the sides and diagonals of a parallelogram, kite, trapezoid, rectangle, and rhombus. As you explore new geometric properties, you will formalize your understanding of proof.

Guiding Question

Mathematically proficient students will construct viable arguments and critique the reasoning of others.

As you work through this chapter, ask yourself:

How can I use the given information to construct arguments, how can I justify my conclusions and how can I respond to the arguments of others.

This chapter ends with an exploration of coordinate geometry.

In this chapter, you will learn:

> The relationships of the sides, angles, and diagonals of special quadrilaterals, such as parallelograms, rectangles, kites, and rhombi (plural of rhombus).

> How to write a convincing proof in a variety of formats, such as a flowchart or two-column proof.

> How to find the midpoint of a line segment.

> How to use algebraic tools to explore quadrilaterals on coordinate axes.

Chapter Outline

Section 7.1 This section contains four large investigations introducing you to geometry topics that will be explored further in Chapters 8 through 12.

Section 7.2 While investigating what congruent triangles can inform you about the sides, angles, and diagonals of a quadrilateral, you will develop an understanding of proof.

Section 7.3 This section begins a focus on coordinate geometry, that is, the study of geometry on coordinate axes. During this section, you will use familiar algebraic tools (such as slope) to make and justify conclusions about shapes.

7.1.1 Does it roll smoothly?

Properties of a Circle

In Chapters 1 through 6, you studied many different types of two-dimensional shapes, explored how they could be related, and developed tools to measure their lengths and areas. In Chapters 7 through 12, you will examine ways to extend these ideas to new shapes (such as polygons and circles) and will thoroughly investigate what you can learn about three-dimensional shapes.

Section 7.1 contains four key investigations that will touch upon the big ideas of the following chapters. As you explore these lessons, take note of what mathematical tools from Chapters 1 through 6 you are using and think about what new directions this course will take. Generate "What if…" questions that can be answered later once new tools are developed.

Since much of the focus of Chapters 7 through 12 is on the study of circles, this lesson will first explore the properties of a circle. What makes a circle special? Today you are going to answer that question and, at the same time, explore other shapes with surprisingly similar qualities.

7-1.   THE INVENTION OF THE WHEEL

One of the most important human inventions was the wheel. Many archeologists estimate that the wheel was probably first invented about 10,000 years ago in Asia. It was an important tool that enabled humans to transport very heavy objects long distances. Most people agree that impressive structures, such as the Egyptian pyramids, could not have been built without the help of wheels.

a.   One of the earliest types of "wheels" used were actually logs. Ancient civilizations laid multiple logs on the ground, parallel to each other, under a heavy item that needed to be moved. As long as the logs had the same diameter and the road was even, the heavy object had a smooth ride. What is special about a circle that allows it to be used in this way? In other words, why do circles enable this heavy object to roll smoothly?

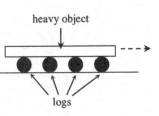

Problem continues on next page →

7-1.   *Problem continued from previous page.*

   b.   What happens to a point on a wheel as it turns? For example, as the wheel at right rolls along the line, what is the path of point *P*? Imagine a piece of gum stuck to a tire as it rolls. On your paper, draw the motion of point *P*. If you need help, find a coin or other round object and test this situation.

   c.   Now turn your attention to the center of the wheel (labeled *C* in the diagram above). As the wheel rolls along the line, what is the path of point *C*? Describe its motion. Why does that happen?

7-2.   DO CIRCLES MAKE THE BEST WHEELS?

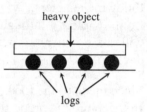
heavy object

logs

   As you read in problem 7-1, ancient civilizations used circular logs to roll heavy objects. However, is a circle the only shape they could have chosen? Are there any other shapes that could rotate between a flat road and a heavy object in a similar fashion?

   Examine the shapes below. Would logs of any of these shapes be able to roll heavy objects in a similar fashion? Be prepared to defend your conclusion!

   a.   b.   c.   d.

7-3.   Stan says that he has a tricycle with square wheels and
        claims that it can ride as smoothly as a tricycle with
        circular wheels! Rosita does not believe him. Analyze
        this possibility with your team as you answer the
        questions below.

   a.   Is Stan's claim possible? Describe what it would be like to ride a tricycle
        with square tires. What type of motion would the rider experience? Why
        does this happen?

   b.   When Rosita challenged him, Stan confessed that he needed a special road
        so that the square wheels would be able to rotate smoothly and would keep
        Stan at a constant height. What would his road need to look like? Draw
        an example on your paper.

   c.   How would Stanley need to change his road to be able to ride a tricycle
        with rectangular (but non-square) wheels? Draw an example on your
        paper.

   d.   As the picture at right[1] shows,
        square wheels are possible if
        the road is specially curved to
        accommodate the change in
        the length of the radius of the
        wheel as it rotates. An
        example is shown below.

        On a level   *On a curved*
        surface   *surface*

        Using mathematical terms, explain why the square wheel needed a
        modified road to ride smoothly, while the circular wheel did not. What is
        different between the two shapes?

---

[1] The picture above shows Stan Wagon riding his special square-wheeled tricycle. This tricycle is on display at
Macalester College in St. Paul, Minnesota. *Reprinted with permission.*

7-4.   REULEAUX CURVES

Reuleaux (pronounced "roo LOW") curves are special
because they have a constant diameter. That means that as a
Reuleaux curve rotates, its height remains constant. Although
the diagram at right is an example of a Reuleaux curve based
on an equilateral triangle, these special curves can be based
on any regular polygon with an odd number of sides.

a.   What happens to the center (point C)
      as the Reuleaux wheel at right rolls?

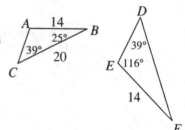

b.   Since logs with a Reuleaux curve shape can also smoothly roll heavy
      objects, why are these shapes not used for bicycle wheels? In other words,
      what is the difference between a circle and a Reuleaux curve?

7-5.   LEARNING LOG

A big focus of Chapters 7 through 12 is on circles. What
did you learn about circles today? Did you learn anything
about other shapes that was new or that surprised you?
Write a Learning Log entry explaining what you learned about the shapes of
wheels. Title this entry "Shapes of Wheels" and label it with today's date.

7-6.   Examine $\triangle ABC$ and $\triangle DEF$ at right.

a.   Assume the triangles at right are not drawn
      to scale. Complete a flowchart to justify
      the relationship between the two triangles.

b.   Find AC and DF.

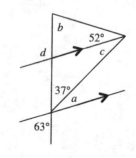

7-7.   Use the relationships in the diagram at right to find the
        values of each variable. Name which geometric
        relationships you used.

7-8.   A rectangle has one side of length 11 mm and a diagonal of 61 mm. Draw a diagram of this rectangle and find its width and area.

7-9.   Troy is thinking of a shape. He says that it has four sides and that no sides have equal length. He also says that no sides are parallel. What is the best name for his shape?

7-10.   Without using your calculator, find the exact values of x and y in each diagram below.

a.

b.

c.

7-11.   Solve each system of equations below, if possible. If it is not possible, explain what the lack of an algebraic solution tells you about the graphs of the equations. Write each solution in the form (x, y). Show all work.

a. $y = -2x - 1$
     $y = \frac{1}{2}x - 16$

b. $y = x^2 + 1$
     $y = -x^2$

7.1.2 What can I build with a circle?

Building a Tetrahedron

In later chapters, you will learn more about polygons, circles, and three-dimensional shapes. Later investigations will require that you remember key concepts you have already learned about triangles, parallel lines, and other angle relationships. Today you will have the opportunity to review some of the geometry you have learned while also beginning to think about what you will be studying in the future.

As you work with your team, consider the following focus questions:

Is there more than one way?

How can you be sure that is true?

What else can we try?

7-12.   IS THERE MORE TO THIS CIRCLE?

Circles can be folded to create many different shapes. Today, you will work with a circle and use properties of other shapes to develop a three-dimensional shape. Be sure to have reasons for each conclusion you make as you work. Each person in your team should start by obtaining a copy of a circle from your teacher and cutting it out.

a.   Fold the circle in half to create a crease that lies on a line of symmetry of the circle. Unfold the circle and then fold it in half again to create a new crease that is perpendicular to the first crease. Unfold your paper back to the full circle. How could you convince someone else that your creases are perpendicular? What is another name for the line segment represented by each crease?

b.   On the circle, label the endpoints of one diameter A and B. Fold the circle so that point A touches the center of the circle and create a new crease. Then label the endpoints of this crease C and D. What appears to be the relationship between $\overline{AB}$ and $\overline{CD}$? Discuss and justify with your team. Be ready to share your reasons with the class.

c.   Now fold the circle twice to form creases $\overline{BC}$ and $\overline{BD}$ and use scissors to cut out $\triangle BCD$. What type of triangle is $\triangle BCD$? How can you be sure? Be ready to convince the class.

7-13.   ADDING DEPTH

Your equilateral triangle should now be flat (also called two-dimensional).
Two-dimensional shapes have length and width, but not depth (or "thickness").

a.   If you cut the labels off when creating your equilateral triangle, label the
vertices of $\triangle BCD$ again. Then, with the unmarked side of the triangle
facedown, fold and crease the triangle so that B touches the midpoint of
$\overline{CD}$. Keep it in the folded position.

What does the resulting shape appear to be? What smaller shapes do you
see inside the larger shape? Justify that your ideas are correct. For
example, if you think that lines are parallel, you must provide evidence.

b.   Open your shape again so that you have the large equilateral triangle in
front of you. How does the length of a side of the large triangle compare
to the length of the side of the small triangle formed by the crease? How
many of the small triangles would fit inside the large triangle? In what
ways are the small and large triangles related?

c.   Repeat the fold in part (a) so that C touches the midpoint of $\overline{BD}$. Unfold
the triangle and fold again so that D touches the midpoint of $\overline{BC}$. Create a
three-dimensional shape by bringing points B, C, and D together. A **three-
dimensional** shape has length, width, and depth. Use tape to hold your
shape together.

d.   Three-dimensional shapes formed with polygons have **faces** and **edges**, as
well as **vertices** (plural of vertex). Faces are the flat surfaces of the shape,
while edges are the line segments formed when two faces meet. Vertices
are the points where edges intersect. Discuss with your team how to use
these words to describe your new shape. Then write a complete
description. If you think you know the name of this shape, include it in
your description.

7-14.   Your team should now have 4 three-dimensional shapes (called tetrahedra). If you are working in a smaller team, you should quickly fold more shapes so that you have a total of four.

a.   Put four tetrahedra together to make an enlarged tetrahedron like the one pictured at right. Is the larger tetrahedron similar to the small tetrahedron? How can you tell?

b.   To determine the edges and faces of the new shape, pretend that it is solid. How many edges does a tetrahedron have? Are all of the edges the same length? How does the length of an edge of the team shape compare with the length of an edge of one of the small shapes?

c.   How many faces of the small tetrahedral would it take to cover the face of the large tetrahedron? Remember to count gaps as part of a face. Does the area of the tetrahedron change in the same way as the length?

Enlarged tetrahedron   Original

METHODS AND MEANINGS

Parts of a Circle

A **circle** is the set of all points on a flat surface that are the same distance from a fixed central point, C, referred to as its **center**. This text will use the notation $\odot C$ to name a circle with center at point C.

The **radius** is a line segment from the center to a point on the circle. Its length is usually denoted r. However, a line segment drawn through the center of the circle with both endpoints on the circle is called a **diameter** and its length is usually denoted d.

Notice that a diameter of a circle is always twice as long as the radius.

7-15.   What is the relationship between $\triangle ABC$ and $\triangle GHJ$ at right? Create a flowchart to justify your conclusion.

7-16.   The area of the trapezoid at right is 56 cm². What is h? Show all work.

7-17.   Line L is perpendicular to the line $6x - y = 7$ and passes through the point $(0, 6)$. Line M is parallel to the line $y = \frac{2}{3}x - 4$ and passes through the point $(-3, -1)$. Where do these lines intersect? Explain how you found your solution.

7-18.   Examine the geometric relationships in each of the diagrams below. For each one, write and solve an equation to find the value of the variable. Name any geometric property or conjecture that you used.

a.

b.

c. $\triangle ABC$ is equilateral.

d.   Point C is the center of the circle.
      $AB = 11x - 1$ and $CD = 3x + 12$

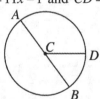

7-19.   In the Shape Factory, you created many shapes by rotating triangles about the midpoint of its sides. (Remember that the **midpoint** is the point exactly halfway between the endpoints of the line segment.) However, what if you rotate a trapezoid instead?

Carefully draw the trapezoid above on graph paper, along with the given midpoints. Then rotate the trapezoid 180° about one of the midpoints and examine the resulting shape formed by both trapezoids (the original and its image). Continue this process with each of the other midpoints, until you discover all the shapes that can be formed by a trapezoid and its image when rotated 180° about the midpoint of one of its sides.

7-20.   On graph paper, plot the points $A(-5, 7)$ and $B(3, 1)$.

a.   Find AB (the length of $\overline{AB}$).

b.   Locate the midpoint of $\overline{AB}$ and label it C. What are the coordinates of C?

c.   Find AC. Can you do this without using the Pythagorean Theorem?

7.1.3 What is the shortest distance?

Shortest Distance Problems

Questions such as, "What length will result in the largest area?" or "When was the car traveling the slowest?" concern *optimization*. To optimize a quantity is to find the "best" possibility. Calculus is often used to solve optimization problems, but geometric tools can sometimes offer surprisingly simple and elegant solutions.

7-21.   INTERIOR DESIGN

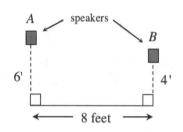

Laura needs your help. She needs to order expensive wire to connect her sound system to her built-in speakers and would like your help to save her money.

She plans to place her sound system somewhere on a cabinet that is 8 feet wide. Speaker A is located 6 feet above one end of the cabinet, while speaker B is located 4 feet above the other end. She will need wire to connect the sound system to speaker A, and additional wire to connect it to speaker B.

Where should she place her sound system that she needs the least amount of wire?

Your Task: Before you discuss this with your team, make your own guess. What does your intuition tell you? Then, using the Lesson 7.1.3 Resource Page, work with your team to determine where on the cabinet the sound system should be placed. How can you be sure that you found the best answer? In other words, how do you know that the amount of wire you found is the least amount possible?

Discussion Points

What is this problem about? What are you supposed to find?

What is a reasonable estimate of the total length of speaker wire?

What mathematical tools could be helpful to solve this problem?

Further Guidance

7-22.   To help solve problem 7-21, first collect some data.

a.   Calculate the total length of wire needed if the sound system is placed 2 feet from the left edge of the cabinet (the edge below Speaker A), as shown in the diagram at right.

b.   Now calculate the total length of wire needed if the sound system is placed 3 feet from the same edge. Does this placement require more or less wire than that from part (a)?

c.   Continue testing placements for the sound system and create a table with your results. Where should the sound system be placed to minimize the amount of wire?

——————   *Further Guidance section ends here.*   ——————

7-23.   This problem reminds Bradley of problem 3-105, *You Are Getting Sleepy…*, in which you and a partner created two triangles by standing and gazing into a mirror. He remembered that the only way two people could see each other's eyes in the mirror was when the triangles were similar. Examine your solution to problem 7-21. Are the two triangles created by the speaker wires similar? Justify your conclusion.

7-24.   Bradley enjoyed solving problem 7-21 so much that he decided to create other "shortest distance" problems. For each situation below, first predict where the shortest path would be using visualization and intuition. Then find a way to determine whether the path you chose is, in fact, the shortest.

a.   In this first puzzle, Bradley decided to test what would happen on the side of a cylinder, such as a soup can. On a can provided by your teacher, find points A and B labeled on the outside of the can. With your team, determine the shortest path from point A to point B along the surface of the can. (In other words, no part of your path can go inside the can.) Describe how you found your solution.

b.   What if the shape is a cube? Using a cube provided by your teacher, predict which path would be the shortest path from opposite corners of the cube (labeled points C and D in the diagram at right). Then test your prediction. Describe how you found the shortest path.

7-25.   MAKING CONNECTIONS

As Bradley looked over his answer from
problem 7-21, he couldn't help but wonder if
there is a way to change this problem into a
straight-line problem like those in problem 7-24.

a.   On the Lesson 7.1.3 Resource Page, reflect
      one of the speakers so that when the two
      speakers are connected with a straight line,
      the line passes through the horizontal cabinet.

b.   When the speakers from part (a) are
      connected with a straight line, two triangles
      are formed. How are the two triangles
      related? Justify your conclusion.

c.   Use the fact that the triangles are similar to find
      where the sound system should be placed. Did
      your answer match that from problem 7-21?

7-26.   TAKE THE SHOT

While playing a game of pool,
Montana Mike needed to hit the
last remaining ball into pocket A,
as shown in the diagram below.
However, to show off, he decided
to make the ball first hit at least
one of the rails of the table.

Your Task: On the Lesson 7.1.3
Resource Page provided by your
teacher, determine where Mike
could bounce the ball off a rail so
that it will land in pocket A.
Work with your team to find as
many possible locations as you
can. Can you find a way he
could hit the ball so that it would
rebound twice before entering
pocket A?

Be ready to share your solutions with the class.

7-27.   LEARNING LOG

Look over your work from this lesson. What mathematical
ideas did you use? What connections, if any, did you find?
Can any other problems you have seen so far be solved
using a straight line? Describe the mathematical ideas you developed during
this lesson in your Learning Log. Title this entry "Shortest Distance" and label
it with today's date.

7-28. $\triangle XYZ$ is reflected across $\overline{XZ}$, as shown at right.

a.   How can you justify that the points Y, Z, and Y'
all lie on a straight line?

b.   What is the relationship between $\triangle XYZ$ and $\triangle X'Y'Z'$? Why?

c.   Read the Math Notes box for this lesson. Then make all the statements
you can about the corresponding parts of these two triangles.

7-29.   Remember that a midpoint of a line segment is the point that divides the segment into two segments of equal length. On graph paper, plot the points $P(0, 3)$ and $Q(0, 11)$. Where is the midpoint M if $PM = MQ$? Explain how you found your answer.

7-30.   Examine the diagram at right. Find two equivalent expressions that represent the area of the *inner* square.

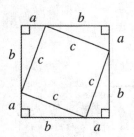

7-31.   For each pair of triangles below, decide whether the triangles are similar and/or congruent. Justify each conclusion.

a.

b.

c.

d.

7-32.   On graph paper, plot and connect the points $A(1, 1)$, $B(2, 3)$, $C(5, 3)$, and $D(4, 1)$ to form quadrilateral $ABCD$.

a.   What is the best name for quadrilateral $ABCD$? Justify your answer.

b.   Find and compare $m\angle DAB$ and $m\angle BCD$. What is their relationship?

c.   Find the equations of diagonals $\overline{AC}$ and $\overline{BD}$. Are the diagonals perpendicular?

d.   Find the point where diagonals $\overline{AC}$ and $\overline{BD}$ intersect.

7-33.   Solve each system of equations below, if possible. If it is not possible, explain what having "no solution" tells you about the graphs of the equations. Write each solution in the form (x, y). Show all work.

a. $y = -\frac{1}{3}x + 7$

$y = -\frac{1}{3}x - 2$

b. $y = 2x + 3$

$y = x^2 - 2x + 3$

7-34.   How long is the longest line segment that will fit inside a square of area 50 square units? Show all work.

7-35.   Graph and connect the points $G(-2, 2)$, $H(3, 2)$, $I(6, 6)$, and $J(1, 6)$ to form $GHIJ$.

a.   What specific type of shape is quadrilateral $GHIJ$? Justify your conclusion.

b.   Find the equations of the diagonals $\overline{GI}$ and $\overline{HJ}$.

c.   Compare the slopes of the diagonals. How do the diagonals of a rhombus appear to be related?

d.   Find J' if quadrilateral $GHIJ$ is rotated 90° clockwise (↻) about the origin.

e.   Find the area of quadrilateral $GHIJ$.

7-36.   The four triangles at right are placed in a bag. If you reach into the bag without looking and pull out one triangle at random, what is the probability that:

a.   The triangle is scalene?

b.   The triangle is isosceles?

c.   at least one side of the triangle is 6 cm?

7-37. Examine the relationships in the diagrams below. For each one, write an equation and solve for the given variable(s). Show all work.

a.

b.

c.

d.

7-38. Copy the table below on your paper and complete it for the equation $y = x^2 + 2x - 3$. Then graph and connect the points on graph paper. Name the roots (x-intercepts).

x	−4	−3	−2	−1	0	1	2
y							

7-39. Find the perimeter of the shape at right. Show all work.

7.1.4 How can I create it?

Using Symmetry to Study Polygons

In Chapter 1, you used a hinged mirror to study the special angles associated with regular polygons. In particular, you investigated what happens as the angle formed by the sides of the mirror is changed. Today, you will use a hinged mirror to determine if there is more than one way to build each regular polygon using the principles of symmetry. And what about other types of polygons? What can a hinged mirror help you understand about them?

As your work with your study team, keep these focus questions in mind:

> Is there another way?

> What types of symmetry can I find?

> What does symmetry tell me about the polygon?

7-40. THE HINGED MIRROR TEAM CHALLENGE

Obtain a hinged mirror, a piece of unlined colored paper, and a protractor from your teacher.

With your team, spend five minutes reviewing how to use the mirror to create regular polygons. Remember that a **regular polygon** has equal sides and angles. Once everyone remembers how the hinged mirror works, select a team member to read the directions of the task below.

Your Task: Below are four challenges for your team. Each requires you to find a creative way to position the mirror in relation to the colored paper. You can tackle the challenges in any order, but you must work together as a team on each of them. Whenever you successfully create a shape, do not forget to measure the angle formed by the mirror, as well as draw a diagram on your paper of the core region in front of the mirror. If your team decides that a shape is impossible to create with the hinged mirror, explain why.

- Create a regular hexagon.
- Create an equilateral triangle at least *two* different ways.
- Create a rhombus that is *not* a square.
- Create a circle.

Core region

Core Connections Geometry

7-41.   ANALYSIS

How can symmetry help you to learn more about shapes? Discuss each question below with the class.

a.   One way to create a regular hexagon with a hinged mirror is with six triangles, as shown in the diagram at right. Note: The gray lines represent reflections of the bottom edges of the mirrors and the edge of the paper, while the core region is shaded.

What is special about each of the triangles in the diagram? What is the relationship between the triangles? Support your conclusions. Would it be possible to create a regular hexagon with 12 triangles? Explain.

b.   If you have not done so already, create an equilateral triangle so that the core region in front of the mirror is a right triangle. Draw a diagram of the result that shows the different reflected triangles like the one above. What special type of right triangle is the core region? Can all regular polygons be created with a right triangle in a similar fashion?

c.   In problem 7-40, your team formed a rhombus that is not a square. On your paper, draw a diagram like the one above that shows how you did it. How can you be sure your resulting shape is a rhombus? Using what you know about the angle of the mirror, explain what must be true about the diagonals of a rhombus.

7-42.   Use what you learned today to answer the questions below.

a.   Examine the regular octagon at right. What is the measure of angle θ? Explain how you know.

b.   Quadrilateral *ABCD* at right is a rhombus. If *BD* = 10 units and *AC* = 18 units, then what is the perimeter of *ABCD*? Show all work.

METHODS AND MEANINGS

MATH NOTES

Regular Polygons

A polygon is **regular** if all its sides are congruent and its angles have equal measure. An equilateral triangle and a square are each regular polygons since they are both *equilateral* and *equiangular*. See the diagrams of common regular polygons below.

| Equilateral Triangle | Square | Regular Hexagon | Regular Octagon | Regular Decagon |

Review & Preview

7-43.   Felipe set his hinged mirror so that its angle was 36° and the core region was isosceles, as shown at right.

a.   How many sides did his resulting polygon have? Show how you know.

b.   What is another name for this polygon?

7-44.   In problem 7-41 you learned that the diagonals of a rhombus are perpendicular bisectors. If *ABCD* is a rhombus with side length 15 mm and if *BD* = 24 mm, then find the length of the other diagonal, $\overline{AC}$. Draw a diagram and show all work.

7-45.   Joanne claims that $(2, 4)$ is the midpoint of the segment connecting the points $(-3, 5)$ and $(7, 3)$. Is she correct? Explain how you know.

7-46. For each pair of triangles below, determine whether or not the triangles are similar. If they are similar, show your reasoning in a flowchart. If they are not similar, explain how you know.

a.

b.

c.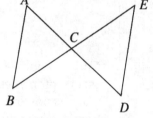

7-47. If $\triangle ABC \cong \triangle DEC$, which of the statements below must be true? Justify your conclusion. Note: More than one statement may be true.

a. $\overline{AC} \cong \overline{DC}$ b. $m\angle B = m\angle D$

c. $\overline{AB} \parallel \overline{DE}$ d. $AD = BE$

e. None of these are true.

7-48. On graph paper, graph the points $A(2, 9)$, $B(4, 3)$, and $C(9, 6)$. Which point (A or C) is closer to point B? Justify your conclusion.

7.2.1 What can congruent triangles tell me?

Special Quadrilaterals and Proof

In earlier chapters you studied the relationships between the sides and angles of a triangle, and solved problems involving congruent and similar triangles. Now you are going to expand your study of shapes to quadrilaterals. What can triangles tell you about parallelograms and other special quadrilaterals?

By the end of this lesson, you should be able to answer these questions:

> What are the relationships between the sides, angles, and diagonals
> of a parallelogram?
>
> How are congruent triangles useful?

7-49.   Carla is thinking about parallelograms and wondering if there are as many special properties for parallelograms as there are for triangles. She remembers that it is possible to create a shape that looks like a parallelogram by rotating a triangle about the midpoint of one of its sides.

a.   Carefully trace the triangle at right onto tracing paper. Be sure to copy the angle markings as well. Then rotate the triangle about a midpoint of a side to make a shape that looks like a parallelogram.

b.   Is Carla's shape truly a parallelogram? Use the angles to convince your teammates that the opposites sides must be parallel. Then write a convincing argument.

c.   What else can the congruent triangles tell you about a parallelogram? Look for any relationships you can find between the angles and sides of a parallelogram.

d.   Does this work for all parallelograms? That is, does the diagonal of a parallelogram always split the shape into two congruent triangles? Draw the parallelogram at right on your paper. Knowing only that the opposite sides of a parallelogram are parallel, create a flowchart to show that the triangles are congruent.

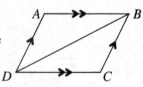

7-50.   CHANGING A FLOWCHART INTO A PROOF

The flowchart you created for part (d) of problem 7-49 shows how you can conclude that if a quadrilateral is a parallelogram, then its each of its diagonals splits the quadrilateral into two congruent triangles.

However, to be convincing, the facts that you listed in your flowchart need to have justifications. This shows the reader how you know the facts are true and helps to prove your conclusion.

Therefore, with the class or your team, decide how to add reasons to each statement (bubble) in your flowchart. You may need to add more bubbles to your flowchart to add justification and to make your proof more convincing.

7-51.   Kip is confused. He put his two triangles from problem 7-49 together as shown at right, but he did not get a parallelogram.

a.   What shape did he make? Justify your conclusion.

b.   What transformation(s) did Kip use to form his shape?

c.   What do the congruent triangles tell you about the angles of this shape?

7-52.   KITES

Kip shared his findings about his kite with his teammate,
Carla, who wants to learn more about the diagonals of a kite.
Carla quickly sketched the kite at right onto her paper with a
diagonal showing the two congruent triangles.

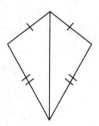

a.   **EXPLORE:** Trace this diagram onto tracing paper and
     carefully add the other diagonal. Then, with your team,
     consider how the diagonals may be related. Use tracing
     paper to help you explore the relationships between the
     diagonals. If you make an observation you think is true,
     move on to part (b) and write a conjecture.

b.   **CONJECTURE:** If you have not already done so, write a conjecture
     based on your observations in part (a).

c.   **PROVE:** When she drew the second diagonal, Carla noticed that four new
     triangles appeared. *"If any of these triangles are congruent, then they may
     be able to help us prove our conjecture from part (b),"* she said. Examine
     $\triangle ABC$ below. Are $\triangle ACD$ and $\triangle BCD$ congruent? Create a flowchart proof
     like the one from problem 7-50 to justify your conclusion.

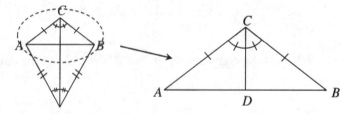

d.   Now extend your proof from part (c) to prove your conjecture from
     part (b).

7-53.   Reflect on all of the interesting facts about parallelograms
and kites you have proven during this lesson. Obtain a
Theorem Toolkit (Lesson 7.2.1A Resource Page) from your
teacher. On it, record each **theorem** (proven conjecture) that
you have proven about the sides, angles, and diagonals of a
parallelogram in this lesson. Do the same for a kite. Be sure
your diagrams contain appropriate markings to represent
equal parts.

Core Connections Geometry

METHODS AND MEANINGS

Reflexive Property of Equality

In this lesson, you used the fact that two triangles formed by the diagonal of a parallelogram share a side of the same length to help show that the triangles were congruent.

The **Reflexive Property of Equality** states that the measure of any side or angle is equal to itself. For example, in the parallelogram at right, $\overline{BD} \cong \overline{DB}$ because of the Reflexive Property.

7-54. Use the information given for each diagram below to solve for x. Show all work.

a. $\overrightarrow{BD}$ bisects $\angle ABC$. (Remember that this means it divides the angle into two equal parts.) If $m\angle ABD = 5x - 10°$ and $m\angle ABC = 65°$, solve for x.

b. Point M is a midpoint of $\overline{EF}$. If $EM = 4x - 2$ and $MF = 3x + 9$, solve for x.

c. $WXYZ$ at right is a parallelogram. If $m\angle W = 9x - 3°$ and $m\angle Z = 3x + 15°$, solve for x.

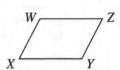

7-55. Jamal used a hinged mirror to create a regular polygon like you did in Lesson 7.1.4.

a. If his hinged mirror formed a 72° angle and the core region in front of the mirror was isosceles, how many sides did his polygon have?

b. Now Jamal has decided to create a regular polygon with 9 sides, called a nonagon. If his core region is again isosceles, what angle is formed by his mirror?

7-56.   Sandra wants to park her car so that she optimizes the distance she has to walk to the art museum and the library. That is, she wants to park so that her total distance directly to each building is the shortest. Find where she should park.

7-57.   Write an expression for the following sequences.

a. $40, 60, 80, ...$

b. $3, \frac{3}{2}, \frac{3}{4}, ...$

7-58.   Earl (from Chapter 6) still hates to wash the dishes and take out the garbage. He found his own weighted coin, one that would randomly land on heads 30% of the time. He will flip a coin once for each chore and will perform the chore if the coin lands on heads.

a.   What is the probability that Earl will get out of doing both chores?

b.   What is the probability that Earl will have to take out the garbage, but will not need to wash the dishes?

7-59.   Which pairs of triangles below are congruent and/or similar? For each part, explain how you know using an appropriate triangle congruence or similarity condition. Note: The diagrams are not necessarily drawn to scale.

a.

b.

c.

d.

7-60.   For part (b) of problem 7-59, explain how the triangles are congruent using a sequence of rigid transformations.

7.2.2 What is special about a rhombus?

Properties of Rhombi

In Lesson 7.2.1, you learned that congruent triangles can be a useful tool to discover new information about parallelograms and kites. But what about other quadrilaterals? Today you will use congruent triangles to investigate and prove special properties of rhombi (the plural of rhombus). At the same time, you will continue to develop your ability to make conjectures and prove them convincingly.

7-61.   Audrey has a favorite quadrilateral – the rhombus. Even though a rhombus is defined as having four congruent sides, she suspects that the sides of a rhombus have other special properties.

a.   **EXPLORE:** Draw a rhombus like the one at right on your paper. Mark the side lengths equal.

b.   **CONJECTURE:** What else might be special about the sides of a rhombus? Write a conjecture.

c.   **PROVE:** Audrey knows congruent triangles can help prove other properties about quadrilaterals. She starts by adding a diagonal $\overline{PR}$ to her diagram so that two triangles are formed. Add this diagonal to your diagram and prove that the created triangles are congruent. Then use a flowchart with reasons to show your logic. Be prepared to share your flowchart with the class.

d.   How can the triangles from part (c) help you prove your conjecture from part (b) above? Discuss with the class how to extend your flowchart to convince others. Be sure to justify any new statements with reasons.

7-62.   Now that you know the opposite sides of a rhombus are parallel, what else can you prove about a rhombus? Consider this as you answer the questions below.

a.   **EXPLORE:** Remember that in Lesson 7.1.4, you explored the shapes that could be formed with a hinged mirror. During this activity, you used symmetry to form a rhombus. Think about what you know about the reflected triangles in the diagram. What do you think is true about the diagonals $\overline{SQ}$ and $\overline{PR}$? What is special about $\overline{ST}$ and $\overline{QT}$? What about $\overline{PT}$ and $\overline{RT}$?

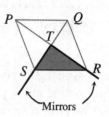

b.   **CONJECTURE:** Use your observations from part (a) to write a conjecture on the relationship of the diagonals of a rhombus.

c.   **PROVE:** Write a flowchart proof that proves your conjecture from part (b). Remember that to be convincing, you need to justify each statement with a reason. To help guide your discussion, consider the questions below. Which triangles should you use? Find two triangles that involve the segments $\overline{ST}$, $\overline{QT}$, $\overline{PT}$, and $\overline{RT}$.

   • How can you prove these triangles are congruent? Create a flowchart proof with reasons to prove these triangles must be congruent.

   • How can you use the congruent triangles to prove your conjecture from part (b)? Extend your flowchart proof to include this reasoning and prove your conjecture.

7-63.   There are often many ways to prove a conjecture. You have rotated triangles to create parallelograms and used congruent parts of congruent triangles to justify that opposite sides are parallel. But is there another way?

Ansel wants to prove the conjecture "*If a quadrilateral is a parallelogram, then opposite angles are congruent.*" He started by drawing parallelogram *TUVW* at right. Copy and complete his flowchart. Make sure that each statement has a reason.

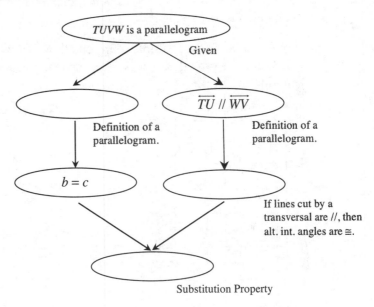

| TUVW is a parallelogram |
| Given |

| | $\overleftrightarrow{TU} \parallel \overleftrightarrow{WV}$ |
| Definition of a parallelogram. | Definition of a parallelogram. |

| $b = c$ | |
| | If lines cut by a transversal are //, then alt. int. angles are ≅. |

| |
| Substitution Property |

7-64.   Think about the new facts you have proven about rhombi during this lesson. On your Theorem Toolkit (Lesson 7.2.1A Resource Page), record each new theorem you have proven about the angles and diagonals of a rhombus. Include clearly labeled diagrams to illustrate your findings.

METHODS AND MEANINGS

MATH NOTES

Exponential Functions

An **exponential function** has the general form $y = a \cdot b^x$, where a is the **initial value** (the y-intercept) and b is the **multiplier** (the growth). Be careful: The independent variable x has to be in the exponent. For example, $y = x^2$ is *not* an exponential equation, even though it has an exponent.

For example, in the multiple representations below, the y-intercept is $(0, 4)$ and the growth factor is 3 because the y-value is increasing by multiplying by 3.

$$y = 4 \cdot 3^x$$

x	y
-3	$\frac{4}{3^3}$ or $\frac{4}{27}$
-2	$\frac{4}{3^2}$ or $\frac{4}{9}$
-1	$\frac{4}{3}$
0	4
1	12
2	36
3	108

To increase or decrease a quantity by a percentage, use the multiplier for that percentage. For example, the multiplier for an increase of 7% is $100\% + 7\% = 1.07$. The multiplier for a decrease of 7% is $100\% - 7\% = 0.93$.

Review & Preview

7-65.   Point M is the midpoint of $\overline{AB}$ and B is the midpoint of $\overline{AC}$. What are the values of x and y? Show all work and reasoning.

$\underset{A}{\bullet} \overset{4x-1}{} \underset{M}{\bullet} \overset{x+8}{} \underset{B}{\bullet} \overset{5y+2}{} \underset{C}{\bullet}$

426

7-66.   Read the Math Notes box in this lesson and then answer following questions. The cost of large flat-screen televisions is decreasing 20% per year.

   a.   What is the multiplier?

   b.   If a 50-inch flat-screen now costs $1200, what will it cost in three years?

   c.   At the same rate, what did it cost two years ago?

7-67.   A light directed from point E is pointed at a hinged mirror with right angle as shown at right.

   a.   If $\angle x$ measures 36°, find the measures of $\angle a, \angle r, \angle m, \angle y$, and $\angle z$.

   b.   Why must the arrows at points A and E be parallel?

7-68.   On graph paper, graph quadrilateral $MNPQ$ if $M(-3, 6), N(2, 8), P(1, 5)$, and $Q(-4, 3)$.

   a.   What shape is $MNPQ$? Show how you know.

   b.   Use the function $x \to x, y \to -y$ to reflect $MNPQ$ across the x-axis and create $M'N'P'Q'$. What are the coordinates of P'?

7-69.   Jester started to prove that the triangles at right are congruent. He was only told that point E is the midpoint of segments $\overline{AC}$ and $\overline{BD}$.

Copy and complete his flowchart below. Be sure that a reason is provided for every statement.

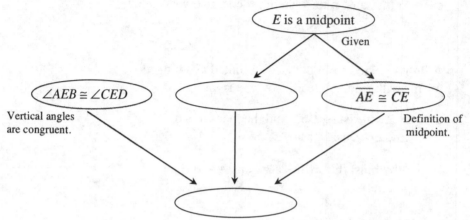

7-70.   For a school fair, Donny is going to design a spinner with red, white, and blue regions. Since he has a certain proportion of three types of prizes, he wants the P(red) = 40% and P(white) = 10%.

a.   If the spinner only has red, white, and blue regions, then what is P(blue)? Explain how you know.

b.   Find the central angles of this spinner if it has only three sections. Then draw a sketch of the spinner. Be sure to label the regions accurately.

c.   Is there a different spinner that has the same probabilities? If so, sketch another spinner that has the same probabilities. If not, explain why there is no other spinner with the same probabilities.

7-71.   On graph paper, graph and shade the solutions for the inequality below.

$$y < -\tfrac{2}{3}x + 5$$

7.2.3 What else can be proved?

More Proofs with Congruent Triangles

In Lessons 7.2.1 and 7.2.2, you used congruent triangles to learn more about parallelograms, kites, and rhombi. You now possess the tools to do the work of a geometer (someone who studies geometry): to discover and prove new properties about the sides and angles of shapes.

As you investigate these shapes, focus on proving your ideas. Remember to ask yourself and your teammates questions such as, *"Why does that work?"* and *"Is it always true?"* Decide whether your argument is convincing and work with your team to provide all of the necessary justification.

7-72.   Carla decided to turn her attention to rectangles. Knowing that a rectangle is defined as a quadrilateral with four right angles, she drew the diagram at right.

After some exploration, she conjectured that all rectangles are also parallelograms. Help her prove that her rectangle *ABCD* must be a parallelogram. That is, prove that the opposite sides must be parallel. Then add this theorem to your Theorem Toolkit (Lesson 7.2.1A Resource Page).

7-73.   For each diagram below, find the value of x, if possible. If the triangles are congruent, state which triangle congruence condition was used. If the triangles are not congruent or if there is not enough information, state, "Cannot be determined."

a.   *ABC* below is a triangle.

b.

c.

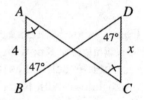

d. $\overline{AC}$ and $\overline{BD}$ are straight line segments.

7-74.   With the class or your team, create a flowchart to prove your answer to part (b) of problem 7-73. That is, prove that $\overline{AD} \cong \overline{CB}$. Be sure to include a diagram for your proof and reasons for every statement. Make sure your argument is convincing and has no "holes."

METHODS AND **M**EANINGS

Definitions of Quadrilaterals

When proving properties of shapes, it is necessary to know exactly how a shape is defined. Below are the definitions of several quadrilaterals that you developed in Lesson 1.3.2 and that you will need to refer to in this chapter and the chapters that follow.

Quadrilateral: A closed four-sided polygon.

Kite: A quadrilateral with two distinct pairs of consecutive congruent sides.

Trapezoid: A quadrilateral with at least one pair of parallel sides.

Parallelogram: A quadrilateral with two pairs of parallel sides.

Rhombus: A quadrilateral with four sides of equal length.

Rectangle: A quadrilateral with four right angles.

Square: A quadrilateral with four sides of equal length and four right angles.

7-75.   Identify if each pair of triangles below is congruent or not. Remember that the diagram may not be drawn to scale. Justify your conclusion.

a.

b.

c.

d.

7-76.   For either part (a), (c) or (d) of problem 7-75, create a flowchart to prove your conclusion. Remember to start with the given information and include a reason or justification for each "bubble" in your flowchart.

7-77.   In the diagram at right, ∠DCA is referred to as an **exterior angle** of △ABC because it lies outside the triangle and is formed by extending a side of the triangle.

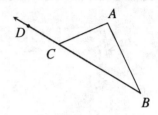

a.   If $m\angle CAB = 46°$ and $m\angle ABC = 37°$, what is $m\angle DCA$? Show all work.

b.   If $m\angle DCA = 135°$ and $m\angle ABC = 43°$, then what is $m\angle CAB$?

7-78.   Tromika wants to find the area of the isosceles triangle at right.

a.   She decided to start by drawing a height from vertex A to side $\overline{BC}$ as shown below. Will the two smaller triangles be congruent? In other words, is $\triangle ABC \cong \triangle ABD$? Why or why not?

b.   What is $m\angle DAB$? BD?

c.   Find AD. Show how you got your answer.

d.   Find the area of $\triangle ABC$.

7-79.   On graph paper, graph quadrilateral $ABCD$ if $A(0,0)$, $B(6,0)$, $C(8,6)$, and $D(2,6)$.

a.   What is the best name for $ABCD$? Justify your answer.

b.   Find the equation of the lines containing each diagonal. That is, find the equations of lines $\overleftrightarrow{AC}$ and $\overleftrightarrow{BD}$.

7-80.   It is often useful to estimate the value of a square root to determine if your answer is reasonable.

a.   What would be a reasonable estimate of $\sqrt{68}$? Explain your thinking. After you have made an estimate, check your estimation with a calculator.

b.   Repeat this process to estimate the values below.

    (1) $\sqrt{5}$ (2) $\sqrt{85}$ (3) $\sqrt{50}$ (4) $\sqrt{22}$

Core Connections Geometry

7-81.   For each diagram below, solve for x. Show all work.

a.

b.

c.

d.

7.2.4 What else can I prove?

More Properties of Quadrilaterals

Today you will work with your team to apply what you have learned to other shapes. Remember to ask yourself and your teammates questions such as, *"Why does that work?"* and *"Is it always true?"* Decide whether your argument is convincing and work with your team to provide all of the necessary justification. By the end of this lesson, you should have a well-crafted mathematical argument proving something new about a familiar quadrilateral.

7-82.   WHAT ELSE CAN CONGRUENT TRIANGLES TELL US?

Your Task: For each situation below, determine how congruent triangles can tell you more information about the shape. Then prove your conjecture using a flowchart. Be sure to provide a reason for each statement. For example, stating *"m∠A = m∠B"* is not enough. You must give a convincing reason, such as *"Because vertical angles are equal"* or *"Because it is given in the diagram."* Use your triangle congruence conditions to help prove that the triangles are congruent.

Later, your teacher will select one of these flowcharts for you to place on a poster. On your poster, include a diagram and all of your statements and reasons. Clearly state what you are proving and help the people who look at your poster understand your logic and reasoning.

a.   In Chapter 1, you used the symmetry of an isosceles triangle to show that the base angles must be congruent. How can you prove this result using congruent triangles?

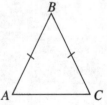

Assume that $\overline{AB} \cong \overline{CB}$ for the triangle at right. With your team, decide how to split $\triangle ABC$ into two triangles that you can show are congruent to show that $\angle BAC \cong \angle BCA$.

Problem continues on next page →

Core Connections Geometry

7-82.   *Problem continued from previous page.*

b.   What can congruent triangles tell us about the
     diagonals and angles of a rhombus? Examine
     the diagram of the rhombus at right. With
     your team, decide how to prove that the
     diagonals of a rhombus bisect the angles.
     That is, prove that $\angle ABD \cong \angle CBD$.

c.   What can congruent triangles tell us about the
     diagonals of a rectangle? Examine the
     rectangle at right. Using the fact that the
     opposite sides of a rectangle are parallel
     (which you proved in problem 7-72), prove
     that the diagonals of the rectangle are
     congruent. That is, prove that $AC = BD$.

METHODS AND **M**EANINGS

MATH NOTES

Diagonals of a Rhombus

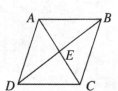

A **rhombus** is defined as a quadrilateral
with four sides of equal length. In addition, you
proved in problem 7-62 that the diagonals of a
rhombus are perpendicular bisectors of each
other.

For example, in the rhombus at right, E is a
midpoint of both $\overline{AC}$ and $\overline{DB}$. Therefore, $AE = CE$ and $DE = BE$. Also,
$m\angle AEB = m\angle BEC = m\angle CED = m\angle DEA = 90°$.

In addition, you proved in problem 7-82 that the diagonals bisect the
angles of the rhombus. For example, in the diagram above,
$m\angle DAE = m\angle BAE$.

7-83.   Use Tromika's method from problem 7-78 to find the area of an equilateral
         triangle with side length 12 units. Show all work.

7-84.   The guidelines set forth by the National
         Kitchen & Bath Association recommends that
         the perimeter of the triangle connecting the
         refrigerator (F), stove, and sink of a kitchen be
         26 feet or less. Lashayia is planning to
         renovate her kitchen and has chosen the
         design at right. Does her design conform to
         the National Kitchen and Bath Association's
         guidelines? Show how you got your answer.

7-85.   Examine the triangles below. For each, solve for x and name which tool you
         use. Show all work.

a.

b.

c.

7-86.   For each figure below, determine if the two smaller triangles in each figure are
         congruent. If so, create a flowchart to explain why. Then, solve for x. If the
         triangles are not congruent, explain why not.

a.

b.

7-87.   The diagonals of a rhombus are 6 units and 8 units long. What is the area of the
         rhombus? Draw a diagram and show all reasoning.

7-88.   Kendrick is frantic. He remembers
that several years ago he buried his
Amazing Electron Ring in his little
sister's sandbox, but he cannot
remember where. A few minutes
ago he heard that someone is
willing to pay $1000 for it. He has
his shovel and is ready to dig.

a.   The sandbox is rectangular, measuring 4 feet by
5 feet, as shown at right. If Kendrick only has
time to search in the 2 foot-square shaded
region, what is the probability that he will find
the ring?

b.   What is the probability that he will not find the ring?
Explain how you found your answer.

c.   Kendrick decides instead to dig in the square
region shaded at right. Does this improve his
chances for finding the ring? Why or why not?

7-89.   What is the 50th term in this sequence?

$$17, 14, 11, 8, \ldots$$

7.2.5   How else can I write it?

Two-Column Proofs

Today you will continue to work with constructing a convincing argument, otherwise known as writing a proof. In this lesson, you will use what you know about flowchart proofs to write a convincing argument using another format, called a two-column proof.

7-90.   The following pairs of triangles are not necessarily congruent even though they appear to be. Use the information provided in the diagram to show why. Justify your statements.

a.

b.

7-91.   Write a flowchart to prove that if point P on line l (not on $\overline{AB}$) is a point on the perpendicular bisector of $\overline{AB}$, then $\overline{PA} \cong \overline{PB}$. That is, point P is the same distance from points A and B *(called "equidistant" in mathematics)*. Assume the intersection of $\overline{AB}$ and line l is point M as shown in the diagram.

Core Connections Geometry

7-92.   Another way to organize a proof is called a **two-column proof**. Instead of using arrows to indicate the order of logical reasoning, this style of proof lists statements and reasons in a linear order, first to last, in columns.

The proof from problem 7-91 has been converted to a two-column proof below. Copy and complete the proof on your paper using your statements and reasons from problem 7-91.

   If: M is on $\overline{AB}$ and $\overline{PM}$ is the perpendicular bisector of $\overline{AB}$

   Prove: $\overline{PA} \cong \overline{PB}$

Statements	Reasons (This statement is true because...)
Point M is on $\overline{AB}$ and $\overline{PM}$ is the perpendicular bisector of $\overline{AB}$.	Given
$m\angle PMB = m\angle PMB = 90°$	Definition of perpendicular and angles with the same measure are congruent.
	Definition of a bisector.
$\overline{PM} \cong \overline{PM}$	

7-93.   Examine the posters of flowchart proofs from problem 7-82. Convert each flowchart proof to a two-column proof. Remember that one column must contain the ordered statements of fact while the other must provide the reason (or justification) explaining why that fact must be true.

7-94.   So far in Section 7.2, you have proven many special properties of quadrilaterals and other shapes. Remember that when a conjecture is proven, it is called a theorem. For example, once you proved the relationship between the lengths of the sides of a right triangle, you were able to refer to that relationship as the Pythagorean Theorem. Find your Theorem Toolkit (Lesson 7.2.1A Resource Page) and make sure it contains all of the theorems you and your classmates have proven so far about various quadrilaterals. Be sure that your records include diagrams for each statement.

7-95.   LEARNING LOG

Reflect on the new proof format you learned today.
Compare it to the flowchart proof format that you have used
earlier. What are the strengths and weaknesses of each
style of proof? Which format is easier for you to use? Which is
easier to read? Title this entry "Two-Column Proofs" and label
it with today's date.

7-96.   Suppose you know that $\triangle TAP \cong \triangle DOG$ where $TA = 14$, $AP = 18$, $TP = 21$, and
$DG = 2y + 7$.

a.   On your paper, draw a reasonable sketch of $\triangle TAP$ and $\triangle DOG$.

b.   Find y. Show all work.

7-97.   Graph the equation $y = -\frac{3}{2}x + 6$ on graph paper. Label the points where the line
intersects the x- and y-axes.

7-98. $\angle a$, $\angle b$, and $\angle c$ are exterior angles of the triangle at right.
Find $m\angle a$, $m\angle b$, and $m\angle c$. Then find
$m\angle a + m\angle b + m\angle c$.

7-99.   The principal's new car cost $35,000 but in three years it will only be worth
$21,494. What is the annual percent of decrease?

7-100. What else can you prove about parallelograms? Prove that if a pair of opposite sides of a quadrilateral are congruent and parallel, then the quadrilateral must be a parallelogram. For example, for the quadrilateral *ABCD* at right, given that $\overline{AB} \parallel \overline{CD}$ and $\overline{AB} \cong \overline{CD}$, show that $\overline{BC} \parallel \overline{AD}$. Organize your reasoning in a flowchart. Then record your theorem in your Theorem Toolkit (Lesson 7.2.1A Resource Page).

7-101. As Ms. Dorman looked from the window of her third-story classroom, she noticed Pam in the courtyard. Ms. Dorman's eyes were 52 feet above ground and Pam was 38 feet from the building. Draw a diagram of this situation. What is the angle at which Ms. Dorman had to look down, that is, what is the angle of depression? (Assume that Ms. Dorman was looking at the spot on the ground below Pam.)

7-102. For each pair of triangles below, determine if the triangles are congruent. If the triangles are congruent,

- complete the correspondence statement,
- state the congruence property,
- and record any other ideas you use that make your conclusion true.

Otherwise, explain why you cannot conclude that the triangles are congruent. Note that the figures are not necessarily drawn to scale.

a. $\triangle ABC \cong \triangle$ _____   b. $\triangle SQP \cong \triangle$ _____   c. $\triangle PLM \cong \triangle$ _____

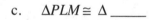

d. $\triangle WXY \cong \triangle$ _____   e. $\triangle EDG \cong \triangle$ _____   f. $\triangle ABC \cong \triangle$ _____

midpoint of
$\overline{WT}$ and $\overline{XZ}$

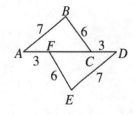

7.2.6   What can I prove?

Explore-Conjecture-Prove

So far, congruent triangles have helped you to discover and prove many new facts about triangles and quadrilaterals. But what else can you discover and prove? Today your work will mirror the real work of professional mathematicians. You will investigate relationships, write a conjecture based on your observations, and then prove your conjecture.

7-103.   TRIANGLE MIDSEGMENT THEOREM

As Sergio was drawing shapes on his paper, he drew a line segment that connected the midpoints of two sides of a triangle. This is called the **midsegment** of a triangle. *"I wonder what we can find out about this midsegment,"* he said to his team. Examine his drawing at right.

a.   **EXPLORE:** Examine the diagram of $\triangle ABC$, drawn to scale above. How do you think $\overline{DE}$ is related to $\overline{AB}$? How do their lengths seem to be related?

b.   **CONJECTURE:** Write a conjecture about the relationship between segments $\overline{DE}$ and $\overline{AB}$.

c.   **PROVE:** Sergio wants to prove that $AB = 2BE$. However, he does not see any congruent triangles in the diagram. How are the triangles in this diagram related? How do you know? Prove your conclusion with a flowchart.

d.   What is the common ratio between side lengths in the similar triangles? Use this to write a statement relating lengths DE and AB.

e.   Now Sergio wants to prove that $\overline{DE} \parallel \overline{AB}$. Use the similar triangles to find all the pairs of equal angles you can in the diagram. Then use your knowledge of angle relationships to make a statement about parallel segments.

7-104.   The work you did in problem 7-103 mirrors the work of many professional mathematicians. In the problem, Sergio examined a geometric shape and thought there might be something new to learn. You then helped him by finding possible relationships and writing a conjecture. Then, to find out if the conjecture was true for all triangles, you wrote a convincing argument (or proof). This process is summarized in the diagram below.

Discuss this process with the class and describe when you have used this process before (either in this class or outside of class). Why do mathematicians rely on this process?

7-105.   RIGHT TRAPEZOIDS

Consecutive angles of a polygon occur at opposite ends of a side of the polygon. What can you learn about a quadrilateral with two consecutive right angles?

a.   **EXPLORE:** Examine the quadrilateral at right with two consecutive right angles. What do you think is true about $\overline{AB}$ and $\overline{DC}$?

b.   **CONJECTURE:** Write a conjecture about what type of quadrilateral has two consecutive right angles. Write your conjecture in conditional ("If..., then...") form.

c.   **PROVE:** Prove that your conjecture from part (b) is true for all quadrilaterals with two consecutive right angles. Write your proof using the two-column format introduced in Lesson 7.2.4. Hint: Look for angle relationships.

d.   The quadrilateral you worked with in this problem is called a **right trapezoid**. Are all quadrilaterals with two right angles a right trapezoid?

7-106.   ISOSCELES TRAPEZOIDS

An **isosceles trapezoid** is a trapezoid with a pair
of congruent base angles. What can you learn
about the sides of an isosceles trapezoid?

a.   **EXPLORE:** Examine trapezoid *EFGH* at
right. How do the non-parallel side lengths
appear to be related?

b.   **CONJECTURE:** Write a conjecture about side
lengths in an isosceles trapezoid. Write your
conjecture in conditional ("If…, then…") form.

c.   **PROVE:** Now prove that your conjecture
from part (b) is true for all isosceles
trapezoids. Write your proof using the two-
column format introduced in Lesson 7.2.5.
To help you get started, the isosceles
trapezoid is shown at right with its sides
extended to form a triangle.

7-107.   Add the theorems you have proved in this lesson to your
Theorem Toolkit (Lesson 7.2.1A Resource Page). Be sure
to include diagrams for each statement.

7-108. What else can you prove about parallelograms? Prove that the diagonals of a parallelogram bisect each other. For example, assuming that quadrilateral *WXYZ* at right is a parallelogram, prove that $\overline{WM} \cong \overline{YM}$ and $\overline{ZM} \cong \overline{XM}$. Organize your reasoning in a flowchart. Then record your theorem in your Theorem Toolkit (Lesson 7.2.1A Resource Page).

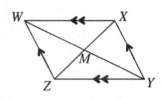

7-109. One way a shape can be special is to have two congruent sides. For example, an isosceles triangle is special because it has a pair of sides that are the same length. Think about all the shapes you know and list the other special properties shapes can have. List as many as you can. Be ready to share your list with the class at the beginning of Lesson 7.3.1.

7-110. Carefully examine each diagram below and explain why the geometric figure cannot exist. Support your statements with reasons. If a line looks straight, assume that it is.

a.

b.

c.

d.

e.

f.

7-111. Remember that if a triangle has two equal sides, it is called isosceles. Decide whether each triangle formed by the points below is isosceles. Explain how you decided.

a. $(6, 0), (0, 6), (6, 6)$

b. $(-3, 7), (-5, 2), (-1, 2)$

c. $(4, 1), (2, 3), (9, 2)$

d. $(1, 1), (5, -3), (1, -7)$

7-112. For each pair of numbers, find the number that is exactly halfway between them.

a. 9 and 15

b. 3 and 27

c. 10 and 21

7-113. Penn started the proof below to show that if $\overline{AD} \parallel \overline{EH}$ and $\overline{BF} \parallel \overline{CG}$, then $a = d$. Unfortunately, he did not provide reasons for his proof. Copy his proof and provide a justification for each statement.

Statements	Reasons
1. $\overline{AD} \parallel \overline{EH}$ and $\overline{BF} \parallel \overline{CG}$	
2. $a = b$	
3. $b = c$	
4. $a = c$	
5. $c = d$	
6. $a = d$	

7-114. After finding out that her kitchen does not conform to industry standards, Lashayia is back to the drawing board (see problem 7-84). Where can she locate her sink along her top counter so that its distance from the stove and refrigerator is as small as possible? And will this location keep her perimeter below 26 feet? Show all work.

7.3.1 What makes a quadrilateral special?

Studying Quadrilaterals on a Coordinate Grid

In Section 7.2 you investigated special types of quadrilaterals, such as parallelograms, kites, and rhombi. Each of these quadrilaterals has special properties you have proved: parallel sides, sides of equal length, equal opposite angles, bisected diagonals, etc.

But not all quadrilaterals have a special name. How can you tell if a quadrilateral belongs to one of these types? And if a quadrilateral does not have a special name, can it still have special properties? In Section 7.3 you will use both algebra and geometry to investigate quadrilaterals defined on coordinate grids.

7-115.   PROPERTIES OF SHAPES

Think about the special quadrilaterals you have studied in this chapter. Each shape has some properties that make it special. For example, a rhombus has two diagonals that are perpendicular. With the class, brainstorm the other types of properties that a shape can have. You may want to refer to your work from problem 7-109. Be ready to share your list with the class.

7-116.   Review some of the algebra tools you already have. Consider two line segments $\overline{AB}$ and $\overline{CD}$, given $A(0, 8)$, $B(9, 2)$, $C(1, 3)$, and $D(9, 15)$.

   a.   Draw these two segments on a coordinate grid. Find the length of each segment.

   b.   Find the equation of $\overleftrightarrow{AB}$ and the equation of $\overleftrightarrow{CD}$. Write both equations in $y = mx + b$ form.

   c.   Is $\overline{AB} \parallel \overline{CD}$? Is $\overline{AB} \perp \overline{CD}$? Justify your answer.

   d.   Use algebra to find the coordinates of the point where $\overline{AB}$ and $\overline{CD}$ intersect.

7-117.   AM I SPECIAL?

Shayla just drew quadrilateral *SHAY*, shown at
right. The coordinates of its vertices are:

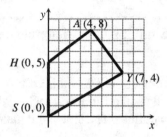

S(0, 0)   H(0, 5)   A(4, 8)   Y(7, 4)

a.   Shayla thinks her quadrilateral is a trapezoid.
Is she correct? Be prepared to justify your
answer to the class.

b.   Does Shayla's quadrilateral look like it is one of the other kinds of special
quadrilaterals you have studied? If so, which one?

c.   Even if Shayla's quadrilateral does not have a special name, it may still
have some special properties like the ones you listed in problem 7-115.
Use algebra and geometry tools to investigate Shayla's quadrilateral and
see if it has any special properties. If you find any special properties, be
ready to justify your claim that this property is present.

7-118.   MUST BE, COULD BE

Mr. Quincey likes to play a game with his class. He
says, *"My quadrilateral has four right angles."* His
students say, *"Then it MUST BE a rectangle"* and *"It
COULD BE a square."* For each description of a
quadrilateral below, say what special type the
quadrilateral *must be* and/or what special type the
quadrilateral *could be*. Look out, some descriptions
may have no *must be* statements and some
descriptions may have many *could be* statements!

a.   My quadrilateral has four equal sides.

b.   My quadrilateral has two pairs of opposite parallel sides.

c.   My quadrilateral has two consecutive right angles.

d.   My quadrilateral has two pairs of equal sides.

Core Connections Geometry

7-119. The diagram at right shows three bold segments. Find the coordinates of the midpoint of each segment.

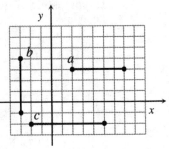

7-120. Examine the diagram at right.

a. Are the triangles in this diagram similar? Justify your answer using similarity transformations.

b. What is the relationship between the lengths of *HR* and *AK*? Between the lengths of *SH* and *SA*? Between the lengths of *SH* and *HA*?

c. If *SK* = 20 units and *RH* = 8 units, what is *HA*?

7-121. Examine the spinner at right. Assume that the probability of spinning a –8 is equal to that of spinning a 0.

a. Find the spinner's expected value if the value of region *A* is 8.

b. Find the spinner's expected value if the value of region *A* is – 4.

c. What does the value of region *A* need to be so that the expected value of the spinner is 0?

7-122.   For each pair of triangles below, determine if the triangles are congruent. If the triangles are congruent, state the triangle congruence condition that justifies your conclusion. If you cannot conclude that the triangles are congruent, explain why not.

a. $\triangle CAB \cong \triangle$____

b. $\triangle CBD \cong \triangle$____

c. $\triangle LJI \cong \triangle$____

d. $\triangle PRQ \cong \triangle$____

7-123.   For one of parts (a), (b) or (c) of problem 7-122, create a flowchart or a two-column proof for your conclusion. Remember to start with the given facts and to provide a justification for each step.

450

7-124. Carolina compared her proof to Penn's work in problem 7-113. Like him, she wanted to prove that if $\overline{AD}$ // $\overline{EH}$ and $\overline{BF}$ // $\overline{CG}$, then $a = d$. Unfortunately, her statements were in a different order. Examine her proof below and help her decide if her statements are in a logical order in order to prove that $a = d$.

Statements	Reasons
1. $\overline{AD}$ // $\overline{EH}$ and $\overline{BF}$ // $\overline{CG}$	Given
2. $a = b$	If lines are parallel, alternate interior angles are equal.
3. $a = c$	Substitution
4. $b = c$	If lines are parallel, corresponding angles are equal.
5. $c = d$	Vertical angles are equal.
6. $a = d$	Substitution

7-125. Describe the minimum information you would need to know about the shapes below in order to identify it correctly. For example, to know that a shape is a square, you must know that it has four sides of equal length and at least one right angle. Be as thorough as possible.

a. rhombus

b. trapezoid

7.3.2 How can I find the midpoint?

Coordinate Geometry and Midpoints

In Lesson 7.3.1, you applied your existing algebraic tools to analyze geometric shapes on a coordinate grid. What other algebraic processes can help us analyze shapes? And what else can be learned about geometric shapes?

7-126.   Cassie wants to confirm her theorem on triangle midsegments (from Lesson 7.2.6) using a coordinate grid. She started with $\triangle ABC$ with $A(0, 0)$, $B(2, 6)$, and $C(7, 0)$.

   a.   Graph $\triangle ABC$ on graph paper.

   b.   With your team, find the coordinates of P, the midpoint of $\overline{AB}$. Likewise, find the coordinates of Q, the midpoint of $\overline{BC}$.

   c.   Prove that the length of the midsegment, $\overline{PQ}$, is half the length of $\overline{AC}$. Also verify that $\overline{PQ}$ is parallel to $\overline{AC}$.

7-127.   As Cassie worked on problem 7-126, her teammate, Esther, had difficulty finding the midpoint of $\overline{BC}$. The study team decided to try to find another way to find the midpoint of a line segment.

   a.   To help Cassie, draw $\overline{AM}$ with $A(3, 4)$ and $M(8, 11)$ on graph paper. Then extend the line segment to find a point B so that M is the midpoint of $\overline{AB}$. Justify your location of point B by drawing and writing numbers on the graph.

   b.   Esther thinks she understands how to find the midpoint on a graph. *"I always look for the middle of the line segment. But what if the coordinates are not easy to graph?"* she asks. With your team, find the midpoint of $\overline{KL}$ if $K(2, 125)$ and $L(98, 15)$. Be ready to share your method with the class.

   c.   Test your team's method by verifying that the midpoint between $(-5, 7)$ and $(9, 4)$ is $(2, 5.5)$.

7-128.   Randy has decided to study the triangle graphed at right.

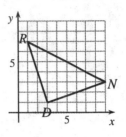

a.   Consider all the special properties this triangle can have. Without using any algebra tools, predict the best name for this triangle.

b.   For your answer to part (a) to be correct, what is the minimum amount of information that must be true about $\triangle RND$?

c.   Use your algebra tools to verify each of the properties you listed in part (b). If you need, you may change your prediction of the shape of $\triangle RND$.

d.   Randy wonders if there is anything special about the midpoint of $\overline{RN}$. Find the midpoint M, and then find the lengths of $\overline{RM}$, $\overline{DM}$, and $\overline{MN}$. What do you notice?

7-129.   On a map, Cary drew a set of coordinate axes. He noticed that the town of Coyner is located at the point $(3, 1)$ and Woottonville is located at $(15, 7)$, where 1 grid unit represents 1 mile.

a.   If the towns want to place a school at the midpoint between the towns, where should it be located? How far would it be from each town?

b.   Woottonville argues that since it will have twice as many students attending the school, it should be closer to Woottonville. Where should the school be if it is:

i. $\frac{1}{3}$ of the way from Woottonville to Coyner?

ii. $\frac{1}{4}$ of the way from Woottonville to Coyner?

iii. $\frac{2}{3}$ of the way from Coyner to Woottonville?

c.   Cary's brother is confused and needs help. Describe how he can find a point a certain fraction of the distance from one point to another?

7-130.   LEARNING LOG

In your Learning Log, explain what a midpoint is and the method you prefer for finding midpoints of a line segment when given the coordinates of its endpoints. Include any diagram or example that helps explain why this method works. Title this entry "Finding a Midpoint" and label it with today's date.

Methods and Meanings

Coordinate Geometry

Coordinate geometry is the study of geometry on a coordinate grid. Using common algebraic and geometric tools, you can learn more about a shape, such as, *"Does it have a right angle?"* or *"Are there two sides with the same length?"*

One useful tool is the Pythagorean Theorem. For example, the Pythagorean Theorem could be used to determine the length of side $\overline{AB}$ of $ABCD$ at right. By drawing the slope triangle between points A and B, the length of $\overline{AB}$ can be found to be $\sqrt{2^2 + 5^2} = \sqrt{29}$ units.

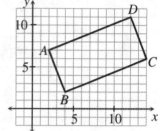

Similarly, slope can help analyze the relationships between the sides of a shape. If the slopes of two sides of a shape are equal, then those sides are **parallel**. For example, since the slope of $\overline{BC} = \frac{2}{5}$ and the slope of $\overline{AD} = \frac{2}{5}$, then $\overline{BC} \mathbin{/\mkern-5mu/} \overline{AD}$.

Also, if the slopes of two sides of a shape are opposite reciprocals, then the sides are **perpendicular** (meaning they form a 90° angle). For example, since the slope of $\overline{BC} = \frac{2}{5}$ and the slope of $\overline{AB} = -\frac{5}{2}$, then $\overline{BC} \perp \overline{AB}$.

By using multiple algebraic and geometric tools, you can identify shapes. For example, further analysis of the sides and angles of $ABCD$ above shows that $AB = DC$ and $BC = AD$. Furthermore, all four angles measure 90°. These facts together indicate that $ABCD$ must be a rectangle.

7-131.   Tomika remembers that the diagonals of a rhombus are perpendicular to each other.

   a.   Graph on *ABCD* if $A(1, 4)$, $B(6, 6)$, $C(4, 1)$, and $D(-1, -1)$. Is *ABCD* a rhombus? Show how you know.

   b.   Find the equation of the lines on which the diagonals lie. That is, find the equations of $\overleftrightarrow{AC}$ and $\overleftrightarrow{BD}$.

   c.   Compare the slopes of $\overleftrightarrow{AC}$ and $\overleftrightarrow{BD}$. What do you notice?

7-132.   Find another valid, logical order for the statements for Penn's proof from problem 7-113. Explain how you know that changing the order the way you did does not affect the logic.

7-133.   Each of these number lines shows a segment in bold. Find the midpoint of the segment in bold. Note that the diagrams are *not* drawn to scale.

   a.   [number line with 3 and 9]

   b.   [number line with -1 and 7]

   c.   [number line with -15 and 2]

7-134.   Examine the diagram at right.

   a.   Are the triangles in this diagram similar? If they are, use a flowchart with justifications or a two-column proof to prove similarity. If they are not similar, explain why not. Explain.

   b.   Name all the pairs of congruent angles in this diagram you can.

   c.   Are $\overline{GH}$ and $\overline{IJ}$ parallel? Explain how you know.

   d.   If $GH = 4x - 3$ and $IJ = 3x + 14$, find x. Then find the length of $\overline{GH}$.

7-135.   Consider $\triangle ABC$ with vertices $A(2, 3)$, $B(6, 6)$, and $C(8, -5)$.

a.   Draw $\triangle ABC$ on graph paper. What kind of triangle is $\triangle ABC$? Prove your result.

b.   Reflect $\triangle ABC$ across $\overline{AC}$. Find the location of B'. What name best describes the resulting figure? Prove your claim.

7-136.   This problem is a checkpoint for solving with trigonometric ratios and the Pythagorean Theorem. It will be referred to as Checkpoint 7.

a.   Compute the perimeter.   b.   Solve for x.

c.   Solve for x.   60 m

d.   Juanito is flying a kite at the park and realizes that all 500 feet of string are out. Margie measures the angle of the string with the ground using her clinometer and finds it to be 42°. How high is Juanito's kite above the ground? Draw a diagram and use the appropriate trigonometric ratio.

Check your answers by referring to the Checkpoint 7 materials located at the back of your book.

If you needed help solving these problems correctly, then you need more practice. Review the Checkpoint 7 materials and try the practice problems. Also, consider getting help outside of class time. From this point on, you will be expected to do problems like these quickly and easily.

7-137.   MUST BE, COULD BE

Here are some more challenges from Mr. Quincey. For each description of a quadrilateral below, say what special type the quadrilateral *must be* and/or what special type the quadrilateral *could be*. Look out: Some descriptions may have no *must be* statements, and some descriptions may have many *could be* statements!

a.   My quadrilateral has a pair of equal sides and a pair of parallel sides.

b.   The diagonals of my quadrilateral bisect each other.

Core Connections Geometry

7.3.3 What kind of quadrilateral is it?

Identifying Quadrilaterals on a Coordinate Grid

Today you will use algebra tools to investigate the properties of a quadrilateral and then will use those properties to identify the type of quadrilateral it is.

7-138.   MUST BE, COULD BE

Mr. Quincey has some new challenges for you! For each description below, decide what special type the quadrilateral *must be* and/or what special type the quadrilateral *could be*. Look out: Some descriptions may have no *must be* statements, and some descriptions may have many *could be* statements!

a.   My quadrilateral has three right angles.

b.   My quadrilateral has a pair of parallel sides.

c.   My quadrilateral has two consecutive equal angles.

7-139.   THE SHAPE FACTORY

You just got a job in the Quadrilaterals Division of your uncle's Shape Factory. In the old days, customers called up your uncle and described the quadrilaterals they wanted over the phone: *"I'd like a parallelogram with…"*.

"But nowadays," your uncle says, *"customers using computers have been emailing orders in lots of different ways."* Your uncle needs your team to help analyze his most recent orders listed below to identify the quadrilaterals and help the shape-makers know what to produce.

Your Task: For each of the quadrilateral orders listed below,

- Create a diagram of the quadrilateral on graph paper.

- Decide if the quadrilateral ordered has a special name. To help the shape-makers, your name must be as specific as possible. (For example, do not just call a shape a rectangle when it is also a square!)

- Record and be ready to present a proof that the quadrilateral ordered must be the kind you say it is. It is not enough to say that a quadrilateral *looks* like it is of a certain type or *looks* like it has a certain property. Customers will want to be sure they get the type of quadrilateral they ordered!

Problem continues on next page →

7-139. *Problem continued from previous page.*

Discussion Points

What special properties might a quadrilateral have?

What algebra tools could be useful?

What types of quadrilaterals might be ordered?

The orders:

a.   A quadrilateral formed by the intersection of these lines:

$$y = -\tfrac{3}{2}x + 3 \qquad y = \tfrac{3}{2}x - 3 \qquad y = -\tfrac{3}{2}x + 9 \qquad y = \tfrac{3}{2}x + 3$$

b.   A quadrilateral with vertices at these points:

$$A(0, 2) \qquad B(1, 0) \qquad C(7, 3) \qquad D(4, 4)$$

c.   A quadrilateral with vertices at these points:

$$W(0, 5) \qquad X(2, 7) \qquad Y(5, 7) \qquad Z(5, 1)$$

M ETHODS AND MEANINGS

MATH NOTES

Finding a Midpoint

A **midpoint** is a point that divides a line segment into two parts of equal length. For example, M is the midpoint of $\overline{AB}$ at right.

There are several ways to find the midpoint of a line segment if the coordinates of the endpoints are known. One way is to add half the change in x ($\tfrac{1}{2}\Delta x$) and half of the change in y ($\tfrac{1}{2}\Delta y$) to the x- and y-coordinates of the starting point, respectively.

Thus, if $A(1, 3)$ and $B(5, 8)$, then $\Delta x = 5 - 1 = 4$ and $\Delta y = 8 - 3 = 5$. Then the x-coordinate of M is $1 + \tfrac{1}{2}(4) = 3$ and the y-coordinate is $3 + \tfrac{1}{2}(5) = 5.5$. So point M is at $(4, 5.5)$.

This strategy can be used to find other points between A and B that are a proportion of the way from a starting point. For example, if you wanted to find a point $\tfrac{4}{5}$ of the way from point A to point B, then this could be found by adding $\tfrac{4}{5}$ of Δx to the x-coordinate of point A and adding $\tfrac{4}{5}$ of Δy to the y-coordinate of point A. This would be the point $((1 + \tfrac{4}{5}(4), 3 + \tfrac{4}{5}(5))$ which is $(4.2, 7)$. Generally, a point a ratio r from $A(x_0, y_0)$ to $B(x_1, y_1)$ is at $(x_0 + r(x_1 - x_0), y_0 + r(y_1 - y_0))$.

7-140. Each problem below gives the endpoints of a segment. Find the coordinates of the midpoint of the segment. If you need help, consult the Math Notes box for this lesson.

a. $(5, 2)$ and $(11, 14)$

b. $(3, 8)$ and $(10, 4)$

7-141. Below are the coordinates of three points and the equations of two lines. For each line, determine which of the points, if any, lie on that line. (There may be more than one!)

$$X(0, 15) \quad Y(3, 16) \quad Z(7, 0)$$

a. $y = \frac{1}{3}x + 15$

b. $y - 16 = -4(x - 3)$

7-142. MUST BE, COULD BE

Here are some more challenges from Mr. Quincey. For each description of a quadrilateral below, say what special type the quadrilateral *must be* and/or what special type the quadrilateral *could be*. Look out: Some descriptions may have no *must be* statements, and some descriptions may have many *"could be*" statements!

a. My quadrilateral has two right angles.

b. The diagonals of my quadrilateral are perpendicular.

7-143. Examine the arrow diagram below.

Polygon is a parallelogram → *area of the polygon equals base times height.*

a. Write this conjecture as a conditional ("If, then") statement.

b. Write the converse of this conditional statement. Is the converse statement a true statement?

c. Write a similar conjecture about triangles. Write it once as a conditional statement and once as an arrow diagram.

d. Write the converse of your triangle conjecture from part (c). Is the converse statement true?

7-144. The angle created by a hinged mirror when forming a regular polygon is called a **central angle**. For example, ∠ABC in the diagram at right is the central angle of the regular hexagon.

a. If the central angle of a regular polygon measures 18°, how many sides does the polygon have?

b. Can a central angle measure 90°? 180°? 13°? For each angle measure, explain how you know.

7-145. Jamika designed a game that allows some people to win money and others to lose money, but overall Jamika will neither win nor lose money. Each player will spin the spinner at right and will win the amount of money shown in the result. How much should each player pay to spin the spinner? Explain your reasoning.

7-146. Suppose ADBC is a quadrilateral and the diagonal $\overline{AB}$ lies on $y = -\frac{4}{3}x + 5$ and diagonal $\overline{CD}$ lies on $y = \frac{3}{4}x - 1$. Assume the diagonals intersect at point E.

a. Without graphing, what is the relationship between the diagonals? How do you know?

b. Graph the lines on graph paper. If E is a midpoint of $\overline{CD}$, what type of quadrilateral could ADBC be? Is there more than one possible type? Explain how you know.

Chapter 7 Closure   What have I learned?

Reflection and Synthesis

The activities below offer you a chance to reflect about what you have learned during this chapter. As you work, look for concepts that you feel very comfortable with, ideas that you would like to learn more about, and topics you need more help with. Look for connections between ideas as well as connections with material you learned previously.

①   TEAM BRAINSTORM

What have you studied in this chapter? What ideas were important in what you learned? With your team, brainstorm a list. Be as detailed as you can. To help get you started, a list of Learning Log entries, Toolkit Entries, and Math Notes boxes are below.

What topics, ideas, and words that you learned *before* this chapter are connected to the new ideas in this chapter? Again, be as detailed as you can.

Next consider the Standards for Mathematical Practice that follow Activity ③: Portfolio. What Mathematical Practices did you use in this chapter? When did you use them? Give specific examples.

How long can you make your lists? Challenge yourselves. Be prepared to share your team's ideas with the class.

Learning Log Entries
- Lesson 7.1.1 – Shapes of Wheels
- Lesson 7.1.3 – Shortest Distance
- Lesson 7.2.5 – Two-Column Proofs
- Lesson 7.3.2 – Finding a Midpoint

Toolkit Entries
- Theorem Toolkit (Lesson 7.2.1A Resource Page and problems 7-53, 7-64, 7-72, 7-94, 7-100, 7-107, and 7-108.)

Math Notes
- Lesson 7.1.2 – Parts of a Circle
- Lesson 7.1.3 – Congruent Triangles → Congruent Corresponding Parts
- Lesson 7.1.4 – Regular Polygons
- Lesson 7.2.1 – Reflexive Property of Equality
- Lesson 7.2.2 – Exponential Functions
- Lesson 7.2.3 – Definitions of Quadrilaterals
- Lesson 7.2.4 – Diagonals of a Rhombus
- Lesson 7.2.6 – Triangle Midsegment Theorem
- Lesson 7.3.2 – Coordinate Geometry
- Lesson 7.3.3 – Finding a Midpoint

Below is a list of the vocabulary used in this chapter. Make sure that you are familiar with all of these words and know what they mean. Refer to the glossary or index for any words that you do not yet understand.

bisect	center	central angle
circle	congruent	conjecture
consecutive angles	coordinate geometry	diagonal
diameter	edge	exterior angle
face	flowchart	isosceles trapezoid
kite	midpoint	midsegment
opposite	parallel	parallelogram
perpendicular	proof	quadrilateral
radius	rectangle	Reflexive Property
regular polygon	rhombus	right trapezoid
square	tetrahedron	theorem
three-dimensional	trapezoid	two-column proof
two-dimensional	vertex	

Make a concept map showing all of the connections you can find among the key words and ideas listed above. To show a connection between two words, draw a line between them and explain the connection, as shown in the model below. A word can be connected to any other word as long as you can justify the connection. For each key word or idea, provide an example or sketch that shows the idea.

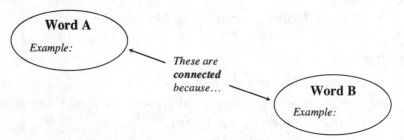

Your teacher may provide you with vocabulary cards to help you get started. If you use the cards to plan your concept map, be sure either to re-draw your concept map on your paper or to glue the vocabulary cards to a poster with all of the connections explained for others to see and understand.

While you are making your map, your team may think of related words or ideas that are not listed here. Be sure to include these ideas on your concept map.

Re-create your proof from problem 7-100 to showcase your current understanding of formal proof. Make sure your flowchart includes given information, bubbles that contain statements, and justifications for the statements. Do *not* use quadrilateral theorems from your Theorem Toolkit or elsewhere in this chapter as part of your flowchart. In other words, start with the given information and make statements based on angle relationships, shape definitions, triangle properties, and triangle similarity, as needed, but do not use quadrilateral theorems (such as "diagonals of a parallelogram bisect each other").

Then rewrite your proof, showcasing your ability to write a two-column proof.

Your teacher may give you the Chapter 7 Closure Resource Page: Quadrilaterals Graphic Organizer to record your work. A Graphic Organizer is a tool you can use to organize your thoughts, showcase your knowledge, and communicate your ideas clearly.

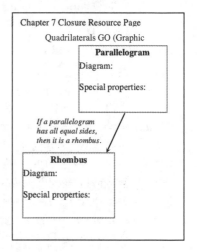

Next, consider the Standards for Mathematical Practice that follow. What Mathematical Practices did you use in this chapter? When did you use them? Give specific examples.

BECOMING MATHEMATICALLY PROFICIENT
The Common Core State Standards For Mathematical Practice

This book focuses on helping you use some very specific Mathematical Practices. The Mathematical Practices describe ways in which mathematically proficient students engage with mathematics everyday.

Make sense of problems and persevere in solving them:

Making sense of problems and persevering in solving them means that you can solve problems that are full of different kinds of mathematics. These types of problems are not routine, simple, or typical. Instead, they combine lots of math ideas and everyday situations. You have to stick with challenging problems, try different strategies, use multiple representations, and use a different method to check your results.

Reason abstractly and quantitatively:

Throughout this course, everyday situations are used to introduce you to new math ideas. Seeing mathematical ideas within a context helps you make sense of the ideas. Once you learn about a math idea in a practical way, you can "**reason abstractly**" by thinking about the concept more generally, representing it with symbols, and manipulating the symbols. **Reasoning quantitatively** is using numbers and symbols to represent an everyday situation, taking into account the units involved, and considering the meaning of the quantities as you compute them.

Construct viable arguments and critique the reasoning of others:

To **construct a viable argument** is to present your solution steps in a logical sequence and to justify your steps with conclusions, relying on number sense, facts and definitions, and previously established results. You communicate clearly, consider the real-life context, and provide clarification when others ask. In this course, you regularly share information, opinions, and expertise with your study team. You **critique the reasoning of others** when you analyze the approach of others, build on each other's ideas, compare the effectiveness of two strategies, and decide what makes sense and under what conditions.

Model with mathematics:

When you **model with mathematics**, you take a complex situation and use mathematics to represent it, often by making assumptions and approximations to simplify the situation. Modeling allows you to analyze and describe the situation and to make predictions. For example, to find the density of your body, you might model your body with a more familiar shape, say, a cylinder of the same diameter and height. Although a model may not be perfect, it can still be very useful for describing data and making predictions. When you interpret the results, you may need to go back and improve your model by revising your assumptions and approximations.

Core Connections Geometry

Use appropriate tools strategically:

To **use appropriate tools strategically** means that you analyze the task and decide which tools may help you model the situation or find a solution. Some of the tools available to you include diagrams, graph paper, calculators, computer software, databases, and websites. You understand the limitations of various tools. A result can be check or estimated by strategically choosing a different tool.

Attend to precision:

To **attend to precision** means that when solving problems, you need to pay close attention to the details. For example, you need to be aware of the units, or how many digits your answer requires, or how to choose a scale and label your graph. You may need to convert the units to be consistent. At times, you need to go back and check whether a numerical solution makes sense in the context of the problem.

You need to **attend to precision** when you communicate your ideas to others. Using the appropriate vocabulary and mathematical language can help make your ideas and reasoning more understandable to others.

Look for and make use of structure:

Looking for and making use of structure is a guiding principal of this course. When you are involved in analyzing the structure and in the actual development of mathematical concepts, you gain a deeper, more conceptual understanding than when you are simply told what the structure is and how to do problems. You often use this practice to bring closure to an investigation.

There are many concepts that you learn by looking at the underlying structure of a mathematical idea and thinking about how it connects to other ideas you have already learned. For example, geometry theorems are developed from the structure of translations.

Look for and express regularity in repeated reasoning:

To **look for and express regularity in repeated reasoning** means that when you are investigating a new mathematical concept, you notice if calculations are repeated in a pattern. Then you look for a way to generalize the method for use in other situations, or you look for shortcuts. For example, the investigations with simple shapes can be applied to more complex shapes using repeated reasoning.

④   WHAT HAVE I LEARNED?

Most of the problems in this section
represent typical problems found in
this chapter. They serve as a gauge
for you. You can use them to
determine which types of problems
you can do well and which types of
problems require further study and
practice. Even if your teacher does
not assign this section, it is a good
idea to try these problems and find
out for yourself what you know and what you still need to work on.

Solve each problem as completely as you can. The table at the end of the
closure section has answers to these problems. It also tells you where you
can find additional help and practice with problems like these.

CL 7-147.   Julius set his hinged mirror so that its angle was 72° and the
core region was isosceles, as shown at right.

a.   How many sides did his resulting polygon have?
      Show how you know.

b.   What is another name for this polygon?

CL 7-148.   Kelly started the proof below to show that if $\overline{TC} \cong \overline{TM}$
and $\overline{AT}$ bisects $\angle CTM$, then $\overline{CA} \cong \overline{MA}$. Copy and
complete her proof.

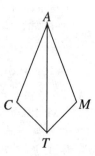

Statements	Reasons
1. $\overline{TC} \cong \overline{TM}$ and $\overline{AT}$ bisects $\angle CTM$	
2.	Definition of bisect
3. $\overline{AT} \cong \overline{AT}$	
4.	
5.	$\cong \Delta s \rightarrow \cong$ parts

CL 7-149.   Examine the spinner at right.

    a.   Find the expected value of the spinner if $x = 4$.

    b.   Find the expected value of the spinner if $x = -8$.

    c.   Find x so that the expected value of the spinner is 6.

CL 7-150.   *ABCD* is a parallelogram. If $A(3, -4), B(6, 2), C(4, 6)$, then what are the possible locations of point *D*? Draw a graph and justify your answer.

CL 7-151.   Each problem below gives the endpoints of a segment. Find the coordinates of the midpoint of the segment.

    a. $(-3, 11)$ and $(5, 6)$ b. $(-4, -1)$ and $(8, 9)$

CL 7-152.   For each diagram below, solve for the variable.

    a.   b.   c.

CL 7-153.   On graph paper, draw quadrilateral *MNPQ* if $M(1, 7), N(-2, 2), P(3, -1)$, and $Q(6, 4)$.

    a.   Find the slopes of $\overline{MN}$ and $\overline{NP}$. What can you conclude about $\angle MNP$?

    b.   What is the best name for *MNPQ*? Justify your answer.

    c.   Which diagonal is longer? Explain how you know your answer is correct.

    d.   Find the midpoint of $\overline{MN}$.

CL 7-154.   Examine the geometric relationships in each of the diagrams below. For each one, write and solve an equation to find the value of the variable. Name any geometric property or conjecture that you used.

a.

b.   *PQRS* is a rhombus with perimeter = 28 units and *PR* = 8 units, find *b* (*QT*)

c.

d.

CL 7-155.   Given the information in the diagram at right, use a flowchart to prove that $\triangle WXY \cong \triangle YZW$.

CL 7-156.   MUST BE, COULD BE

Here are some more challenges from Mr. Quincey. For each description of a quadrilateral below, say what special type the quadrilateral *must be* and/or what special type the quadrilateral *could be*. Remember: Some descriptions may have no *must be* statements, and some descriptions may have many "*could be* statements!

a.   The diagonals of my quadrilateral are equal.

b.   My quadrilateral has one right angle.

c.   My quadrilateral has one pair of equal adjacent sides.

CL 7-157.   Check your answers using the table at the end of the closure section. Which problems do you feel confident about? Which problems were hard? Use the table to make a list of topics you need help on and a list of topics you need to practice more.

Answers and Support for Closure Activity #4
What Have I Learned?

Note: MN = Math Note, LL = Learning Log

Problem	Solution	Need Help?	More Practice
CL 7-147.	a. $360° \div 72° = 5$ sides b. regular pentagon	Lesson 7.1.4 MN: 7.1.4	Problems 7-43, 7-55, and 7-144
CL 7-148.	<table><tr><th>Statements</th><th>Reasons</th></tr><tr><td>1. $\overline{TC} \cong \overline{TM}$ and $\overline{AT}$ bisects $\angle CTM$</td><td>Given</td></tr><tr><td>2. $\angle CTA \cong \angle MTA$</td><td>Definition of bisect</td></tr><tr><td>3. $\overline{AT} \cong \overline{AT}$</td><td>Reflexive Property</td></tr><tr><td>4. $\triangle CAT \cong \triangle MAT$</td><td>SAS $\cong$</td></tr><tr><td>5. $\overline{CA} \cong \overline{MA}$</td><td>$\cong \triangle s \rightarrow \cong$ parts</td></tr></table>	Lesson 7.2.5 MN: 7.1.3 and 7.2.1 LL: 7.2.5 Theorem Toolkit	Problems 7-102, 7-113, 7-122, and 7-124
CL 7-149.	a. 4.5 b. 0 c. $x = 8$	Lesson 4.2.5 MN: 5.2.2	Problems CL 5-141, CL 6-107, 7-121, and 7-145
CL 7-150.	Point D is at $(1, 0), (5, -8)$, or $(7, 12)$.	Lessons 7.3.1 and 7.3.3 MN: 7.2.3 and 7.3.2	Problems 7-32, 7-35, 7-68, and 7-79
CL 7-151.	a. $(1, 8.5)$ b. $(2, 4)$	Lesson 7.3.2 MN: 7.3.3 LL: 7.3.2	Problems 7-20, 7-29, 7-45, 7-119, and 7-140
CL 7-152.	a. $x \approx 7.43$ b. $x \approx 8.28$ c. $\theta \approx 33.7°$	Lesson 2.3.2, Sections 4.1 and 5.1 MN: 2.3.2, 4.1.2, 4.1.4, 5.1.2, and 5.1.4 LL: 2.3.2, 4.1.3, 4.1.4, 5.1.2, 5.1.3, and 5.3.1 Triangle Toolkit	Problems CL 3-119(a), CL 4-122, CL 5-139, 7-10, 7-85, and 7-136

Problem	Solution	Need Help?	More Practice
CL 7-153.	a. Slope of $\overline{MN} = \frac{5}{3}$ and $\overline{NP} = -\frac{3}{5}$, $\angle MNP$ is a right angle. b. It is a square because all sides are equal and all angles are right angles. c. The diagonals have equal length. Each is $\sqrt{68}$ units long. d. $(-\frac{1}{2}, \frac{9}{2})$	Section 7.3 MN: 7.2.3, 7.3.2, and 7.3.3 LL: 7.3.3	Problems 7-20, 7-32, 7-35, 7-48, 7-79, and 7-131
CL 7-154.	a. $2(3m+5) = 5m+11$, $m = 1$ b. $b^2 + 4^2 = 7^2$, so $b = \sqrt{33} \approx 5.74$ units c. $3x+17° + x - 5° = 180°$, so $x = 42°$ d. $2x - 5° = x + 13°$, so $x = 18°$	Section 2.1, Lessons 2.3.2 and 7.2.6 MN: 2.1.1, 2.1.4, 2.3.2, 7.2.4, and 7.2.6 LL: 2.1.1, 2.3.2 Angle Relationships Toolkit Theorem Toolkit	Problems 7-7, 7-18, 7-37, and 7-81
CL 7-155.		Section 3.2 and Lessons 6.1.1 through 6.1.4 MN: 3.2.2, 3.2.4, 6.1.4, and 7.2.1 LL: 3.2.2	Problems CL 3-121, CL 4-123, CL 5-140, CL 6-101, 7-6, 7-15, 7-46, 7-69, 7-76, 7-86, 7-100, 7-108, 7-123, and 7-134(a)
CL 7-156.	a. Must be: rectangle; Could be: square b. Must be: none; Could be: any quadrilateral c. Must be: none; Could be: kite, rhombus, square	Lessons 7.3.1 and 7.3.3 MN: 7.2.3	Problems 7-9, 7-125, 7-137, and 7-142

CHAPTER 8　　　　　　Polygons and Circles

In previous chapters, you have extensively studied triangles and quadrilaterals to learn more about their sides and angles. In this chapter, you will broaden your focus to include polygons with 5, 8, 10, and even 100 sides. You will develop a way to find the area and perimeter of a regular polygon and will study how the area and perimeter changes as the number of sides increases.

In Section 8.2, you will re-examine similar shapes to study what happens to the area and perimeter of a shape when the shape is enlarged or reduced.

Finally, in Section 8.3, you will connect your understanding of polygons with your knowledge of the area ratios of similar figures to find the area and circumference of circles of all sizes.

Guiding Question

Mathematically proficient students express regularity in repeated reasoning.

As you work through this chapter, ask yourself:

Can I find the shortcuts and generalize the rules for finding perimeters and areas of polygons?

In this chapter, you will learn:

➤ About special types of polygons, such as regular and non-convex polygons.

➤ How the measures of the interior and exterior angles of a regular polygon are related to the number of sides of the polygon.

➤ How the areas of similar figures are related.

➤ How to find the area and circumference of a circle and parts of circles and use this ability to solve problems in various contexts.

Chapter Outline

Section 8.1　This section begins with an investigation of the interior and exterior angles of a polygon and ends with a focus on the areas and perimeters of regular polygons.

Section 8.2　In this section, similar figures are revisited in order to investigate the ratio of the areas of similar figures.

Section 8.3　While answering the question, "*What if the polygon has an infinite number of sides?*", a process will be developed to find the area and circumference of a circle.

8.1.1 How can I build it?

· ·

Pinwheels and Polygons

In previous chapters, you have studied triangles and quadrilaterals. In Chapter 8, you will broaden your focus to include all polygons and will study what triangles can tell us about shapes with 5, 8, or even 100 sides.

By the end of this lesson, you should be able to answer these questions:

> How can you use the number of sides of a regular polygon to find the
> measure of the central angle?

> What type of triangle is needed to form a regular polygon?

8-1. **PINWHEELS AND POLYGONS**

Inez loves pinwheels. One day in class, she noticed that if she put three congruent triangles together so that one set of corresponding angles are adjacent, she could make a shape that looks like a pinwheel.

a. Can you determine any of the angles of her triangles? Explain how you found your answer.

b. The overall shape (outline) of Inez's pinwheel is shown at right. How many sides does it have? What is another name for this shape?

c. Inez's shape is an example of a **polygon** because it is a closed, two-dimensional figure made of non-intersecting straight line segments connected end-to-end. As you study polygons in this course, it is useful to use the names below because they identify how many sides a particular polygon has. Some of these words may be familiar, while others may be new. On your paper, draw an example of a *heptagon*.

Name of Polygon	Number of Sides
Triangle	3
Quadrilateral	4
Pentagon	5
Hexagon	6
Heptagon	7

Name of Polygon	Number of Sides
Octagon	8
Nonagon	9
Decagon	10
11-gon	11
n-gon	*n*

8-2.   Inez is very excited. She wants to know if
you can build a pinwheel using *any* angle
of her triangle. Obtain a Lesson 8.1.1
Resource Page from your teacher and cut
out Inez's triangles. Then work with your
team to build pinwheels and polygons by
placing different corresponding angles
together at the center. You will need to
use the triangles from all four team
members together to build one shape. Be
ready to share your results with the class.

8-3.   Jorge likes Inez's pinwheels but wonders, *"Will all triangles build a pinwheel
or a polygon?"*

a. If you have not already done so, cut out the remaining triangles on the
Lesson 8.1.1 Resource Page. Work together to determine which congruent
triangles can build a pinwheel (or polygon) when corresponding angles are
placed together at the center. For each successful pinwheel, answer the
questions below.

- How many triangles did it take to build the pinwheel?

- Calculate the measure of a central angle of the pinwheel. (Remember
that a central angle is an angle of a triangle with a vertex at the center
of the pinwheel.)

- Is the shape familiar? Does it have a name? If so, what is it?

b. Explain why one triangle may be able to create a pinwheel or polygon
while another triangle cannot.

c. Jorge has a triangle with angle measures 32°, 40°, and 108°. Will this
triangle be able to form a pinwheel? Explain.

8-4.   Jasmine wants to create a pinwheel with equilateral triangles.

a.   How many equilateral triangles will she need? Explain how you know.

b.   What is the name for the polygon she created?

c.   Jasmine's shape is an example of a **convex polygon**, while Inez's shape, shown at right, is **non-convex**. Study the examples of convex and non-convex polygons below and then write a definition of a convex polygon on your paper.

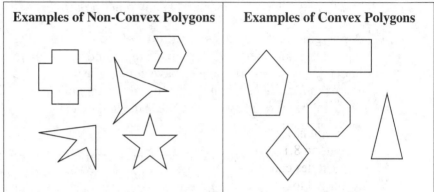

Examples of Non-Convex Polygons	Examples of Convex Polygons

8-5.   When corresponding angles are placed together, why do some triangles form convex polygons while others result in non-convex polygons? Consider this as you answer the following questions.

a.   Carlisle wants to build a convex polygon using congruent triangles. He wants to select one of the triangles below to use. Which triangle(s) will build a convex polygon if multiple congruent triangles are placed together so that they share a common vertex and do not overlap? Explain how you know.

b.   For each triangle from part (a) that creates a convex polygon, how many sides would the polygon have? What name is most appropriate for the polygon?

METHODS AND MEANINGS

Convex and Non-Convex Polygons

A **polygon** is defined as a two-dimensional closed figure made up of straight line segments connected end-to-end. These segments may not cross (intersect) at any other points.

A polygon is referred to as a **regular polygon** if it is equilateral (all sides have the same length) and equiangular (all interior angles have equal measure). For example, the hexagon shown at right is a regular hexagon because all sides have the same length and each interior angle has the same measure.

A polygon is called **convex** if each pair of interior points can be connected by a segment without leaving the interior of the polygon. See the example of convex and non-convex shapes in problem 8-4.

Review & Preview

8-6.   Solve for x in each diagram below.

a.

b.

c.

d.

Core Connections Geometry

8-7.   Using the definition of polygon from the Math Notes box in this lesson determine whether each of the following figures is or is not a polygon. Justify your decisions for each figure.

a.   b.   c.   d.

e.   f.   g.   h.

8-8.   After solving for *x* in each of the diagrams in problem 8-6, Jerome thinks he sees a pattern. He notices that the measure of an exterior angle of a triangle is related to two of the angles of a triangle.

a.   Do you see a pattern? To help find a pattern, study the results of problem 8-6.

b.   In the example at right, angles *a* and *b* are called **remote interior angles** of the given exterior angle because they are not adjacent to the exterior angle. Write a conjecture about the relationships between the remote interior and exterior angles of a triangle.

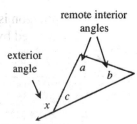

c.   Prove that the conjecture you wrote for part (b) is true for all triangles. Your proof can be written in any form, as long as it is convincing and provides reasons for all statements.

8-9.   Examine the geometric relationships in the diagram at right. Show all of the steps in your solutions for *x* and *y*.

8-10.   Steven has 100 congruent triangles that each has an angle measuring 15°. How many triangles would he need to use to make a pinwheel? Explain how you found your answer.

8-11.   Find the value of x in each diagram below, if possible. If the triangles are congruent, state which triangle congruence property was used. If the triangles are not congruent or if there is not enough information, state, "Cannot be determined."

a.

b.

c.

d.

8-12.   Decide if the following statements are true or false. If a statement is false, provide a diagram of a counterexample.

a.   All squares are rectangles.

b.   All quadrilaterals are parallelograms.

c.   All rhombi are parallelograms.

d.   All squares are rhombi.

e.   The diagonals of a parallelogram bisect the angles.

8.1.2 What is its measure?

Interior Angles of Polygons

In an earlier chapter you discovered that the sum of the interior angles of a triangle is always 180°. What about other polygons, such as hexagons or decagons? What about the sum of their interior angles? Do you think it matters if the polygon is convex or not? Consider these questions today as you investigate the angles of a polygon.

8-13.   Copy the diagram of the regular pentagon at right onto your paper. Then, with your team, find the *sum* of the measures of its interior angles *as many ways as you can*. You may want to use the fact that the sum of the angles of a triangle is 180°. Be prepared to share your team's methods with the class.

8-14.   SUM OF THE INTERIOR ANGLES OF A POLYGON

In problem 8-13, you found the sum of the angles of a regular pentagon. But what about other polygons?

a.   Obtain a Lesson 8.1.2 Resource Page from your teacher. Then use one of the methods from problem 8-13 to find the sum of the interior angles of other polygons. Complete the table (also shown below) on the resource page.

Number of Sides of the Polygon	3	4	5	6	7	8	9	10	12
Sum of the Interior Angles of the Polygon	180°								

b.   Does the interior angle sum depend on whether the polygon is convex? Test this idea by drawing a few non-convex polygons (like the one at right) on your paper and determine if it matters whether the polygon is convex. Explain your findings.

c.   Find the sum of the interior angles of a 100-gon. Explain your reasoning.

d.   LEARNING LOG

In your Learning Log, write an expression that represents the sum of the interior angles of an *n*-gon. Title this entry "Sum of Interior Angles of a Polygon" and include today's date.

8-15. The pentagon at right has been dissected (broken up) into three triangles with the angles labeled as shown. Use the three triangles to prove that the sum of the interior angles of *any* pentagon is always 540°. If you need help doing this, answer the questions below.

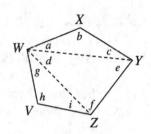

a. What is the sum of the angles of a triangle? Use this fact to write three equations based on the triangles in the diagram.

b. Add the three equations to create one long equation that represents the sum of all nine angles.

c. Substitute the three-letter name for each angle of the pentagon for the lower case letters at each vertex of the pentagon. For example, $m\angle XYZ = c + e$.

8-16. Use the angle relationships in each of the diagrams below to solve for the given variables. Show all work.

a.

b.

c.

d.

Mᴇᴛʜᴏᴅs ᴀɴᴅ Mᴇᴀɴɪɴɢs

Special Quadrilateral Properties

In Chapter 7, you examined several special quadrilaterals and proved conjectures regarding many of their special properties. Review what you learned below.

Parallelogram: Opposite sides of a parallelogram are congruent and parallel. Opposite angles are congruent. Also, since the diagonals create two pair of congruent triangles, the diagonals bisect each other.

Parallelogram

Rhombus: Since a rhombus is a parallelogram, it has all of the properties of a parallelogram. Its diagonals are perpendicular bisectors and bisect the angles of the rhombus. In addition, the diagonals create four congruent triangles.

Rhombus

Rectangle: Since a rectangle is a parallelogram, it has all of the properties of a parallelogram. In addition, its diagonals must be congruent.

Rectangle

Isosceles Trapezoid: The base angles (angles joined by a base) of an isosceles trapezoid are congruent.

Isosceles Trapezoid

8-17.   On graph paper, graph $\triangle ABC$ if $A(3, 0)$, $B(2, 7)$, and $C(6, 4)$.

   a.   What is the most specific name for this triangle? Prove your answer is correct using both slope and side length.

   b.   Find $m\angle A$. Explain how you found your answer.

8-18.   The exterior angles of a quadrilateral are labeled a, b, c, and d in the diagram at right. Find the measures of a, b, c, and d and then find the sum of the exterior angles.

8-19.   Find the area and perimeter of the shape at right. Show all work.

8-20.   Crystal is amazed! She graphed $\triangle ABC$ using the points $A(5, -1)$, $B(3, -7)$, and $C(6, -2)$. Then she rotated $\triangle ABC$ 90° counterclockwise (↺) about the origin to find $\triangle A'B'C'$. Meanwhile, her teammate took a different triangle ($\triangle TUV$) and rotated it 90° clockwise (↻) about the origin to find $\triangle T'U'V'$. Amazingly, $\triangle A'B'C'$ and $\triangle T'U'V'$ ended up using exactly the same points! Name the coordinates of the vertices of $\triangle TUV$.

8-21.   Write an equation for each of the following sequences.

   a. $-30, -15, 0, ...$ b. $9, 3, 1, ...$

8-22.   Suzette started to set up a proof to show that if $\overline{BC} \parallel \overline{EF}$, $\overline{AB} \parallel \overline{DE}$, and $AF = DC$, then $\overline{BC} \cong \overline{EF}$. Examine her work below. Then complete her missing statements and reasons.

Statements	Reasons
1. $\overline{BC} \parallel \overline{EF}$, $\overline{AB} \parallel \overline{DE}$, and $AF = DC$	1.
2. $m\angle BCF = m\angle EFC$ and $m\angle EDF = m\angle CAB$	2.
3.	3. Reflexive Property
4. $AF + FC + CD = FC$	4. Additive Property of Equality (adding the same amount to both sides of an equation keeps the equation true)
5. $AC = DF$	5. Segment addition
6. $\triangle ABC \cong \triangle DEF$	6.
7.	7. $\cong \triangle s \rightarrow \cong$ parts

8-23.   **Multiple Choice:** Which equation below is *not* a correct statement based on the information in the diagram?

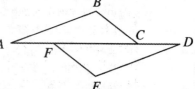

   a. $3x + y = 180°$ b. $2x - 1° = 4° - x$

   c. $2x - 1° = 5y - 10°$ d. $2x - 1° + 3x = 180°$

   e.   None of these is correct

8.1.3 What if it is a regular polygon?

. . . .

Angles of Regular Polygons

In Lesson 8.1.2 you discovered how to determine the sum of the interior angles of a polygon with any number of sides. What more can you learn about a polygon? Today you will focus on the interior and exterior angles of regular polygons.

As you work today, keep the following focus questions in mind:

Does it matter if the polygon is regular?

Is there another way to find the answer?

What's the connection?

8-24.   Diamonds, a very valuable naturally-occurring gem, have been popular for centuries because of their beauty, durability, and ability to reflect a spectrum of light. In 1919, a diamond cutter from Belgium, Marcel Tolkowsky, used his knowledge of geometry to design a new shape for a diamond, called the "round brilliant cut" (top view shown at right). He discovered that when diamonds are carefully cut with flat surfaces (called facets or faces) in this design, the angles maximize the brilliance and reflective quality of the gem.

Notice that at the center of this design is a regular octagon with equal sides and equal interior angles. For a diamond cut in this design to achieve its maximum value, the octagon must be cut carefully and accurately. One miscalculation, and the value of the diamond can be cut in half!

a.   Determine the measure of each interior angle of a regular octagon. Explain how you found your answer.

interior angle

b.   What about the interior angles of other regular polygons? Find the interior angles of a regular nonagon and a regular 100-gon.

c.   Will the process you used for part (a) work for any regular polygon? Write an expression that will calculate the interior angle of an n-gon.

8-25.   Fern states, *"If a triangle is equilateral, then all angles have equal measure and it must be a regular polygon."* Does this reasoning work for polygons with more than three sides? Investigate this idea below.

   a.   If all of the sides of a polygon, such as a quadrilateral, are equal, does that mean that the angles must be equal? If you can, draw a counterexample.

   b.   What if all of the angles are equal? Does that force a polygon to be equilateral? Explain your thinking. Draw a counterexample on your paper, if possible.

8-26.   Jeremy asks, *"What about exterior angles? What can we learn about them?"*

   a.   Examine the regular hexagon shown at right. Angle *a* is an example of an **exterior angle** because it is formed on the outside of the hexagon by extending one of its sides. Are all of the exterior angles of a regular polygon equal? Explain how you know.

   b.   Find *a*. Be prepared to share how you found your answer.

   c.   This regular hexagon has six exterior angles, as shown in the diagram above. What is the sum of the exterior angles of a regular hexagon?

   d.   What can you determine about the exterior angles of other regular polygons? Explore this with your team. Have each team member choose a different shape from the list below to analyze. For each shape:

   •   Find the measure of one exterior angle of that shape, and

   •   Find the sum of the exterior angles.

   (1) equilateral triangle   (2) regular octagon

   (3) regular decagon   (4) regular dodecagon (12-gon)

   e.   Compare your results from part (d). As a team, write a conjecture about the sum of the exterior angles of polygons based on your observations. Be ready to share your conjecture with the rest of the class.

   f.   Is your conjecture from part (e) true for all polygons or for only regular polygons? Does it matter if the polygon is not convex? Explore these questions using a dynamic geometric tool or obtain the Lesson 8.1.3 Resource Page and tracing paper from your teacher. Write a statement explaining your findings.

8-27.   Use your understanding of polygons to answer the questions below, if possible.
         If there is no solution, explain why not.

    a.   Gerardo drew a regular polygon that had exterior angles measuring 40°.
          How many sides did his polygon have? What is the name for this
          polygon?

    b.   A polygon has an interior angle sum of 2520°. How many sides does it
          have?

    c.   A quadrilateral has four sides. What is the measure of each of its interior
          angles?

    d.   What is the measure of an interior angle of a regular 360-gon? Is there
          more than one way to find this answer?

8-28.   LEARNING LOG

         How can you find the interior angle of a regular polygon?
         What is the sum of the exterior angles of a polygon? Write a
         Learning Log entry about what you learned during this
         lesson. Title this entry "Interior Angles and Sum of Exterior
         Angles of a Polygon" and include today's date.

8-29.   Find the area and perimeter of each shape below. Show all work.

    a.   b.

5 ft
10 ft
2 ft
11 ft

20 cm
20 cm

8-30.   In the figure at right, if $PQ = RS$ and $PR = SQ$,
         prove that $\angle P \cong \angle S$. Write your proof either in a
         flowchart or in two-column proof form.

8-31.   Joey used 10 congruent triangles to create a regular decagon.

   a.   What kind of triangles is he using?

   b.   Find the three angle measures of one of the triangles. Explain how you know.

   c.   If the area of each triangle is 14.5 square inches, then what is the area of the regular decagon? Show all work.

8-32.   On graph paper, plot $A(2, 2)$ and $B(14, 10)$.

   a.   If C is the midpoint of $\overline{AB}$, D is the midpoint of $\overline{AC}$, and E is the midpoint of $\overline{CD}$, find the coordinates of E.

   b.   What fraction of the distance from A to B is E?

   c.   Use the ratio from part (b) to find the coordinates of E directly as a point a certain ratio between A and B. Show your work.

8-33.   Use the geometric relationships in the diagrams below to solve for x.

   a.   b.

8-34.   The arc at right is called a quarter circle because it is one-fourth of a circle.

   a.   Copy Region A at right onto your paper. If this region is formed using 4 quarter circles, can you find another shape that must have the same area as Region A? Justify your conclusion.

   b.   Find the area of Region A. Show all work.

8-35.   **Multiple Choice:** Which property below can be used to prove that the triangles at right are similar?

   a.   AA ~   b.   SAS ~

   c.   SSS ~   d.   HL ~   e.   None of these

Core Connections Geometry

8.1.4 Is there another way?

Regular Polygon Angle Connections

During Lessons 8.1.1 through 8.1.3, you have discovered several ways the number of sides of a regular polygon is related to the measures of the interior and exterior angles of the polygon. These relationships can be represented in the diagram at right.

Regular Polygon Angle Web

How can these relationships be useful? What is the most efficient way to go from one measurement to another? This lesson will explore these questions so that you will have a complete set of tools to analyze the angles of a regular polygon.

8-36. Which connections in the Regular Polygon Angle Web do you already have? Which do you still need? Explore this as you answer the questions below.

    a. If you know the number of sides of a regular polygon, how can you find the measure of an interior angle directly? Find the measurements of an interior angle of a 15-gon.

    b. If you know the number of sides of a regular polygon, how can you find the measure of an exterior angle directly? Find the measurements of an exterior angle of a 10-gon.

    c. What if you know that the measure of an interior angle of a regular polygon is 162°? How many sides must the polygon have? Show all work.

    d. If the measure of an exterior angle of a regular polygon is 15°, how many sides does it have? What is the measure of an interior angle? Show how you know.

8-37. Suppose a regular polygon has an interior angle measuring 120°. Find the number of sides using *two* different strategies. Show all work. Which strategy was most efficient?

8-38.   Use your knowledge of polygons to answer the questions below, if possible.

   a.   How many sides does a polygon have if the sum of the measures of the interior angles is 1980°? 900°?

   b.   If the exterior angle of a regular polygon is 90°, how many sides does it have? What is another name for this shape?

   c.   Each interior angle of a regular pentagon has measure $2x + 4°$. What is x? Explain how you found your answer.

   d.   The measures of four of the exterior angles of a pentagon are 57°, 74°, 56°, and 66°. What is the measure of the remaining angle?

   e.   Find the sum of the interior angles of an 11-gon. Does it matter if it is regular or not?

8-39.   LEARNING LOG

In a Learning Log entry, copy the Regular Polygon Angle Web that your class created. Explain what it represents and give an example of at least two of the connections. Title this entry "Regular Polygon Angle Web" and include today's date.

8-40.   Esteban used a hinged mirror to create an equilateral triangle, as shown in the diagram at right. If the area of the shaded region is 11.42 square inches, what is the area of the entire equilateral triangle? Justify your solution.

8-41.   A house purchased for $135,000 has an annual appreciation of 4%.

   a.   What is the multiplier?

   b.   Write a function of the form $f(t) = ab^t$ that represents the situation, where t is the time in years after the house was purchased.

   c.   At the current rate, what will be the value of the house in 10 years?

8-42.   Copy each shape below on your paper and state if the shape is convex or non-convex. You may want to compare each figure with the examples provided in problem 8-4.

a.   b.   c.   d.

8-43.   Find the area of each figure below. Show all work.

a.   b.   c.

8-44.   Find the number of sides in a regular polygon if each interior angle has the following measures.

a.   60°   b.   156°   c.   90°   d.   140°

8-45.   Determine if the figures below (not drawn to scale) are similar. Justify your decision.

8-46.   At right is a scale drawing of the floor plan for
Nzinga's dollhouse. The actual dimensions of
the dollhouse are 5 times the measurements
provided in the floor plan at right.

a.   Use the measurements provided in
the diagram to find the area and
perimeter of her floor plan.

b.   Draw a similar figure on your paper. Label the sides with the actual
measurements of Nzinga's dollhouse. What is the perimeter and area of
the floor of her actual dollhouse? Show all work.

c.   Find the ratio of the perimeters of the two figures.
What do you notice?

d.   Find the ratio of the areas of the two figures.
How does the ratio of the areas seem to be
related to the zoom factor?

$8.1.5$ What is the area?

Finding Areas of Regular Polygons

In Lesson 8.1.4, you developed a method to find the measures of the interior and exterior angles of a regular polygon. How can this be useful? Today you will use what you know about the angles of a regular polygon to explore how to find the area of any regular polygon with n sides.

8-47.   USING MULTIPLE STRATEGIES

With your team, find the area of each shape below *twice*, each time using a distinctly different method or strategy. Make sure that your results from using different strategies are the same. Be sure that each member of your team understands each method.

a.   square

b.   regular hexagon

8-48.   Create a presentation that shows the two different methods that your team used to find the area of the regular hexagon in part (b) of problem 8-47.

Then, as you listen to other teams present, look for strategies that are different than yours. For each one, consider the questions below.

- *Which geometric tools does this method use?*

- *Would this method help find the area of other regular polygons (like a pentagon or 100-gon)?*

8-49.   Which method presented by teams in problem 8-48 seemed able to help find the
         area of other regular polygons? Discuss this with your team. Then find the area
         of the two regular polygons below. If your method does not work, switch to a
         different method. Assume C is the center of each polygon.

a.

b.

8-50.   LEARNING LOG

So far, you have found the area of a regular hexagon,
nonagon, and decagon. How can you calculate the area of
any regular polygon? Write a Learning Log entry
describing a general process for finding the area of a polygon with n sides.
Title this entry "Area of a Regular Polygon" and label it with today's date.

8-51.   Beth needs to fertilize her flowerbed,
         which is in the shape of a regular
         pentagon. A bag of fertilizer states that it
         can fertilize up to 150 square feet, but
         Beth is not sure how many bags of
         fertilizer she should buy.

Beth does know that each side of the
pentagon is 15 feet long. Copy the
diagram of the regular pentagon below
onto your paper. Find the area of the
flowerbed and tell Beth how many bags
of fertilizer to buy. Explain how you
found your answer.

15 ft

8-52.   GO, ROWDY RODENTS!

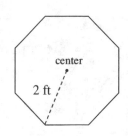

Recently, your school ordered a stained-glass window
with the design of the school's mascot, the rodent.
Your student body has decided that the shape of the
window will be a regular octagon, shown at right. To
fit in the space, the window must have a radius of
2 feet. The **radius of a regular polygon** is the
distance from the center to each vertex.

a.   A major part of the cost of the
window is the amount of glass
used to make it. The more glass
used, the more expensive the
window. Your principal has
turned to your class to determine
how much glass the window will
need. Copy the diagram onto your
paper and find its area. Explain
how you found your answer.

b.   The edge of the window will have a
polished brass trim. Each foot of
trim will cost $48.99. How much
will the trim cost? Show all work.

METHODS AND MEANINGS

Interior and Exterior Angles of a Polygon

The properties of interior and exterior angles in polygons (which includes regular and non-regular polygons), where n represents the number of sides in the polygon (n-gon), can be summarized as follows:

- The sum of the measures of the interior angles of an n-gon is $180°(n - 2)$.

- The sum of the measures of the exterior angles of an n-gon is always $360°$.

- The measure of any interior angle plus its corresponding exterior angle is $180°$.

In addition, for *regular* polygons:

- The measure of each interior angle in a regular n-gon is $\frac{180°(n-2)}{n}$.

- The measure of each exterior angle in a regular n-gon is $\frac{360°}{n}$.

Review & Preview

8-53.   The exterior angle of a regular polygon is 20°.

a.   What is the measure of an interior angle of this polygon? Show how you know.

b.   How many sides does this polygon have? Show all work.

8-54.   Examine the triangle and line of reflection at right.

a.   On your paper, trace the triangle and the line of reflection. Then draw the image of the triangle after it is reflected across the line. Verify your reflection is correct by folding your paper along the line of reflection.

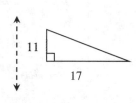

b.   Find the perimeter of the image. How does it compare with the perimeter of the original figure?

c.   Find the measure of both acute angles in the original triangle.

Core Connections Geometry

8-55.   Find the coordinates of the point at which the diagonals of parallelogram $ABCD$ intersect if $B(-3, -17)$ and $D(15, 59)$. Explain how you found your answer.

8-56.   Find the area of an equilateral triangle with side length 20 mm. Draw a diagram and show all work.

8-57.   A hotel in Las Vegas is famous for its large-scale model of the Eiffel Tower. The model, built to scale, is 128 meters tall and 41 meters wide at its base. If the real tower is 324 meters tall, how wide is the base of the real Eiffel Tower?

8-58.   For each equation below, solve for w, if possible. Show all work.

    a. $5w^2 = 17$ b. $5w^2 - 3w - 17 = 0$ c. $2w^2 = -3$

8-59.   **Multiple Choice:** The triangles at right are congruent because of:

    a.   SSA $\cong$ b.   HL $\cong$ c.   SAS $\cong$

    d.   SSS $\cong$ e.   None of these

8-60.   Solve for x in each diagram below.

    a.   b.

    c.   d.

8-61.   What is another (more descriptive) name for each polygon described below?

a.   A regular polygon with an exterior angle measuring 120°.

b.   A quadrilateral with four equal angles.

c.   A polygon with an interior angle sum of 1260°.

d.   A quadrilateral with perpendicular diagonals.

8-62.   If $\triangle ABC$ is equilateral and if $A(0,0)$ and $B(12,0)$, then what do you know about the coordinates of vertex C? Prove your answer is true.

8-63.   In the figure at right, $\overline{AB} \cong \overline{DC}$ and $\angle ABC \cong \angle DCB$.

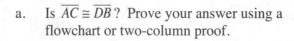

a.   Is $\overline{AC} \cong \overline{DB}$? Prove your answer using a flowchart or two-column proof.

b.   Do the measures of $\angle ABC$ and $\angle DCB$ make any difference in your solution to part (a)? Explain why or why not.

8-64.   On graph paper, graph the parabola $y = 2x^2 - x - 15$.

a.   What are the roots (x-intercepts) of the parabola? Write your points in (x, y) form.

b.   How would the graph of $y = -(2x^2 - x - 15)$ be the same or different? Can you tell without graphing?

8-65.   **Multiple Choice:** To decide if his class would take a quiz today, Mr. Chiu will flip a coin three times. If all three results are heads or all three results are tails, he will give the quiz. Otherwise, his students will not be tested. What is the probability that his class will take the quiz?

a. $\frac{1}{8}$ b. $\frac{1}{4}$ c. $\frac{1}{2}$ d.   1

8-66.   **Multiple Choice:** Approximate the length of $\overline{AB}$.

a.   15.87   b.   21.84   c.   37.16

d.   19.62   e.   None of these

8.2.1 How does the area change?

Area Ratios of Similar Figures

Much of this course has focused on similarity. In Chapter 3, you investigated how to enlarge and reduce a shape to create a similar figure. You also have studied how to use proportional relationships to find the measures of sides of similar figures. Today you will study how the areas of similar figures are related. That is, as a shape is enlarged or reduced in size, how does the area change?

8-67.　MIGHTY MASCOT

Enlargement ⟶

Archie's version

To celebrate the victory of your school's championship girls' ice hockey team, the student body has decided to hang a giant flag with your school's mascot on the gym wall.

To help design the flag, your friend Archie has created a scale version of the flag measuring 1 foot wide and 1.5 feet tall.

a.　The student body thinks the final flag should be 3 feet tall. How wide would this enlarged flag be? Justify your solution.

b.　If Archie used $2 worth of cloth to create his scale model, then how much will the cloth cost for the full-sized flag? Discuss this with your team. Explain your reasoning.

c.　Obtain the Lesson 8.2.1A Resource Page and scissors from your teacher. Carefully cut enough copies of Archie's scale version to fit into the large flag. How many did it take? Does this confirm your answer to part (b)? If not, what will the cloth cost for the flag?

d.

The student body is reconsidering the size of the flag. It is now considering enlarging the flag so that it is 3 or 4 times the width of Archie's model. How much would the cloth for a similar flag that is 3 times as wide as Archie's model cost? What if the flag is 4 times as wide?

To answer this question, first *estimate* how many of Archie's drawings would fit into each enlarged flag. Then obtain one copy of the Lesson 8.2.1B Resource Page for your team and confirm each answer by fitting Archie's scale version into the enlarged flags.

8-68.   Write down any observations or patterns you found while working on problem 8-61. For example, if the area of one shape is 100 times larger than the area of a similar shape, then what is the ratio of the corresponding sides (also called the **linear scale factor**)? And if the linear scale factor is r, then how many times larger is the area of the new shape?

8-69.   Use your pattern from problem 8-68 to answer the following questions.

a.   Kelly's shape at right has an area of 17 mm². If she enlarges the shape with a linear scale (zoom) factor of 5, what will be the area of the enlargement? Show how you got your answer.

b.   Examine the two similar shapes at right. What is the linear scale factor? What is the area of the smaller figure?

c.   Rectangle *ABCD* at right is divided into nine smaller congruent rectangles. Is the shaded rectangle similar to *ABCD*? If so, what is the linear scale factor? And what is the ratio of the areas? If the shaded rectangle is not similar to *ABCD*, explain how you know.

d.   While ordering carpet for his rectangular office, Trinh was told by the salesperson that a 16' by 24' piece of carpet costs $800. Trinh then realized that he read his measurements wrong and that his office is actually 8' by 12'. "*Oh, that's no problem,*" said the salesperson. "*That is half the size and will cost $400 instead.*" Is that fair? Decide what the price should be.

8-70.   If the side length of a hexagon triples, how does the area increase? First make a prediction using your pattern from problem 8-68. Then confirm your prediction by calculating and comparing the areas of the two hexagons shown at right.

METHODS AND MEANINGS

Ratios of Similarity

Since Chapter 3, you have used the term **zoom factor** to refer to the ratio of corresponding dimensions of two similar figures. However, now that you will be using other ratios of similar figures (such as the ratio of the areas), this ratio needs a more descriptive name. From now on, this text will refer to the ratio of corresponding sides as the **linear scale factor**. The word "linear" is a reference to the fact that the ratio of the lengths of line segments is a comparison of a single dimension of the shapes. Often, this value is represented with the letter r, for ratio.

For example, notice that the two triangles at right are similar because of AA ~. Since the corresponding sides of the new and original shape are 9 and 6, it can be stated that $r = \frac{9}{6} = \frac{3}{2}$.

Original   **New**

Review & Preview

8-71.   Examine the shape at right.

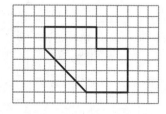

a.   Find the area and perimeter of the shape.

b.   On graph paper, enlarge the figure so that the linear scale factor is 3. Find the area and perimeter of the new shape.

c.   What is the ratio of the perimeters of both shapes? What is the ratio of the areas?

8-72.   Sandip noticed that when he looked into a mirror that was lying on the ground 8 feet from him, he could see a clock on the wall. If Sandip's eyes are 64 inches off the ground, and if the mirror is 10 feet from the wall, how high above the floor is the clock? Include a diagram in your solution.

8-73.   Mr. Singer has a dining table in the shape of a regular
          hexagon. While he loves this design, he has trouble finding
          tablecloths to cover it. He has decided to make his own
          tablecloth!

          In order for his tablecloth to drape over each edge, he will
          add a rectangular piece along each side of the regular hexagon
          as shown in the diagram at right. Using the dimensions given in
          the diagram, find the total area of the cloth Mr. Singer will need.

8-74.   What is the probability that $x^2 + 7x + k$ is factorable if $0 \le k \le 20$ and k is an
          integer?

8-75.   Your teacher has offered your class extra credit.
          She has created two spinners, shown at right.
          Your class gets to spin only one of the spinners.
          The number that the spinner lands on is the
          number of extra credit points each member of
          the class will get. Study both spinners carefully.

          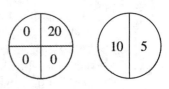

          a.   Assuming that each spinner is divided into equal portions, which spinner
               do you think the class should choose to spin and why?

          b.   What if the spot labeled "20" were changed to "100"? Would that make
               any difference?

8-76.   If the rectangles below have the same area, find x. Is there more than one
          answer? Show all work.

8-77.   **Multiple Choice:** A cable 100 feet long is attached 70 feet up the side of a
          building. If it is pulled taut (i.e., there is no slack) and staked to the ground as
          far away from the building as possible, approximately what angle does the cable
          make with the ground?

          a.   39.99°   b.   44.43°   c.   45.57°   d.   12.22°

8.2.2 How does the area change?

Ratios of Similarity

Today you will continue investigating the ratios between similar figures. As you solve today's problems, look for connections between the ratios of similar figures and what you already know about area and perimeter.

8-78.   TEAM PHOTO

Alice has a 4-inch by 5-inch photo of
your school's championship girls' ice
hockey team. To celebrate their
recent victory, your principal wants
Alice to enlarge her photo for a
display case near the main office.

a.   When Alice went to the print shop,
she was confronted with many
choices of sizes: 7-inch by 9-inch,
8-inch by 10-inch, and 12-inch by 16-inch.

She's afraid that if she picks the wrong size, part of the photo will be cut
off. Which size should Alice pick and why?

b.   The cost of the photo paper to print Alice's 4-inch-by-5-inch picture is
$0.45. Assuming that the cost per square inch of photo paper remains
constant, how much should it cost to print the enlarged photo? Explain
how you found your answer.

c.   Unbeknownst to her, the vice-principal also went out and ordered an
enlargement of Alice's photo. However, the photo paper for his
enlargement cost $7.20! What are the dimensions of his photo?

8-79.   So far, you have discovered and used the relationship between the areas of
          similar figures. How are the perimeters of similar figures related? Confirm
          your intuition by analyzing the pairs of similar shapes below. For each pair,
          calculate the areas and perimeters and complete a table like the one shown
          below. To help see patterns, reduce fractions to lowest terms or find the
          corresponding decimal values.

	Ratio of Sides	Perimeter	Ratio of Perimeters	Area	Ratio of Areas
small figure					
large figure					

a.

b.

c.

8-80.   While Jessie examines the two figures at right, she wonders
          if they are similar. Decide with your team if there is
          enough information to determine if the shapes are similar.
          Justify your conclusion.

8-81.   Your teacher enlarged the figure at right so that the
          area of the similar shape is 900 square cm. What is
          the perimeter of the enlarged figure? Be prepared to
          explain your method to the class.

Area = 100 cm²

8-82.   LEARNING LOG

Reflect on what you have learned in Lessons 8.2.1 and
8.2.2. Write a Learning Log entry that explains what you
know about the areas and perimeters of similar figures.
What connections can you make with other geometric concepts? Be sure to
include an example. Title this entry "Areas and Perimeters of Similar Figures"
and include today's date.

8-83.   Assume Figure A and Figure B, at right, are similar.

a.   If the ratio of similarity is $\frac{3}{4}$, then what is the
       ratio of the perimeters of Figures A and B?

b.   If the perimeter of Figure A is p and the
       linear scale factor is r, what is the
       perimeter of Figure B?

Figure A   **Figure B**

c.   If the area of Figure A is a and the linear scale factor is r, what is the area
       of Figure B?

8-84.   Always a romantic, Marris decided to bake his girlfriend a cookie in the shape of
a regular dodecagon (12-gon) for Valentine's Day.

a.   If the edge of the dodecagon is 6 cm, what is the area of the top of the
       cookie?

b.   His girlfriend decides to divide the cookie into 12 separate but congruent
       pieces. After 9 of the pieces have been eaten, what area of cookie is left?

8-85.   As her team was building triangles with linguini, Karen asked for help building
a triangle with sides 5, 6, and 1. *"I don't think that's possible,"* said her
teammate, Kelly.

a.   Why is this triangle not possible?

b.   Change the lengths of one of the sides so that the triangle is possible.

8-86.   What is the 150th term in this sequence?

$$17, 16\tfrac{1}{2}, 16, 15\tfrac{1}{2}, \dots$$

8-87.   Callie started to prove that given the information in the diagram at right, then $\overline{AB} \cong \overline{CD}$. Copy her flowchart below on your paper and help her by justifying each statement.

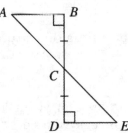

8-88.   For each pair of triangles below, decide if the triangles are congruent. If the triangles are congruent:

- State which triangle congruence property proves that the triangles are congruent.

- Write a congruence statement (such as $\triangle ABC \cong \triangle$ _____).

a.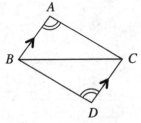

b.

8-89.   **Multiple Choice:** What is the solution to the system of equations at right?

$$y = \tfrac{1}{2}x - 4$$
$$x - 4y = 12$$

a. $(2, 0)$ b. $(16, 4)$

c. $(-2, -5)$ d. $(4, -2)$

e.   None of these

8.3.1 What if it has infinitely many sides?

A Special Ratio

In Section 8.1, you developed a method to find the area and perimeter of a regular polygon with *n* sides. You carefully calculated the area of regular polygons with 5, 6, 8, and even 10 sides. But what if the regular polygon has an infinite number of sides? How can you predict its area?

As you investigate this question today, keep the following focus questions in mind:

What is the connection?

Do I see any patterns?

How are the shapes related?

8-90. POLYGONS WITH INFINITELY MANY SIDES

In order to predict the area and perimeter of a polygon with infinitely many sides, your team is going to work with other teams to generate data in order to find a pattern.

Your teacher will assign your team three of the regular polygons below. For each polygon, find the area and perimeter if the radius is 1 (as shown in the diagram of the regular pentagon at right). Leave your answer accurate to the nearest 0.01. Place your results into a class chart to help predict the area and perimeter of a polygon with infinitely many sides.

a. equilateral triangle   b. regular octagon   c. regular 30-gon

d. square   e. regular nonagon   f. regular 60-gon

g. regular pentagon   h. regular decagon   i. regular 90-gon

j. regular hexagon   k. regular 15-gon   l. regular 180-gon

8-91.   ANALYSIS OF DATA

With your team, analyze the chart created by the class.

a.   What do you predict the area will be for a regular polygon with infinitely many sides? What do you predict its perimeter will be?

b.   What is another name for a regular polygon with infinitely many sides?

c.   Does the number 3.14… look familiar? If so, share what you know with your team. Be ready to share your idea with the class.

8-92.   LEARNING LOG

Record the area and circumference of a circle with radius 1 in your Learning Log. Then, include a brief description of how you "discovered" π. Title this entry "Pi" and include today's date.

ETHODS AND MEANINGS

MATH NOTES

Area of a Regular Polygon

If a polygon is regular with n sides, it can be subdivided into n congruent isosceles triangles. One way to calculate the area of a regular polygon is to multiply the area of one isosceles triangle by n.

***n*-gon**

To find the area of the isosceles triangle, it is helpful to first find the measure of the polygon's central angle by dividing 360° by n. The height of the isosceles triangle divides the top vertex angle in half.

For example, suppose you want to find the area of a regular decagon with side length 8 units. The central angle is $\frac{360°}{10} = 36°$. Then the top angle of the shaded right triangle at right would be $36° \div 2 = 18°$.

Use right triangle trigonometry to find the measurements of the right triangle, then calculate its area. For the shaded triangle above, $\tan 18° = \frac{4}{h}$ and $h \approx 12.311$. Use the height and the base to find the area of the isosceles triangle: $\frac{1}{2}(8)(12.311) \approx 49.242$ sq. units. Then the area of the regular decagon is approximately $10 \cdot 49.242 \approx 492.42$ sq. units.

Core Connections Geometry

8-93.   Find the area of the shaded region for the regular pentagon at right if the length of each side of the pentagon is 10 units. Assume that point *C* is the center of the pentagon.

10

8-94.   For each triangle below, find the value of *x*, if possible. Name the triangle tool that you used. If the triangle cannot exist, explain why.

a.

b.

c.

d.

Area of the shaded region is 96 square units.

8-95.   Find the measure of each interior angle of a regular 30-gon using two different methods.

8-96.   Examine the diagram at right. Assume that $\overline{AD}$ and $\overline{BE}$ are line segments, and that $\overline{BC} \cong \overline{DC}$ and $\angle A \cong \angle E$. Prove that $\overline{AB} \cong \overline{ED}$. Use the form of proof that you prefer (such as the flowchart or two-column proof format). Be sure to copy the diagram onto your paper and add any appropriate markings.

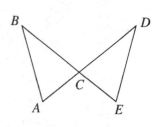

8-97.   For each diagram below, write and solve an equation to find *x*.

a.

b.

8-98.   On graph paper, plot the points $A(-3, -1)$ and $B(6, 11)$.

   a.   Find the midpoint M of $\overline{AB}$.

   b.   Find the point P, on $\overline{AB}$, that is $\frac{2}{3}$ of the way from A to B.

   c.   Find the equation of the line that passes through points A and B.

   d.   Find the distance between points M and P.

8-99.   **Multiple Choice:** What fraction of the circle at right is shaded?

   a. $\frac{60}{360}$ b. $\frac{300}{360}$ c. $\frac{60}{180}$

   d. $\frac{120}{180}$ e.   None of these

8.3.2 What is the relationship?

Area and Circumference of a Circle

In Lesson 8.3.1, your class discovered that the area of a circle with radius 1 unit is π units^2 and that the circumference is 2π units. But what if the radius of the circle is 5 units or 13.6 units? Today you will develop a method to find the area and circumference of circles when the radius is not 1. You will also explore parts of circles (called sectors and arcs) and learn about their measurements.

As you and your team work together, remember to ask each other questions such as:

Is there another way to solve it?

What is the relationship?

What is area? What is circumference?

8-100.   AREA AND CIRCUMFERENCE OF A CIRCLE

Now that you know the area and circumference (perimeter) of a circle with radius 1, how can you find the area and circumference of a circle with any radius?

a.   First examine how the circles at right are related. Since circles always have the same shape, what is the relationship between any two circles?

b.   What is the ratio of the circumferences (perimeters)? What is the ratio of the areas? Explain.

c.   If the area of a circle with radius of 1 is π square units, what is the area of a circle with radius 3 units? With radius 10 units? With radius r units?

d.   Likewise, if the circumference (perimeter) of a circle is 2π units, what is the circumference of a circle with radius 3? With radius 7? With radius r?

8-101.   Read the definitions of radius and diameter in the Math Notes box for this lesson. Then answer the questions below.

a.   Find the area of a circle with radius 10 units.

b.   Find the circumference of a circle with diameter 7 units.

c.   If the area of a circle is 121π square units, what is its diameter?

d.   If the circumference of a circle is 20π units, what is its area?

8-102.   The giant sequoia trees in California are famous for their immense size and old age. Some of the trees are more than 2500 years old and tourists and naturalists often visit to admire their size and beauty. In some cases, you can even drive a car through the base of a tree!

One of these trees, the General Sherman tree in Sequoia National Park, is the largest living thing on the earth. The tree is so gigantic, in fact, that the base has a circumference of 102.6 feet! Assuming that the base of the tree is circular, how wide is the base of the tree? That is, what is its diameter? How does that diameter compare with the length and width of your classroom?

8-103.   To celebrate their victory, the girls'
ice-hockey team went out for pizza.

a.   The goalie ate half of a pizza that
had a diameter of 20 inches! What
was the area of pizza that she ate?
What was the length of crust that she
ate? Leave your answers in exact
form. That is, do not convert your
answer to decimal form.

b.   Sonya chose a slice from another pizza that had a diameter of 16 inches.
If her slice had a central angle of 45°, what is the area of this slice? What
is the length of its crust? Show how you got your answers.

c.   As the evening drew to a close, Sonya noticed that
there was only one slice of the goalie's pizza
remaining. She measured the central angle and found
out that it was 72°. What is the area of the remaining
slice? What is the length of its crust? Show how you
got your answer.

d.   A portion of a circle (like the crust of a slice of pizza) is
called an **arc**. This is a set of connected points a fixed
distance from a central point. The length of an arc is a part
of the circle's circumference. If a circle has a radius of
6 cm, find the length of an arc with a central angle of 30°.

arc

e.   A region that resembles a slice of pizza is called a **sector**. It
is formed by two radii of a central angle and the arc between
their endpoints on the circle. If a circle has radius 10 feet,
find the area of a sector with a central angle of 20°.

sector

8-104.   LEARNING LOG

Reflect on what you have learned today. How did you use
similarity to find the areas and circumferences of circles?
How are the radius and diameter of a circle related? Write
a Learning Log entry about what you learned today. Title this entry
"Area and Circumference of a Circle" and include today's date.

MATH NOTES

Circle Facts

The area of a circle with radius $r = 1$ unit is π units^2. (Remember that $\pi \approx 3.1415926...$)

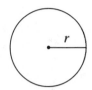

Since all circles are similar, their areas increase by a square of the linear scale (zoom) factor. That is, a circle with radius 6 has an area that is 36 times the area of a circle with radius 1. Thus, a circle with radius 6 has an area of 36π units^2, and a circle with radius r has **area** $A = \pi r^2$ units^2.

Area = πr^2
Circumference = $2\pi r = \pi d$

The **circumference** of a circle is its perimeter. It is the distance around a circle. The circumference of a circle with radius $r = 1$ unit is 2π units. Since the perimeter ratio is equal to the ratio of similarity, a circle with radius r has circumference $C = 2\pi r$ units. Since the diameter of a circle is twice its radius, another way to calculate the circumference is $C = \pi d$ units.

A part of a circle is called an **arc**. This is a set of points a fixed distance from a center and is defined by a central angle. Since a circle does not include its interior region, an arc is like the edge of a crust of a slice of pizza.

arc

A region that resembles a slice of pizza is called a **sector**. It is formed by two radii of a central angle and the arc between their endpoints on the circle.

sector

8-105.   A regular hexagon with side length 4 has the same area as a square. What is the length of the side of the square? Explain how you know.

8-106.   Use what you know about similar figures to complete the following tasks.

13

5   4

8

a.   Find the area and perimeter of the trapezoid at right.

b.   Find the area and perimeter of the trapezoid that is similar to this one, but has been reduced by a linear scale factor of $\frac{1}{3}$.

8-107.　An exterior angle of a regular polygon measures 18°.

    a.　How many sides does the polygon have?

    b.　If the length of a side of the polygon is 2, what is the area of the polygon?

8-108.　Find the missing angle(s) in each problem below using the geometric relationships shown in the diagram at right. Be sure to write down the conjecture that justifies each calculation. Remember that each part is a separate problem.

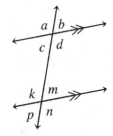

    a.　If $d = 110°$ and $k = 5x - 20°$, write an equation and solve for x.

    b.　If $b = 4x - 11°$ and $n = x + 26°$, write an equation and solve for x. Then find the measure of $\angle n$.

8-109.　Reynaldo has a stack of blocks on his desk, as shown below at right.

    a.　If his stack is 2 blocks wide, 2 blocks long, and 2 blocks tall, how many blocks are in his stack?

    b.　What if his stack instead is 3 blocks wide, 3 blocks long, and 2 blocks tall? How many blocks are in this stack?

    c.　What if his stack contains 99 blocks, is 3 blocks tall, x blocks long, and y blocks wide? What could x and y be?

8-110.　Krista is trying to solve for x in the triangle at right.

    a.　What equation would Krista write?

    b.　Krista does not have a calculator, but she remembered something funny her friend Juanisha told her. Juanisha's favorite sine ratio is $\sin 31.5° \approx 0.522$ because 5/22 is Juanisha's birthday! Without a calculator, use Juanisha's favorite ratio to solve your equation from part (a).

8-111.　**Multiple Choice:** Which type of quadrilateral below does not necessarily have diagonals that bisect each other?

    a.　square   b.　rectangle   c.　rhombus   d.　trapezoid

8.3.3 How can I use it?

Circles in Context

In Lesson 8.3.1, you developed methods to find the area and circumference of a circle with radius r. During this lesson, you will work with your team to solve problems from different contexts involving circles and polygons.

8-112. While the earth's orbit (path) about the sun is slightly elliptical, it can be approximated by a circle with a radius of 93,000,000 miles.

a. How far does the earth travel in one orbit about the sun? That is, what is the approximate circumference of the earth's path?

b. Approximately how fast is the earth traveling in its orbit in space? Calculate your answer in miles per hour.

8-113. A certain car's windshield wiper clears a portion of a sector as shown shaded at right. If the angle the wiper pivots during each swing is 120°, find the area of the windshield that is wiped during each swing.

15 in.　5 in.　120°

8-114. THE GRAZING GOAT

Zoe the goat is tied by a rope to one corner of a 15 meter-by-25 meter rectangular barn in the middle of a large, grassy field. Over what area of the field can Zoe graze if the rope is:

a. 10 meters long?

b. 20 meters long?

c. 30 meters long?

d. Zoe is happiest when she has at least 400 m² to graze. What possible lengths of rope could be used?

8-115.   THE COOKIE CUTTER

A cookie baker has an automatic mixer that
turns out a sheet of dough in the shape of a
square 12 inches wide. His cookie cutter cuts
3-inch diameter circular cookies as shown at
right. The supervisor complained that too much
dough was being wasted and ordered the baker
to find out what size cookie would have the
least amount of waste.

Your Task:

- Analyze this situation and determine how
  much cookie dough is "wasted" when
  3-inch cookies are cut. Then have each
  team member find the amount of dough
  wasted when a cookie of a different
  diameter is used. Compare your results.

- Write a note to the supervisor explaining
  your results. Justify your conclusion.

ⓂETHODS AND MEANINGS

Arc Length and Area of a Sector

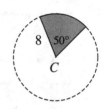

The ratio of the area of a sector to the area of a circle with the same radius equals the ratio of its central angle to 360°. For example, for the sector in circle C at right, the area of the entire circle is $\pi(8)^2 = 64\pi$ square units. Since the central angle is 50°, then the area of the sector can be found with the proportional equation:

$$\frac{50°}{360°} = \frac{\text{area of sector}}{64\pi}$$

Thus, the area of the sector is $\frac{50°}{360°}(64\pi) = \frac{80\pi}{9} \approx 27.93$ sq. units.

The length of an arc can be found using a similar process. The ratio of the length of an arc to the circumference of a circle with the same radius equals the ratio of its central angle to 360°. To find the length of $\overparen{AB}$ at right, first find the circumference of the entire circle, which is $2\pi(5) = 10\pi$ units. Then:

$$\frac{104°}{360°} = \frac{\text{arc length}}{10\pi}$$

Multiplying both sides of the equation by 10π, the arc length is $\frac{104°}{360°}(10\pi) = \frac{26\pi}{9} \approx 9.08$ units.

You may be surprised to learn that there are other units of measure (besides degrees) to measure an angle. A very special angle measure is called a **radian** and is defined as the measure of a central angle when the length of the arc equals the length of the radius. 1 radian $= \frac{360°}{2\pi} \approx 57.296°$.

8-116. Use what you know about the area and circumference of circles to answer the questions below. Show all work. Leave answers in terms of π.

   a. If the radius of a circle is 14 units, what is its circumference? What is its area?

   b. If a circle has diameter 10 units, what is its circumference? What is its area?

   c. If a circle has circumference 100π units, what is its area?

   d. If a circle has circumference C, what is its area in terms of C?

8-117. In 2000 a share of Jiffy Stock was worth $20 and in 2010 it was worth $50. What was the annual multiplier and the annual percent of increase?

8-118. Larry started to set up a proof to show that if $\overline{AB} \perp \overline{DE}$ and $\overline{DE}$ is a diameter of $\odot C$, then $\overline{AF} \cong \overline{FB}$. Examine his work below. Then complete his missing statements and reasons.

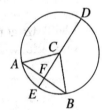

Statements	Reasons
1. $\overline{AB} \perp \overline{DE}$ and $\overline{DE}$ is a diameter of $\odot C$.	1.
2. $\angle AFC$ and $\angle BFC$ are right angles.	2.
3. $FC = FC$	3.
4. $\overline{AC} = \overline{BC}$	4. Definition of a Circle (radii must be equal)
5.	5. HL $\cong$
6. $\overline{AF} \cong \overline{FB}$	6.

8-119.   Match each regular polygon named on the left with a statement about its qualities listed on the right.

a.   regular hexagon

(1)   Central angle of 36°

b.   regular decagon

(2)   Exterior angle measure of 90°

c.   equilateral triangle

(3)   Interior angle measure of 120°

d.   square

(4)   Exterior angle measure of 120°

8-120.   Examine the graph of $f(x)$ at right. Use the graph to find the following values.

a. $f(1)$

b. $f(0)$

c. x if $f(x) = 4$

d. x if $f(x) = 0$

8-121.   Examine the relationships that exist in the diagram at right. Find the measures of angles a, b, c, and d. Remember that you can find the angles in any order, depending on the angle relationships you use.

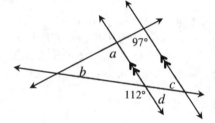

8-122.   **Multiple Choice:** How many cubes with edge length 1 unit would fit in a cube with edge length 3 units?

a.   3

b.   9

c.   10

d.   27

e.   None of these

8-123.   The city of Denver wants you to help build a dog park.
          The design of the park is a rectangle with two
          semicircular ends. (Note: A semicircle is half of a circle.)

30 ft

55 ft

   a.   The entire park needs to be covered with grass. If grass is
         sold by the square foot, how much grass should you order?

   b.   The park also needs a fence for its perimeter. A sturdy chain-linked fence
         costs about $8 per foot. How much will a fence for the entire park cost?

   c.   The local design board has rejected the plan because it was too small.
         "Big dogs need lots of room to run," the president of the board said.
         Therefore, you need to increase the size of the park with a linear scale
         factor of 2. What is the area of the new design? What is the perimeter?

8-124.   This problem is a checkpoint for angle relationships in geometric figures.
          It will be referred to as Checkpoint 8.

          For each diagram, solve for the variable and name the relationship used.

   a. $4x - 3°$ / $3x + 1°$

   b. $5x + 6°$ $2x + 21°$

   c. $4x + 28°$
         $x + 19°$ $3x + 13°$

   d. $40°$ $4x - 10°$

          Check your answers by referring to the Checkpoint 8 materials located at the
          back of your book.

          If you needed help solving these problems correctly, then you need more
          practice. Review the Checkpoint 8 materials and try the practice problems.
          Also, consider getting help outside of class time. From this point on, you will
          be expected to do problems like these quickly and easily.

8-125. $\overline{BE}$ is the midsegment of $\triangle ACD$,
          shown at right.

          B 7 A
          C   6
          11   E
                D

   a.   Find the perimeter of $\triangle ACD$.

   b.   If the area of $\triangle ABE$ is 54 cm^2, what is the area of $\triangle ACD$?

8-126.   Christie has tied a string that is 24 cm long into a closed
          loop, like the one at right.

   a.   She decided to form an equilateral triangle with her
         string. What is the area of the triangle?

   b.   She then forms a square with the same loop of string. What is the area of
         the square? Is it more or less than the equilateral triangle she created in
         part (a)?

   c.   If she forms a regular hexagon with her string, what would be its area?
         Compare this area with the areas of the square and equilateral triangle
         from parts (a) and (b).

   d.   What shape do you think that Christie conjectures will enclose the greatest
         area?

8-127.   Three spinners are shown at right. If
          each spinner is randomly spun and if
          spinners #2 and #3 are each equally
          divided, find the following probabilities.

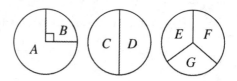

   a.   P(spinning A, C, and E)

   b.   P(spinning at least one vowel)

8-128.   The **Isoperimetric Theorem** states that of all closed figures on a flat surface
          with the same perimeter, the circle has the greatest area. Use this fact to answer
          the questions below.

   a.   What is the greatest area that can be enclosed by a loop of string that is
         24 cm long?

   b.   What is the greatest area that can be enclosed by a loop of string that is
         18π cm long?

8-129.   **Multiple Choice:** The diagram at right is not drawn to scale.
          If $\triangle ABC \sim \triangle KLM$, find KM.

   a.   6   b.   12

   c.   15   d.   21

   e.   None of these

Chapter 8 Closure   What have I learned?

Reflection and Synthesis

The activities below offer you a chance to
reflect about what you have learned during this
chapter. As you work, look for concepts that
you feel very comfortable with, ideas that you
would like to learn more about, and topics you
need more help with. Look for connections
between ideas as well as connections with
material you learned previously.

①   TEAM BRAINSTORM

What have you studied in this chapter? What ideas were important in what you
learned? With your team, brainstorm a list. Be as detailed as you can. To help
get you started, lists of Learning Log entries and Math Notes boxes are below.

What topics, ideas, and words that you learned *before* this chapter are connected
to the new ideas in this chapter? Again, be as detailed as you can.

How long can you make your list? Challenge yourselves. Be prepared to share
your team's ideas with the class.

Learning Log Entries
- Lesson 8.1.2 – Sum of Interior Angles of a Polygon
- Lesson 8.1.3 – Interior Angles and Sum of Exterior
  Angles of a Polygon
- Lesson 8.1.4 – Regular Polygon Angle Web
- Lesson 8.1.5 – Area of a Regular Polygon
- Lesson 8.2.2 – Areas and Perimeters of Similar Figures
- Lesson 8.3.1 – Pi
- Lesson 8.3.2 – Area and Circumference of a Circle

Math Notes
- Lesson 8.1.1 – Convex and Non-Convex Polygons
- Lesson 8.1.2 – Special Quadrilateral Properties
- Lesson 8.1.5 – Interior and Exterior Angles of a Polygon
- Lesson 8.2.1 – Ratios of Similarity
- Lesson 8.3.1 – Area of a Regular Polygon
- Lesson 8.3.2 – Circle Facts
- Lesson 8.3.3 – Arc Length and Area of a Sector

②   MAKING CONNECTIONS

Below is a list of the vocabulary used in this chapter. Make sure that you are familiar with all of these words and know what they mean. Refer to the glossary or index for any words that you do not yet understand.

arc	area	central angle
circumference	convex (polygon)	diameter
exterior angle	interior angle	linear scale factor
non-convex (polygon)	perimeter	pi (π)
polygon	radius	radius of a regular polygon
regular polygon	remote interior angle	sector
similar	zoom factor	

Make a concept map showing all of the connections you can find among the key words and ideas listed above. To show a connection between two words, draw a line between them and explain the connection. A word can be connected to any other word as long as you can justify the connection. For each key word or idea, provide an example or sketch that shows the idea.

While you are making your map, your team may think of related words or ideas that are not listed here. Be sure to include these ideas on your concept map.

③   PORTFOLIO: EVIDENCE OF MATHEMATICAL PROFICIENCY

Write down all the ways that you can find the interior and exterior angles of a regular polygon. Make a sketch of a seven-sided regular polygon and any other regular polygon you choose. Showcase your understanding of regular polygons by finding all the interior and exterior angles of these two polygons.

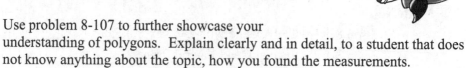

Use problem 8-107 to further showcase your understanding of polygons. Explain clearly and in detail, to a student that does not know anything about the topic, how you found the measurements.

Choose one or two problems from Lesson 8.3.3 that you feel best exhibits your understanding of circles and carefully copy your work, modifying and expanding it if needed. Again, make sure your explanation is clear and detailed. Remember you are not only exhibiting your understanding of the mathematics, but you are also exhibiting your ability to communicate your justifications.

         Core Connections Geometry

④ WHAT HAVE I LEARNED?

Most of the problems in this section represent typical problems found in this chapter. They serve as a gauge for you. You can use them to determine which types of problems you can do well and which types of problems require further study and practice. Even if your teacher does not assign this section, it is a good idea to try these problems and find out for yourself what you know and what you still need to work on.

Solve each problem as completely as you can. The table at the end of the closure section has answers to these problems. It also tells you where you can find additional help and practice with problems like these.

CL 8-130. Mrs. Frank loves the clock in her classroom because it has the school colors, green and purple. The shape of the clock is a regular dodecagon with a radius of 14 centimeters. Centered on the clock's face is a green circle of radius 9 cm. If the region outside the circle is purple, which color has more area? (See problem 8-52 in Lesson 8.1.5 for the definition of the radius of a polygon.)

CL 8-131. Graph the quadrilateral $ABCD$ if $A(-2, 6)$, $B(2, 3)$, $C(2, -2)$, and $D(-2, 1)$.

a. What is the most descriptive name for this quadrilateral? Justify your conclusion.

b. Find the area of $ABCD$.

c. Find the slope of the diagonals, $\overline{AC}$ and $\overline{BD}$. How are the slopes related?

d. Find the point of intersection of the diagonals. What is the relationship between this point and diagonal $\overline{AC}$?

CL 8-132.   Examine the triangle pairs below, which are not necessarily drawn to scale. For each pair, determine:

- If they must be congruent. If they are congruent, write a correct congruence statement (such as $\triangle PQR \cong \triangle STU$) and state the congruence property (such as SAS $\cong$).

- If there is not enough information, explain why you cannot assure congruence.

- If they cannot be congruent, and explain why.

a.   b.   c.

CL 8-133.   Complete the following statements.

a.   If $\triangle YSR \cong \triangle NVD$, then $\overline{DV} \cong$ __?__ and $m\angle RYS =$ __?__ .

b.   If $\overrightarrow{AB}$ bisects $\angle DAC$, then __?__ $\cong$ __?__ .

c.   In $\triangle WQY$, if $\angle WQY \cong \angle QWY$, then __?__ $\cong$ __?__ .

d.   If $ABCD$ is a parallelogram, and $m\angle B = 148°$, then $m\angle C =$ __?__ .

CL 8-134.   Examine the diagram at right. If M is the midpoint of $\overline{KQ}$ and if $\angle P \cong \angle L$, prove that $\overline{KL} \cong \overline{QP}$. Use a flowchart or a two-column proof format.

CL 8-135.   A running track design is composed of two half circles connected by two straight-line segments. Garrett is jogging on the inner lane (with radius r) while Devin is jogging on the outer (with radius R). If $r = 30$ meters and $R = 33$ meters, how much longer does Devin have to run to complete one lap?

CL 8-136.   Use the relationships in the diagrams below to solve for the given variable. Justify your solution with a definition or theorem.

a.

b.   The perimeter of the quadrilateral below is 202 units.

c.   *CARD* is a rhombus.

d.

CL 8-137.   Use the relationships in the diagrams below to find the values of the variables, if possible. The diagrams are not drawn to scale.

a.

b.

c.

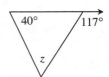

CL 8-138.   Answer the following questions about polygons. If there is not enough information or the problem is impossible, explain why.

a.   Find the sum of the interior angles of a dodecagon.

b.   Find the number of sides of a regular polygon if its central angle measures 35°.

c.   If the sum of the interior angles of a regular polygon is 900°, how many sides does the polygon have?

d.   If the exterior angle of a regular polygon is 15°, find its central angle.

e.   Find the exterior angle of a polygon with 10 sides.

CL 8-139. Examine the diagram at right.

a. Find the measures of each of the angles below, if possible. If it is not possible, explain why it is not possible. If it is possible, state your reasoning.

(1) $m\angle b$ (2) $m\angle f$

(3) $m\angle m$ (4) $m\angle g$

(5) $m\angle h$ (6) $m\angle i$

b. If $m\angle p = 130°$, can you now find the measures of any of the angles from part (a) that you couldn't before? Find the measures for all that you can. Be sure to justify your reasoning.

CL 8-140. Check your answers using the table at the end of the closure section. Which problems do you feel confident about? Which problems were hard? Use the table to make a list of topics you need help on and a list of topics you need to practice more.

Answers and Support for Closure Activity #4
What Have I Learned?

MN: Math Notes, LL: Learning Log

Problem	Solution	Need Help?	More Practice
CL 8-130.	Area of green = $81\pi \approx 254.5$ cm^2; area of purple = $588 - 81\pi \approx 333.5$ cm^2, so the area of purple is greater.	Lessons 8.1.5 and 8.3.2 MN: 8.1.5, 8.3.1, and 8.3.2 LL: 8.1.4, 8.1.5, and 8.3.2	Problems 8-67, 8-84, 8-93, 8-107(b), and 8-126
CL 8-131.	a. Rhombus. It is a quadrilateral with four equal sides. b. 20 square units c. The slopes are –2 and $\frac{1}{2}$. They are opposite reciprocals. d. The point of intersection is $(0, 2)$. It is the midpoint of the diagonal.	Section 7.3 MN: 7.2.3, 7.3.2, 7.3.3, and 8.1.2 LL: 7.3.3	Problems CL 7-153, 8-17, 8-32, 8-55, and 8-98

Problem	Solution	Need Help?	More Practice
CL 8-132.	a. Congruent (SAS ≅), $\triangle ABD \cong \triangle CBD$ b. Not enough information (the triangles are similar (AA ~), but no side lengths are given to know if they are the same size.) c. Congruent (ASA ≅ or AAS ≅), $\triangle ABC \cong \triangle DEF$	Section 3.2 and Lessons 6.1.1 through 6.1.4 MN: 3.2.2 and 6.1.4	Problems CL 3-121, CL 4-123, CL 5-140, CL 6-101, CL 7-155, 8-11, and 8-88
CL 8-133.	a. $\overline{DV} \cong \overline{RS}$, $m\angle RYS = m\angle DNV$ b. $\angle DAB \cong \angle CAB$ c. $\overline{WY} \cong \overline{QY}$ d. $m\angle D = 32°$	MN: 7.1.3	Problems 7-24, 7-38, 7-48, 7-75, 8-22, 8-30, and 8-88
CL 8-134.		Section 3.2 and Lessons 6.1.1 through 6.1.4 MN: 3.2.2, 3.2.4, 6.1.4, and 7.1.3 LL: 3.2.2	Problems CL 3-121, CL 4-123, CL 5-140, CL 6-101, CL 7-155, 8-22, 8-30, 8-63, 8-87, 8-96, and 8-118
CL 8-135.	Devin must run 6π meters farther than Garrett on each lap.	Lesson 8.3.2 MN: 8.3.2 LL: 8.3.2	Problems 8-116 and 8-123(b)

Problem	Solution	Need Help?	More Practice
CL 8-136.	a. $x = 110°$ (Opposite angles in a parallelogram are equal.) b. $t = 18$ (Perimeter equals the sum of the sides.) c. $x = 23°$ (Diagonals of a rhombus are perpendicular.) d. $m = 4$ (Nonparallel sides of an isosceles trapezoid are congruent.)	Section 2.1, Lessons 2.3.2 and 7.2.6 MN: 2.1.1, 2.1.4, 2.3.2, 7.2.4, 7.2.6, and 8.1.2 LL: 2.1.1, 2.3.2 Angle Relationships Toolkit	Problems CL 7-154, 8-6, 8-60, 8-97, 8-108, 8-121, and 8-124
CL 8-137.	a. $x = 4°$ b. Cannot determine because the lines are not marked parallel. c. $z = 77°$	Section 2.1 MN: 2.1.1 and 2.1.4 LL: 2.1.1	Problems 8-6, 8-23, 8-33, 8-60, 8-97, 8-108, 8-121, and 8-124
CL 8-138.	a. $1800°$ b. Impossible. In a regular polygon, the central angle must be a factor of $360°$. c. 7 sides d. $15°$ e. $36°$	Lessons 8.1.2, 8.1.3, and 8.1.4 MN: 7.1.4 and 8.1.5 LL: 8.1.2, 8.1.3, and 8.1.4	Problems 8-8, 8-18, 8-44, 8-53, 8-95, 8-107(a), and 8-119
CL 8-139.	a. (1) $b = 101°$, corres. angles are equal (2) $f = 79°$, supplementary angles (3) not enough information (4) $g = 101°$, vertical angles are equal (5) $h = 79°$, supplementary angles (6) not enough information b. $m = 50°$; $v = 130°$; $i = 51°$	Section 2.1 MN: 2.1.1, 2.1.4, and 2.2.1 LL: 2.1.1	Problems 8-6, 8-23, 8-33, 8-60, 8-97, 8-108, 8-121, and 8-124

SOLIDS AND CONSTRUCTIONS

9

CHAPTER 9   Solids and Constructions

In your study of geometry so far, you have focused your attention on two-dimensional shapes. You have investigated the special properties of triangles, parallelograms, regular polygons and circles, and have developed tools to help you describe and analyze those shapes. For example, you have tools to find an interior angle of a regular hexagon, to calculate the length of the hypotenuse of a right triangle, and to measure the perimeter of a triangle or the area of a circle.

In Section 9.1, you will turn your focus to three-dimensional shapes (called **solids**), such as cubes and cylinders. You will learn several ways to represent three-dimensional solids and develop methods to measure their volumes and surface areas.

Guiding Question

Mathematically proficient students use appropriate tools strategically.

As you work through this chapter, ask yourself:

How can I represent it, what tools can I use, and how can I construct it?

Then, in Section 9.2, you will learn how to use special tools to construct accurate diagrams of two-dimensional shapes and geometric relationships. During this investigation, you will revisit many of the geometric conjectures and theorems that you have developed so far.

In this chapter, you will learn how to:

> ➤ Find the surface area and volume of three-dimensional solids, such as prisms and cylinders.

> ➤ Represent a three-dimensional solid with a mat plan, a net, and side and top views.

> ➤ Determine the changes to volume when a three-dimensional solid is enlarged proportionally.

> ➤ Construct familiar geometric shapes (such as a rhombus or a regular hexagon) using construction tools such as tracing paper, a compass and straightedge, or a dynamic geometry tool.

Chapter Outline

Section 9.1   This section is devoted to the study of three-dimensional solids and their measurement. You will also learn to use a variety of methods to represent the shapes of solids.

Section 9.2   This section will introduce you to the study of constructing geometric shapes and relationships. For example, you will learn how to construct a perpendicular bisector using only a compass and a straightedge.

9.1.1 How can I build it?

Three-Dimensional Solids

With your knowledge of polygons and circles, you are able to create and explore new, interesting shapes and make elaborate designs such as the one shown in the stained glass window at right. However, in the physical world, the objects you encounter every day are three-dimensional. In other words, physical objects cannot exist entirely on a flat surface, such as a tabletop.

To understand the shapes that you encounter daily, you will need to learn more about how three-dimensional shapes, called **solids**, can be created, described, and measured.

Reprinted with permission by Rob Mielke, Blue Feather Stained Glass Designs.

As you work with your team today, be especially careful to explain to your teammates how you "see" each solid. Remember that spatial visualization takes time and effort, so be patient with your teammates and help everyone understand how each solid is built.

9-1.   Using blocks provided by your teacher, work with your team to build the three-dimensional solid at right. Assume that blocks cannot hover in midair. That is, if a block is on the second level, assume that it has a block below it to prop it up.

   a.   Is there more than one arrangement of blocks that could look like the solid drawn at right? Why or why not?

   b.   To avoid confusion, a **mat plan** can be used to show how the blocks are arranged in the solid. The number in each square represents the number of the blocks stacked in that location if you are looking from above. For example, in the right-hand corner, the solid is only 1 block tall, so there is a "1" in the corresponding corner of its mat plan.

Verify that the solid your team built matches the solid represented in the mat plan above.

   c.   What is the **volume** of the solid? That is, if each block represents a cubic unit, how many blocks (cubic units) make up this solid?

9-2.   Another way to represent a
       three-dimensional solid is by
       its **side** and **top views**.

       For example, the solid from
       problem 9-1 can also be
       represented by a top, front, and
       right-hand view, as shown at right.
       Each view shows *all* of the blocks
       that are visible when looking
       directly at the solid from that
       direction.

       Examine the diagram of blocks at
       right. On graph paper, draw the
       front, right, and top views of this
       solid. Assume that there are no
       hidden blocks.

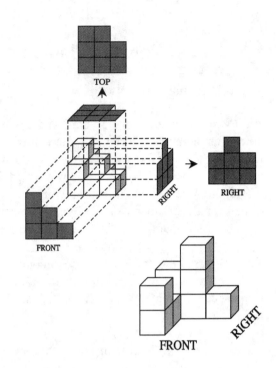

9-3.   For each of the mat plans below:

       •   Build the three-dimensional solid with the blocks provided by your
           teacher.

       •   Find the volume of the solid in cubic units.

       •   Draw the front, right, and top views of the solid on a piece of graph paper.

a.

0	3	0
2	3	1
0	2	0

RIGHT

FRONT

b.

0	2	1
0	3	0
3	2	1

RIGHT

FRONT

c.

1	1	3
2	1	2
0	0	1

RIGHT

FRONT

9-4.   Meagan built a shape with blocks and then drew
       the views shown at right.

       a.   Build Meagan's shape using blocks
            provided by your teacher. Use as few
            blocks as possible.

       b.   What is the volume of Meagan's shape?

       c.   Draw a mat plan for her shape.

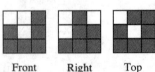

Front   Right   Top

9-5.   Draw a mat plan for each of the following solids. There may be more than one possible answer! Then find the possible volumes of each one.

a.

FRONT   RIGHT

b.

FRONT   RIGHT

9-6.   LEARNING LOG

During this lesson, you have found the volume of several three-dimensional solids. However, what *is* volume? What does it measure? Write a Learning Log entry describing volume. Add at least one example. Title this entry "Volume of a Three-Dimensional Shape" and include today's date.

Review & Preview

9-7.   Examine the solid at right.

   a.   On your paper, draw a possible mat plan for this solid.

   b.   Find the volume of this solid.

9-8.   Assume that two figures on a flat surface, A and B, are similar.

   a.   If the linear scale factor is $\frac{2}{5}$, then what is the ratio of the areas of A and B?

   b.   If the ratio of the perimeters of A and B is 14:1, what is the ratio of the areas?

   c.   If the area of A is 81 times that of B, what is the ratio of the perimeters?

9-9.   Find the area of a regular decagon with perimeter 100 units. Show all work.

9-10.   The diagram at right shows a circle inscribed in a square. Find the area of the shaded region if the side length of the square is 6 meters.

9-11.   Solve each system of equations below. Write your solution in the form (x, y). Check your solution.

a. $3x - y = 14$
       $x = 2y + 8$

b. $x = 2y + 2$
       $x = -y - 10$

c. $16x - y = -4$
       $2x + y = 13$

9-12.   Gino looked around at the twelve students in his lunchtime computer science club and wrote down the following descriptions of their sex, clothing, and shoes:

male, long pants, tennis shoes   male, shorts, tennis shoes
female, shorts, tennis shoes   male, shorts, other shoes
female, dress or skirt, other shoes   female, dress or skirt, tennis shoes
female, long pants, tennis shoes   male, long pants, other shoes
male, long pants, other shoes   female, shorts, other shoes
female, long pants, other shoes   male, long pants, tennis shoes

a.   Make an area model or tree diagram of all the possible outfits in the sample space. Organize the combinations of sex, clothing, and shoes.

b.   In your model or diagram from part (a), indicate the probabilities for each option. What is the probability that a randomly selected student is wearing long pants?

c.   Which outcomes are in the event which is the union of {long pants} and {tennis shoes}? Which outcomes are in the intersection of {long pants} and {tennis shoes}?

9-13.   **Multiple Choice:** What information would you need to know about the diagram at right in order to prove that $\triangle ABD \cong \triangle CBD$ by SAS $\cong$?

a. $\overline{AD} \cong \overline{CD}$

b. $\overline{AB} \cong \overline{CB}$

c. $\angle A \cong \angle C$

d. $\angle ABD \cong \angle CBD$

e.   None of these

Core Connections Geometry

9.1.2 How can I measure it?

Volumes and Surface Areas of Prisms

Today you will continue to study three-dimensional solids and will practice representing a solid using a mat plan and its side and top views. You will also learn a new way to represent a three-dimensional object, called a net. As you work today, you will learn about a special set of solids called prisms and will study how to find the surface area and volume of a prism.

9-14. The front, top, and right-hand views of Heidi's solid are shown at right.

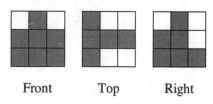

Front   Top   Right

     a. Build Heidi's solid using blocks provided by your teacher. Use the smallest number of blocks possible. What is the volume of her solid?

     b. Draw a mat plan for Heidi's solid. Be sure to indicate where the front and right sides are located.

     c. Oh no! Heidi accidentally dropped her entire solid into a bucket of paint! What is the **surface area** of her solid? That is, what is the area that is now covered in paint?

9-15. So far, you have studied three ways to represent a solid: a three-dimensional drawing, a mat plan, and its side and top views.

Another way to represent a three-dimensional solid is with a **net**, such as the one shown at right. When folded, a net will form the three-dimensional solid it represents.

     a. With your team, predict what the three-dimensional solid formed by this net will look like. Assume the shaded squares make up the base (or bottom) of the solid.

     b. Obtain a Lesson 9.1.2 Resource Page and scissors from your teacher and cut out the net. Fold along the solid lines to create the three-dimensional solid. Did the result confirm your prediction from part (a)?

     c. Now build the shape with blocks and complete the mat plan at right for this solid.

     d. What is the volume of this solid? How did you get your answer?

     e. What is the surface area of the solid? How did you find your answer? Be prepared to share any shortcuts with the class.

9-16.   Paul built a tower by stacking six identical
         layers of the shape at right on top of each
         other.

Each layer

Paul's tower

a.   What is the volume of his tower?
      How can you tell without building
      the shape?

b.   What is the surface area of his tower?

c.   Paul's tower is an example of a **prism** because it is a solid and two of its
      faces (called **bases**) are congruent and parallel. A prism must also have
      sides that connect the bases (called **lateral faces**). Each lateral face must
      be a parallelogram (and thus may also be a rectangle, rhombus or a
      square).

      For each of the prisms below, find the volume and surface area.

(1)   (2)   (3)

                                                              5

                                                          4   3

9-17.   Heidi created several more solids, represented below. Find the volume of each
         one.

a.

0	3	5
22	10	25
18	15	8
16	12	0

RIGHT

FRONT

b.

c.

9-18.   Pilar built a tower by stacking identical layers on top of each other. If her tower
         used a total of 312 blocks and if the bottom layer has 13 blocks, how tall is her
         tower? Explain how you know.

9-19.   LEARNING LOG

What is the relationship between the area of the base of a
prism, its height, and its volume? In a Learning Log
entry, summarize how to find the volume of a solid. Be
sure to include an example. Title this entry "Finding Volume"
and include today's date.

METHODS AND MEANINGS

Polyhedra and Prisms

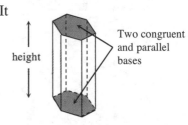

A closed three-dimensional solid that has flat, polygonal faces is
called a **polyhedron**. The plural of polyhedron is **polyhedra**.
"Poly" is the Greek root for "many," and "hedra" is the Greek
root for "faces."

A **prism** is a special type of polyhedron. It
must have two congruent, parallel **bases**
that are polygons. Also, its **lateral faces**
(the faces connecting the bases) are
parallelograms formed by connecting the
corresponding vertices of the two bases.
Note that lateral faces may be any type of
parallelogram, such as rectangles, rhombi, or squares.

height   Two congruent
                            and parallel
                            bases

Review & Preview

9-20.   Mr. Wallis is designing a home. He found
         the plan for his dream house on the Internet
         and printed it out on paper.

30

60°

51

   a.   The design of the home is shown at right.
         If all measurements are in millimeters,
         find the area of the diagram.

   b.   Mr. Wallis took his home design to the copier and enlarged it 400%.
         What is the area of the diagram now? Show how you know.

9-21.   At right is the solid from problem 9-7.

   a.   On graph paper, draw the front, right,
         and top views.

   b.   Find the total surface area of the solid.

9-22.   Review what you know about the angles of polygons below.

   a.   If the exterior angle of a polygon is 29°, what is the interior angle?

   b.   If the interior angle of a polygon is 170°, can it be a regular polygon?
         Why or why not?

   c.   Find the sum of the interior angles of a regular 29-gon.

9-23.   For each geometric relationship represented below, write and solve an equation
         for x. Show all work.

   a.   b.

9-24.   At the band's peak of popularity, a personally signed Black Diamond poster
         sold for $500. Three years later the band was almost forgotten and the poster
         was worth only $10. What were the annual multiplier and annual percent of
         decrease?

Core Connections Geometry

9-25.   On graph paper, graph $\triangle ABC$ if $A(-3, -4)$, $B(-1, -6)$, and $C(-5, -8)$.

   a.   What is AB (the length of $\overline{AB}$)?

   b.   Reflect $\triangle ABC$ across the x-axis to form $\triangle A'B'C'$. What are the coordinates of B'? Describe the function that would change the coordinates of $\triangle ABC$ to $\triangle A'B'C'$.

   c.   Rotate $\triangle A'B'C'$ 90° clockwise (↻) about the origin to form $\triangle A''B''C''$. What are the coordinates of C''?

   d.   Translate $\triangle ABC$ so that $(x,y) \rightarrow (x+5, y+1)$. What are the new coordinates of point A?

9-26.   Compute the volume of the figure at right.

9-27.   **Multiple Choice:** Find the perimeter of the sector at right.

   a. 12π ft   b. 3π ft   c. $6 + 3\pi$ ft

   d. $12 + \pi$ ft   e.   None of these

9.1.3 What if the bases are not rectangles?

Prisms and Cylinders

In Lessons 9.1.1 and 9.1.2, you investigated volume, surface area, and special three-dimensional solids called prisms. Today you will explore different ways to find the volume and surface area of a prism and a related solid called a cylinder. You will also consider what happens to the volume of a prism or cylinder if it slants to one side or if it is enlarged proportionally.

9-28. Examine the three-dimensional solid at right.

a. On graph paper, draw a net that, when folded, will create this solid.

b. Compare your net with those of your teammates. Is there more than one possible net? Why or why not?

c. Find the surface area and volume of this solid.

9-29. SPECIAL PRISMS

The prism in problem 9-28 is an example of a **rectangular prism**, because its bases are rectangular. Similarly, the prism at right is called a **triangular prism** because the two congruent bases are triangular.

a. Carefully draw the prism at right onto your paper. One way to do this is to draw the two triangular bases first and then to connect the corresponding vertices of the bases. Notice that hidden edges are represented with dashed lines.

b. Find the surface area of the triangular prism. Remember that the surface area includes the areas of *all* surfaces – the sides and the bases. Carefully organize your work and verify your solution with your teammates.

c. Find the volume of the triangular prism. Be prepared to share your team's method with the class.

d. Does your method for finding surface area and volume work on other prisms? For example, what if the bases are hexagonal, like the one shown at right? Work with your team to find the surface area and volume of this hexagonal prism. Assume that the bases are regular hexagons with side length 4 inches.

9-30.   CYLINDERS

Carter wonders, *"What if the bases are circular?"* Copy the
cylinder at right onto your paper. Discuss with your team
how to find its surface area and volume if the radius of the
base is 5 units and the height of the cylinder is 8 units.

9-31.   CAVALIERI'S PRINCIPLE

Bonaventura Cavalieri (1598-1647) was a mathematician who helped to
develop calculus, but is best remembered today for a principle named for
him. Cavalieri's Principle can be thought of as a way of finding volumes in a
relatively easy way.

a.   Suppose you have a stack of 25 pennies piled one on top of the
other. You decide to slant the stack by sliding some of the pennies
over. Does the volume of the 25 pennies change even though they are no
longer stacked one on top of another.

b.   Would the same thing be true of a stack of 15 books that you slide to the
side or twist some of them? What about a stack of 1000 sheets of paper?

c.   The idea of viewing solids as slices that can be moved
around without affecting the volume is called **Cavalieri's
Principle**. Use this principle to find the volume of the
cylinder at right. Note that when the lateral faces of a
prism or cylinder are not perpendicular to its base, the
solid is referred to as an **oblique** cylinder or prism. How is the
volume of this prism related to the one in problem 9-30?

9-32.   Hernando needs to replace the hot water tank at his
house. He estimates that his family needs a tank
that can hold at least 75 gallons of water. His local
water tank supplier has a cylindrical model that has
a diameter of 2 feet and a height of 3 feet. If
1 gallon of water is approximately 0.1337 cubic
feet, determine if the supplier's tank will provide
enough water.

METHODS AND MEANINGS

Volume and Total Surface Area of a Solid

Volume measures the size of a three-dimensional space enclosed within an object. It is expressed as the number of $1 \times 1 \times 1$ cubes (or parts of cubes) that fit inside a solid.

For example, the solid shown above right has a volume of 6 cubic units.

Since volume reflects the number of cubes that fit within a solid, it is measured in **cubic units**. For example, if the dimensions of a solid are measured in feet, then the volume would be measured in cubic feet (a cube with dimensions $1' \times 1' \times 1'$).

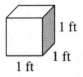

1 ft
1 ft
1 ft

On the other hand, the total **surface area** of a solid is the area of all of the external faces of the solid. For example, the total surface area of the solid above is 24 square units.

Cavalieri's Principle states that when the corresponding slices of two solids (with equal heights) have equal area, then the solids have equal volume. One way to think about Cavalieri's Principle is to think about how the volume of a stack of identical books would not change when you slide or twist some of them in the stack.

Review & Preview

9-33.   In the diagram at right, $\overline{DE}$ is a midsegment of $\triangle ABC$. If the area of $\triangle ABC$ is 96 square units, what is the area of $\triangle ADE$? Explain how you know.

9-34.   A regular hexagonal prism has a volume of 2546.13 cm³ and the base has an edge length of 14 cm. Find the height and surface area of the prism.

9-35.   Are $\triangle EHF$ and $\triangle FGE$ congruent? If so, explain how you know. If not, explain why not.

9-36.   A sandwich shop delivers lunches by bicycle to nearby office buildings. Unfortunately, sometimes the delivery is made later than promised. A delay can occur either because food preparation took too long, or because the bicycle rider got lost. Last month the food preparation took too long or the rider got lost, 7% of the time. During the same month, the food preparation took longer than expected 11 times and the bicycle rider got lost 4 times. There were 200 deliveries made during the month. For a randomly selected delivery last month, find the probability that both the food preparation took too long and the rider got lost.

9-37.   Remember that the absolute value of a number is its positive value. For example, $|-5| = 5$ and $|5| = 5$. Use this understanding to solve the equations below, if possible. If there is no solution, explain how you know.

   a. $|x| = 6$ b. $|x| = -2$ c. $|x + 7| = 10$

9-38.   Cindy's cylindrical paint bucket has a diameter of 12 inches and a height of 14.5 inches. If 1 gallon ≈ 231 in.^{3}, how many gallons does her paint bucket hold?

9-39.   Write the equation of an exponential function that passes through the points (0, 32) and (3, 4).

9-40.   A cork in the shape of a cylinder has a radius of 2 cm, a height of 5 cm, and weighs 2.5 grams.

   a.   What is the volume of the cork?

   b.   What is the cork's density in grams per cubic centimeter? That is, how many grams of cork are there per cubic centimeter?

9.1.4 How does the volume change?

Volumes of Similar Solids

As you continue your study of three-dimensional solids, today you will explore how the volume of a solid changes as the solid is enlarged proportionally.

9-41. HOW DOES THE VOLUME CHANGE?

In Lesson 9.1.3, you began a study of the surface area and volume of solids. Today, you will continue that investigation in order to generalize about the ratios of similar solids.

a. Describe the solid formed by the net at right. What are its dimensions (length, width, and height)?

b. Have each team member select a different enlargement ratio from the list below. On graph paper, carefully draw the net of a similar solid using your enlargement ratio. Then cut out your net and build the solid (so that the gridlines end up on the outside the solid) using scissors and tape.

(1) 1   (2) 2   (3) 3   (4) 4

c. Find the volume of your solid and compare it to the volume of the original solid. What is the ratio of these volumes? Share the results with your teammates so that each person can complete a table like the one below.

Linear Scale Factor	Original Volume	New Volume	Ratio of Volumes
1			
2			
3			
4			
r			

d. How does the volume change when a three-dimensional solid is enlarged or reduced to create a similar solid? For example, if a solid's length, width, and depth are enlarged by a linear scale factor of 10, then how many times bigger does the volume get? What if the solid is enlarged by a linear scale factor of r? Explain.

9-42.   Examine the $1 \times 1 \times 3$ solid at right.

   a.   Build this solid with blocks provided by your teacher.

   b.   If this shape is enlarged by a linear scale factor of 2, how wide will the new shape be? How tall? How deep?

   c.   How many of the $1 \times 1 \times 3$ solids would you need to build the enlargement described in part (b) above? Use blocks to prove your answer.

   d.   What if the $1 \times 1 \times 3$ solid is enlarged with a linear scale factor of 3? How many times larger would the volume of the new solid be? Explain how you found your answer.

9-43.   At the movies, Maurice counted the number of kernels of popcorn that filled his tub and found that it had 320 kernels. He decided that next time, he will get an enlarged tub that is similar, but has a linear scale factor of 1.5. How many kernels of popcorn should the enlarged tub hold?

9-44.   LEARNING LOG

In your Learning Log, explain how the volume changes when a solid is enlarged proportionally. That is, if a three-dimensional object is enlarged by a linear scale factor of 2, by what factor does the volume increase? Title this entry "Volumes of Similar Solids" and include today's date.

9-45.   Koy is inflating a spherical balloon for her brother's birthday party. She has used three full breaths so far and her balloon is only half the width she needs. Assuming that she puts the same amount of air into the balloon with each breath, how many more breaths does she need to finish the task? Explain how you know.

9-46.   Draw a cylinder on your paper. Assume the radius of the cylinder is 6 inches and the height is 9 inches.

a.   What is the surface area of the cylinder? What is the volume?

b.   If the cylinder is enlarged with a linear scale factor of 3, what is the volume of the enlarged cylinder? How do you know?

9-47.   While Katarina was practicing her figure skating, she wondered how far she had traveled. She was skating a "figure 8," which means she starts between two circles and then travels on the boundary of each circle, completing the shape of a sideways 8. If both circles have a radius of 5 feet, how far does she travel when skating one "figure 8"?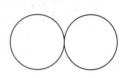

9-48.   For each triangle below, solve for x, if possible. If no solution is possible, explain why.

a. 80° 10 27° x b. 8 6 x c. 6 x 30° 5

9-49.   The mat plan for a three-dimensional solid is shown at right.

a.   On your paper, draw the front, right, and top views of this solid.

b.   Find the volume and surface area of the solid.

3	2	0
1	4	1
0	3	2

RIGHT

FRONT

Mat Plan

9-50.   The graph of the inequality $y > 2x - 3$ is shown at right. On graph paper, graph the inequality $y \le 2x - 3$. Explain what you changed about the graph.

9-51.   An international charity builds homes for disaster victims. Often the materials
          are donated. The charity recently built 45 homes. 20% used granite for the
          kitchen countertops, while the rest used porcelain tile. 15 of the homes used red
          oak for the wooden kitchen floor, 20 used white oak, and 10 used maple. If a
          disaster victim is randomly assigned to a home, what is the probability (in
          percent) of getting an oak floor with granite countertops?

9-52.   **Multiple Choice:** The point $A(-2, 5)$ is rotated $90°$ counter-clockwise (↺).
          What are the new coordinates of point A?

          a. $(2, 5)$ b. $(5, -2)$ c. $(2, -5)$ d. $(-5, -2)$

9.1.5 How does the volume change?

Ratios of Similarity

Today, work with your team to analyze the following problems. As you work, think about whether the problem involves volume or area. Also think carefully about how similar solids are related to each other.

9-53. A statue to honor Benjamin Franklin will be placed outside the entrance to the Liberty Bell exhibit hall in Philadelphia. The designers decide that a smaller, similar version will be placed on a table inside the building. The dimensions of the life-sized statue will be four times those of the smaller statue. Planners expect to need 1.5 pints of paint to coat the small statue. They also know that the small statue will weigh 14 pounds.

a. How much paint will be needed to paint the life-sized statue?

b. If the small statue is made of the same material as the enlarged statue, then its weight will change just as the volume changes as the statue is enlarged. How much will the life-size statue weigh?

9-54. The Blackbird Oil Company is considering the purchase of 20 new jumbo oil storage tanks. The standard model holds 12,000 gallons. Its dimensions are $\frac{4}{5}$ the size of the similarly shaped jumbo model, that is, the ratio of the dimensions is 4:5.

a. How much more storage capacity would the twenty jumbo models give Blackbird Oil?

b. If jumbo tanks cost 50% more than standard tanks, which tank is a better buy?

9-55. In problem 7-14 your class constructed a large tetrahedron like the one at right. Assume the dimensions of the shaded tetrahedron at right are half of the dimensions of the similar enlarged tetrahedron.

a. If the volume of the large tetrahedron is 138 in.³, find the volume of the small shaded tetrahedron.

b. Each face of a tetrahedron is an equilateral triangle. If the small shaded tetrahedron has an edge length of 16 cm, find the total surface area for each of the tetrahedra.

c. Your class tried to construct a tetrahedron using four smaller congruent tetrahedra. However, the result left a gap in the center, as shown in the diagram at right. If the volume of each small shaded tetrahedron is 50 in.³, what is the volume of the gap? Explain how you know.

METHODS AND MEANINGS

The $r : r^2 : r^3$ Ratios of Similarity

When a two-dimensional figure is enlarged proportionally, its perimeter and area also grow. If the linear scale factor is r, then the perimeter of the figure is enlarged by a factor of r while the area of the figure is enlarged by a factor of r^2. Examine what happens when the square at right is enlarged by a linear scale factor of 3.

$P = 4$ units $P = 4 \cdot 3 = 12$ units
$A = 1$ units² $A = 1 \cdot 3^2 = 9$ units²

When a solid is enlarged proportionally, its surface area and volume also grow. If it is enlarged by a linear scale factor of r, then the surface area grows by a factor of r^2 and the volume grows by a factor of r^3. The example at right shows what happens to a solid when it is enlarged by a linear scale factor of 2.

Original solid   Width, height,   **Result:**
SA = 14   and depth are   SA = 56
units²   doubled   units²
V = 3 units³   V = 24 units³

Thus, if a solid is enlarged proportionally by a linear scale factor of r, then:

New edge length = $r \cdot$ (corresponding edge length of original solid)

New surface area = $r^2 \cdot$ (original surface area)

New volume = $r^3 \cdot$ (original volume)

9-56. Consider the two similar solids at right.

a. Create a mat plan and draw the front, right, and top views for the solid on the left.

b. What is the linear scale factor between the two solids?

c. Find the surface area of each solid. What is the ratio of the surface areas? How is this ratio related to the linear scale factor?

d. Now find the volumes of each solid. How are the volumes related? Compare this to the linear scale factor and record your observations.

9-57. Elliot has a modern fish tank that is in the shape of an oblique prism, shown at right.

a. If the slant of the prism makes a 60° angle with the flat surface on which the prism is placed, find the volume of water the tank can hold. Assume that each base is a rectangle.

b. If Elliot has 25 fish, how crowded are the fish? That is, what is the density of fish, measured in number of fish per cubic inch?

c. What is the density of fish in Elliot's tank in fish per cubic *foot*?

9-58. Decide if the following statements are true or false. If they are true, explain how you know. If they are false, provide a counterexample.

a. If a quadrilateral has two sides that are parallel and two sides that are congruent, then the quadrilateral must be a parallelogram.

b. If the interior angles of a polygon add up to 360°, then the polygon must be a quadrilateral.

c. If a quadrilateral has 3 right angles, then the quadrilateral must be a rectangle.

d. If the diagonals of a quadrilateral bisect each other, then the quadrilateral must be a rhombus.

Core Connections Geometry

9-59.   Write and solve an equation based on the geometric relationship shown at right.

9-60.   Solve each equation below. Check your solution.

   a. $20 - 6(5 + 2x) = 10 - 2x$

   b. $2x^2 - 9x - 5 = 0$

   c. $\frac{3}{5x-1} = \frac{1}{x+1}$

   d. $|2x - 1| = 5$

9-61.   A new car purchased for $27,000 loses 15% of its value each year.

   a.   What is the multiplier?

   b.   Write a function of the form $f(t) = ab^t$ that represents the situation.

   c.   At the current rate, what will be the value of the car in 5 years?

9-62.   Examine the information provided in each diagram below. Decide if each figure is possible or not. If the figure is not possible, explain why.

   a.

   b.

   c.

9-63.   **Multiple Choice:** For $\angle ABE \cong \angle BEF$ in the diagram below, what must be true?

   a. $\angle ABE \cong \angle BED$

   b. $\angle ABE \cong \angle GBC$

   c. $\overline{AC} \parallel \overline{GH}$

   d. $\overline{AC} \parallel \overline{DF}$

   e.   None of these.

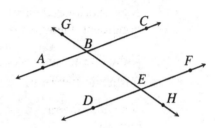

9.2.1 How can I construct it?

•••

Introduction to Constructions

So far in this course, you have used tools such as rulers, tracing paper, protractors, and even computers to draw geometric relationships and shapes. But how did ancient mathematicians accurately construct shapes such as squares or equilateral triangles without these types of tools?

Today you will start by exploring how to construct several geometric relationships and figures with tracing paper. You will then investigate how to construct geometric shapes with tools called a compass and a straightedge, much like the ancient Greeks did more than 2000 years ago. As you study these forms of **construction**, you will not only learn about new geometric tools, but also gain a deeper understanding of some of the special geometric relationships and shapes you have studied so far in this course.

9-64.   CONSTRUCTING WITH TRACING PAPER

To start this focus on construction, you will begin with a familiar tool: tracing paper. Obtain several sheets of tracing paper and a straightedge from your teacher. Note: A straightedge is *not* a ruler. It does not have any markings or measurements on it. For example, a 3" × 5" index card makes a good straightedge.

a.   Starting with a smooth, square piece of tracing paper, find a way to create parallel lines (or creases). Make sure the lines are *exactly* parallel. Be ready to share with the class how you accomplished this.

b.   With a new piece of tracing paper, trace line segment $\overline{AB}$ at right. Use your straightedge for accuracy. Can you fold the tracing paper so that the resulting crease not only finds the midpoint of $\overline{AB}$ but also is perpendicular to $\overline{AB}$? Remember that this is the **perpendicular bisector** of $\overline{AB}$. Prove that your crease is the perpendicular bisector.

Problem continues on next page →

9-64.   *Problem continued from previous page.*

    c.   On the perpendicular bisector from part (b) above, choose a point C and then connect $\overline{AC}$ and $\overline{BC}$ to form $\triangle ABC$. What type of triangle did you construct? Use your geometry knowledge to justify your answer.

    d.   In part (b), you determined how to use tracing paper and a straightedge to construct a line that bisects another line. How can you construct an angle bisector?

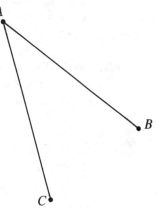

         On a piece of tracing paper, trace $\angle BAC$ at right. Construct the angle bisector. That is, find $\overline{AD}$ such that $\angle BAD \cong \triangle CAD$.

    e.   Did you know that the angle bisectors of a triangle intersect at a single point? On your tracing paper, connect $\overline{BC}$ to form $\triangle ABC$. Then fold to find the angle bisectors of the other two angles, $\angle ABC$ and $\angle BCA$. Mark this special "center" of the triangle, which is sometimes referred to as the **incenter** of the triangle, with a point. Put this tracing paper aside but keep it for problem 9-66.

9-65. CONSTRUCTING WITH A COMPASS AND A STRAIGHTEDGE

Other tools that are often used to construct
geometric figures are a compass and a
straightedge. Obtain a Lesson 9.2.1 Resource
Page from your teacher and explore what types of
shapes you can construct using these tools.

a. Find point *C* on the resource page. Use your compass to construct two
circles with different radii that have a center at point *C*. Circles that have
the same center are called **concentric** circles.

b. With tracing paper, copying a line segment means just putting the tracing
paper over the line and tracing it. But how can you copy a line segment
using only a compass and a straightedge?

On the resource page, find $\overline{AB}$. Next to $\overline{AB}$, use your straightedge to draw
a new line segment. With your team, decide how to use the compass to
mark off two points (*C* and *D*) so that $\overline{AB} \cong \overline{CD}$. Be ready to share your
method with the class.

c. Now construct a new line segment, labeled $\overline{EF}$, that is twice as long as
$\overline{AB}$. How can you be sure that $\overline{EF}$ is twice as long as $\overline{AB}$?

d. How can you use these tools to copy an angle? On
your resource page, find ∠*X*. With your team,
discuss how you can use your compass to construct a
new angle (∠*Y*) on your resource page that is
congruent to ∠*X*. Start by drawing a ray with
endpoint *Y*.

9-66. The incenter of a triangle is special because it is also the center of a circle that
lies inside the triangle and intersects each side of the triangle exactly once. This
circle is called an **inscribed circle**. To construct this circle, you will need to
use both your tracing paper from part (d) and (e) of problem 9-64 and your
compass.

a. As Shui thought about constructing a circle that fits inside the triangle, she
observed, "*I think △ABC is an isosceles triangle.*" Do you agree? How
can you test her conjecture with your tracing paper?

b. Shui thinks that the inscribed circle must pass through the midpoint of
$\overline{BC}$. Is this correct? Explain why or why not.

c. With your compass, construct the inscribed circle of △*ABC* with the center
at the incenter.

9-67.   REGULAR HEXAGON

As Shui was completing her homework, she noticed that a
regular hexagon has a special quality: when dissected into
congruent triangles, the hexagon contains triangles that are
all equilateral! *"I bet I can use this fact to help me
construct a regular hexagon,"* she told her team.

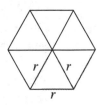

a.   On the Lesson 9.2.1 Resource Page, construct a circle with radius r and
      center H.

b.   Mark one point on the circle to be a starting vertex. Since each side of the
      hexagon has length r, the radius of the circle, carefully use the compass to
      mark off the other vertices of the hexagon on the circle. Then connect the
      vertices to create the regular hexagon.

c.   When all vertices of a polygon lie on the same circle, the polygon is
      inscribed in the circle. For example, the hexagon you constructed in part
      (b) is inscribed in $\odot H$. After consulting with your teammates, construct
      an equilateral triangle that is also inscribed in $\odot H$. You may want to use
      colored markers or pencils to help distinguish between the hexagon and
      the triangle.

9-68.   Examine the diagram of *ABCD* at right.

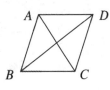

a.   If opposite sides of the quadrilateral are parallel
      and all sides are congruent, what type of
      quadrilateral is *ABCD*?

b.   List what you know about the diagonals of *ABCD*.

c.   Find the area of *ABCD* if $BC = 8$ and $m\angle ABC = 60°$.

9-69.   A butterfly house at a local zoo is a rectangular prism with dimensions
         20' × 15' × 10' and contains 625 butterflies.

   a.   Sketch the prism on your paper.

   b.   What is the volume of the butterfly house? Show your work.

   c.   How many cubic feet of air is there for each butterfly?

   d.   **Density** is the quantity of something per unit measure, especially length,
         area, or volume. For example you might talk about the density of birds on
         a power wire (maybe a flock lands with 7 birds/meter), population density
         (the density of Singapore is 7301 people per square meter), or the mass
         density of an element (iron has density of $7.874 \frac{g}{cm^3}$).

         Assuming the butterflies are equally distributed inside the butterfly house,
         what is the density of butterflies? Explain.

9-70.   Use the relationships given in the diagram
         at right to write and solve an equation for x.
         Show all work.

9-71.   For each pair of triangles below, determine if the triangles are congruent. If
         they are congruent, state the congruence property that assures their congruence
         and write a congruence statement (such as $\triangle ABC \cong \triangle$_____).

   a.   b.   c.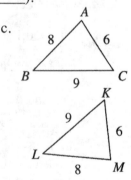

9-72.   Write the equation represented by the table below.

IN (x)	−4	−3	−2	−1	0	1	2	3	4
OUT (y)	−26	−20	−14	−8	−2	4	10	16	22

Core Connections Geometry

9-73. This problem is a checkpoint for finding probabilities. It will be referred to as Checkpoint 9A.

Because students complained that there were not enough choices in the cafeteria, the student council decided to collect data about the sandwich choices that were available. The cafeteria supervisor indicated that she makes 36 sandwiches each day. Each sandwich consists of bread, a protein, and a condiment. Twelve of the sandwiches were made with white bread, and 24 with whole-grain bread. Half of the sandwiches were made with salami, and the other half were evenly split between turkey and ham. Two-thirds of the sandwiches were made with mayonnaise, and the rest were left plain with no condiment.

a. Organize the possible sandwich combinations of bread, protein, and condiment by making an area model or tree diagram, if possible.

b. Wade likes any sandwich that has salami or mayonnaise on it. Which outcomes are sandwiches that Wade likes? If Wade randomly picks a sandwich, what is the probability he will get a sandwich that he likes? (Hint: You can use W and G to abbreviate the breads. Then use S, T, and H to abbreviate the proteins, and M and P to abbreviate the condiments.)

c. Madison does not like salami or mayonnaise. Which outcomes are sandwiches that Madison likes? If Madison randomly picks a sandwich, what is the probability she will get a sandwich that she likes?

d. If you have not already done so in part (c), show how to use a complement to find the probability Madison gets a sandwich that she likes.

e. Which outcomes are in the event for the intersection of {salami} and {mayonnaise}?

Check your answers by referring to the Checkpoint 9A materials located at the back of your book.

If you needed help solving these problems correctly, then you need more practice. Review the Checkpoint 9A materials and try the practice problems. Also, consider getting help outside of class time. From this point on, you will be expected to do problems like these quickly and easily.

9-74. **Multiple Choice:** Which net below will not produce a closed cube?

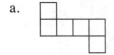

a.   b.   c.   d.

9.2.2 How can I construct it?

Constructing Bisectors

During Lesson 9.2.1, you studied how to construct geometric relationships such as congruent line segments using tools that include a compass and tracing paper. But what other geometric relationships and shapes can you construct using these tools? Today, as you investigate new ways to construct familiar geometric figures, look for connections to previous course material.

9-75.   INTERSECTING CIRCLES

As Ventura was doodling with his compass, he drew the diagram at right. Assume that each circle passes through the center of the other circle.

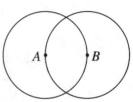

a.   Explain why $\odot A$ and $\odot B$ must have the same radius.

b.   On the Lesson 9.2.2 Resource Page provided by your teacher, construct two intersecting circles so that each passes through the other's center. Label the centers A and B.

c.   On your construction, locate the two points where the circles intersect each other. Label these points C and D. Then construct quadrilateral $ACBD$. What type of quadrilateral is $ACBD$? Justify your answer.

d.   Use what you know about the diagonals of $ACBD$ to describe the relationship of $\overline{AB}$ and $\overline{CD}$. Make as many statements as you can.

e.   What else can this diagram help you construct when given a line segment such as $\overline{AB}$? Share your ideas with the class.

9-76.   In problem 9-75, you constructed a rhombus
         and a perpendicular bisector.

a.   In your own words, describe how this process
      works. That is, given any line segment, how
      can you find its midpoint? How can you find
      a line perpendicular to it? Be sure to justify
      your statements.

b.   Test that your directions in part (a) work
      for line $\overline{KM}$ on the Lesson 9.2.2 Resource Page.
      In other words, construct a perpendicular bisector
      of $\overline{KM}$. Label the midpoint of $\overline{KM}$ point N.

c.   Return to your work from part (b) and use it to construct a 45°- 45°- 90°
      triangle. Prove that your triangle must be isosceles.

9-77.   In problem 9-75, you used the fact that the diagonals of a rhombus are
         perpendicular bisectors of each other to develop a construction. In fact, most
         constructions are rooted in the properties of many of the geometric shapes you
         have studied so far. A rhombus can help you with another important
         construction.

a.   Examine the rhombus $ABCD$ at right. What is the
      relationship between $\angle ABC$ and $\overline{BD}$?

b.   Since the diagonals of a rhombus bisect the angles,
      use this relationship to construct an angle bisector of
      $\angle R$ on the resource page. That is, construct a
      rhombus so that R is one of its vertices. Use only a
      compass, a straightedge, and a pencil.

9-78.   CONSTRUCTION CHALLENGE

         On the Lesson 9.2.2 Resource Page, locate $\overline{PQ}$, $\overline{ST}$, and $\angle V$. In the space
         provided, use the construction strategies you have developed so far to construct
         a triangle with legs congruent to $\overline{PQ}$ and $\overline{ST}$, with an angle congruent to $\angle V$ in
         between. Be sure you know how to do this two ways: with a compass and a
         straightedge and with tracing paper.

METHODS AND **M**EANINGS

Rhombus Facts

Review what you have previously learned about a rhombus below.

A **rhombus** is a quadrilateral with four equal sides. All rhombi (the plural of rhombus) are parallelograms.

Starting with the definition of a rhombus above, there are several facts about rhombi that can be proved. For example, the diagonals of a rhombus are perpendicular bisectors of each other. That is, they intersect each other at their midpoints and form right angles at that point. Also, all four small triangles are congruent (as well as the larger triangles formed by any two of the smaller triangles). In addition, the diagonals of a rhombus bisect the opposite angles.

9-79.   Unlike a straightedge, a ruler has measurement markings. With a ruler, it is fairly simple to construct a line segment of length 6 cm or a line segment with length 3 inches. But how can you construct a line segment of $\sqrt{2} \approx 1.414213562...$ centimeters? Consider this as you answer the questions below.

   a.   With a ruler, construct a line segment of 1 cm.

   b.   What about 1.4 cm? Adjust your line segment from part (a) so that its length is 1.4 cm. Did your line get longer or shorter?

   c.   Now change the line segment so that its length is 1.41 cm. How did it change?

   d.   Karen wants to draw a line segment is exactly $\sqrt{2} \approx 1.414213562...$ centimeters long. Is this possible? Why or why not?

9-80.   Describe a sequence of steps to construct an equilateral triangle.

9-81.   The floor plan of Marina's local drug store is shown at right. While shopping one day, Marina tied her dog, Mutt, to the building at point F. If Mutt's leash is 4 meters long, what is the area that Mutt can roam? Draw a diagram and show all work.

9-82.   Find the area of the Marina's drugstore (*FIDO*) in problem 9-81 Show all work.

9-83.   Compute the volume of the figure at right.

9-84.   Which has greater measure: an exterior angle of an equilateral triangle or an interior angle of a regular heptagon (7-gon)? Show all work.

9-85.   On graph paper, graph the line $y=-\frac{3}{2}x+6$. State the x- and y-intercepts.

9-86.   **Multiple Choice:** A solid with a volume of 26 in.^{3} was enlarged to create a similar solid with a volume of 702 in.^{3}. What is the linear scale factor between the two solids?

    a.   1   b.   2   c.   3   d.   4

9.2.3 How do I construct it?

More Explorations with Constructions

So far, several geometric relationships and properties have helped you develop constructions using a compass and a straightedge. For example, constructing a rhombus helped you construct an angle bisector. Constructing intersecting circles helped you construct a perpendicular bisector. What other relationships can help you develop constructions?

Today you will investigate how to use parallel line theorems to construct a line parallel to a given line through a point not on the line. You will also use the different construction techniques you have learned to construct a square, and will justify that the shape you created meets the definition of a square.

9-87.   CONSTRUCTING PARALLEL LINES

In this chapter you have used geometric concepts such as triangle congruence and the special properties of a rhombus to create constructions. How can angle relationships formed by parallel lines help with construction? Consider this question as you answer the questions below.

a.   Examine the diagram at right. If $l \parallel m$, what do you know about $\angle a$ and $\angle b$? What about $\angle a$ and $\angle c$? Justify your answer.

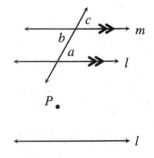

b.   Neelam thinks that angle relationships can help her construct a line parallel to another line through a given point not on the line. On the Lesson 9.2.3 Resource Page, find line l and point P. Help Neelam construct a line parallel to l through point P by first constructing a transversal through point P that intersects line l.

c.   If you have not already done so, complete Neelam's construction by copying an angle formed by the transversal and line l. Explain how you used alternate interior angles or corresponding angles.

Core Connections Geometry

9-88.   CONSTRUCTING A SQUARE

So far, you have developed techniques for constructing congruent angles, congruent line segments, perpendicular and parallel lines, and bisectors of angles and segments. You have constructed a rhombus, a regular hexagon, and an equilateral triangle using just a compass and straightedge. Now you will use what you know to construct a square.

a.   What makes a square a square? In other words, what are its unique characteristics? What shapes is it related to?

b.   Based on the characteristics you identified in part (a), work with your team to develop a strategy for constructing a square. Keep track of the steps you take on the Lesson 9.2.3 Resource Page, so that you can share them with the class.

c.   In order for the shape you constructed in part (c) to be a square, it must have four right angles and four congruent sides. Prove that your shape is a square using the steps of your construction and your geometry knowledge. Be ready to share your justification.

9-89.   Consider what you know about all 30°- 60°- 90° triangles.

a.   Using the information in the triangle at right, how long is the hypotenuse? Explain how you know.

b.   Negin (pronounced "Nay-GEEN") wants to use this relationship to construct a 30°- 60°- 90° triangle. On the Lesson 9.2.3 Resource Page, locate her work so far. She has constructed perpendicular lines and has constructed one side ($\overline{MN}$). Complete her construction so that her triangle has angles 30°, 60°, and 90°.

9-90.   CONSTRUCTING OTHER GEOMETRIC SHAPES

What about constructing a kite? On the Lesson 9.2.3 Resource Page, use a compass and a straightedge to construct a kite. Remember that a kite is defined as a quadrilateral with two pairs of adjacent, congruent sides. Be prepared to explain to the class how you constructed your kite.

MATH NOTES

METHODS AND MEANINGS

Constructing a Perpendicular Bisector

A perpendicular bisector of a given segment can be constructed using tracing paper or using a compass and a straightedge.

With tracing paper: To construct a perpendicular bisector with tracing paper, first copy the line segment onto the tracing paper. Then fold the tracing paper so that the endpoints coincide (so that they lie on top of each other). When the paper is unfolded, the resulting crease is the perpendicular bisector of the line segment.

With a compass and a straightedge: One way to construct a perpendicular bisector with a compass and a straightedge is to construct a circle at each endpoint of the line segment with a radius equal to the length of the line segment. Then use the straightedge to draw a line through the two points where the circles intersect. This line will be the perpendicular bisector of the line segment.

9-91. Examine the mat plan of a three-dimensional solid at right.

a. On your paper, draw the front, right, and top views of this solid.

b. Find the volume of the solid.

c. If the length of each edge of the solid is divided by 2, what will the new volume be? Show how you got your answer.

6	0	0	RIGHT
3	0	1	
2	6	6	

FRONT

Mat Plan

9-92. Examine the diagram at right. Given that $\triangle ABC \cong \triangle EDF$, prove that $\triangle DBG$ is isosceles. Use any format of proof that you prefer.

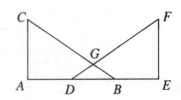

9-93. The Portland Zoo is building a new children's petting zoo pen that will contain 6 goats. One of the designs being considered is shown at right (the shaded portion). Assume the measurements are in meters.

a. What is the area of the petting zoo?

b. How many meters of fence are needed to enclose the petting zoo area.

c. What will be the density of goats in the pen? Show how you got your answer.

9-94. Sylvia has 14 coins, all nickels and quarters. If the value of the coins is $2.90, how many of each type of coin does she have? Explain your method.

9-95. West High School has a math building in the shape of a regular polygon. When Mrs. Woods measured an interior angle of the polygon (which was inside her classroom), she got 135°.

a. How many sides does the math building have? Show how you got your answer.

b. If Mrs. Wood's ceiling is 10 feet high and the length of one side of the building is 25 feet, find the volume of West High School's math building.

9-96. Given the information in the diagram at right, prove that $\angle C \cong \angle D$. Write your proof using any format studied so far.

9-97. Write the equation of an exponential function that passes through the points (2, 48) and (5, 750).

9-98. **Multiple Choice:** Jamila has started to construct a line parallel to line m through point Q at right. Which of the possible strategies below make the most sense to help her find the line parallel to m through point Q?

a. Measure $\angle QPR$ with a protractor.

b. Use the compass to measure the arc centered at P, then place the point of the compass where the arc centered at Q meets $\overline{QP}$, and mark that measure off on the arc.

c. Construct $\overline{QR}$.

d. Measure PR with a ruler.

Other Constructions

So far in this section, you have developed a basic library of constructions that can help create many of the geometric shapes and relationships you have studied in Chapters 1 through 8. For example, you can construct a rhombus, an isosceles triangle, a right triangle, a regular hexagon, and an equilateral triangle.

As you continue your investigation of geometric constructions today, keep in mind the following focus questions:

What geometric principles or properties can I use?

Why does it work?

Is there another way?

9-99.   TEAM CHALLENGE

Albert has a neat trick. Given any triangle, he can place it on the tip of his pencil and it balances on his first try! The whole class wonders, "*How does he do it?*"

Your Task: Construct a triangle and find its point of balance. This point, called a **centroid**, is special not only because it is the center of balance, but also because it is where the **medians** of the triangle meet. Read more about medians of a triangle in the Math Notes box for this lesson and then follow the directions below.

a.   After reading about medians and centroids in the Math Notes box for this lesson, draw a large triangle on a piece of unlined paper provided by your teacher. (Note: Your team will work together on one triangle.)

b.   Working together, carefully construct the three medians and locate the centroid of the triangle.

c.   Once your team is convinced that your centroid is accurate, glue the paper to a piece of cardstock or cardboard provided by your teacher. Carefully cut out the triangle and demonstrate that your centroid is, in fact, the center of balance of your triangle! Good luck!

9-100. In problem 9-99, you constructed a centroid of a triangle, which is special because it is a center of balance in a triangle. However, there are other important points in a triangle. For example, visualize a point inside of △ABC below that is the same distance from each vertex.

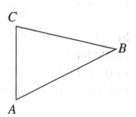

a. Find △ABC on the Lesson 9.2.4 Resource Page provided by your teacher. Using a compass and a straightedge, find a line that represents all the points that are equidistant (the same distance) from point A and point B. Justify your answer.

b. Joanna asks, "*How can we find one point that is the same distance from C, too?*" Talk about this with your team and test out your ideas until you find one point that is equidistant from A, B, and C.

c. Joanna points out that the intersection of the perpendicular bisectors of the sides of the triangle is equidistant from the vertices. "*That means there is a circle that passes through all three vertices!*" she noted. Use your compass to draw this circle. Where is its center?

9-101. As the Math Notes box for this lesson states, the point at which the medians of a triangle meet is called the **centroid**. However, how can you be certain that the medians of a triangle will always meet at a single point? In this problem, you will provide some of the reasoning for a proof that the medians will always meet at a single point.

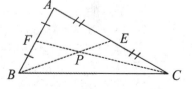

a. △ABC has midpoints E and F on sides $\overline{AC}$ and $\overline{AB}$ as shown in the diagram at right. $\overline{BE}$ and $\overline{CF}$ intersect at P. Why are $\overline{BE}$ and $\overline{CF}$ medians?

b. Draw segment $\overline{FE}$ and explain how you know that $\overline{FE}$ is parallel to $\overline{BC}$ and half its length.

c. Prove that △FPE ~△CPB.

d. Use the relationship of the triangles to identify the ratios $\frac{EP}{PB}$ and $\frac{FE}{BC}$. How does this help explain that $\frac{BP}{PE} = \frac{2}{3}$?

e. What if you had started with a different pair of medians for this triangle? Let point D be the midpoint of $\overline{BC}$. Can the same logic be used to show that $\overline{AD}$ and $\overline{BE}$ will intersect at a point with the same ratio of lengths as in part (d)? Explain.

f. Explain how this proves that the medians will intersect at a single point.

9-102. What other specific triangles can you construct? Choose at least three of the different triangles below and, if possible, construct them using compass and straightedge or tracing paper and the techniques you have developed so far. Be prepared to share your strategies, and to justify your steps for creating each shape or to justify why the shape could not be constructed.

- An isosceles triangle with side length $\overline{AB}$ given at right

- A triangle with side lengths 3, 4, and 5 units

- A 30°-60°-90° triangle

- A triangle with side lengths 2, 3 and 6 units

- An isosceles right triangle with leg length $\overline{PQ}$

- A scalene triangle

METHODS AND MEANINGS

Centroid and Medians of a Triangle

A line segment connecting a vertex of a triangle to the midpoint of the side opposite the vertex is called a **median**.

Since a triangle has three vertices, it has three medians. An example of a triangle with its three medians is provided at right.

The point at which the three medians intersect is called a **centroid**. The centroid is also the center of balance of a triangle.

Since the three medians intersect at a single point, this point is called a **point of concurrency**. You will learn about other points of concurrency in a later chapter.

9-103.   Find the volumes of the solids below.

a.   cylinder with a hole

b.   regular octagonal prism

9-104.   Jillian is trying to construct a square. She
has started by constructing two
perpendicular lines, as shown at right. If
she wants each side of the square to have
length k, as shown at right, describe how
she should finish her construction.

9-105.   Without using a calculator, find the sum of the interior angles of a 1002-gon.
Show all work.

9-106.   York County, Maine, is roughly triangular
in shape. To help calculate its area, Sergio
has decided to use a triangle to model the
region, as shown at right. According to his
map, the border with New Hampshire is
165 miles long, while the coastline along the
Atlantic Ocean is approximately 100 miles
long. If the angle at the tip of Maine is 43°,
as shown in the diagram, what is the
approximate area of York County?

9-107. This problem is a checkpoint for exponential function problems. It will be referred to as Checkpoint 9B.

a. Graph $y = 2(0.75)^x$.

b. Write the equation for the exponential function based on the table at right.

x	$f(x)$
1	23
2	52.9
3	121.67
4	

c. The population of Flood River City is now 42,000. Experts predict the population will decrease 25% each year for the next five years. What will be the population in five years?

d. A share of Orange stock that was worth $25 in 2000 was worth $60 in 2010. What is the annual multiplier and percent increase?

Check your answers by referring to the Checkpoint 9B materials located at the back of your book.

If you needed help solving these problems correctly, then you need more practice. Review the Checkpoint 9B materials and try the practice problems. Also, consider getting help outside of class time. From this point on, you will be expected to do problems like these quickly and easily.

9-108. Copy the following words and their lines of reflection onto your paper. Then use your visualization skills to help draw the reflected images.

a. REFLECT

b. PRISM

9-109. **Multiple Choice:** Solve this problem without a calculator: Examine the triangle at right. Find the approximate value of x. Use the values in the trigonometric table below as needed.

a. 4.69   b. 5.32

c. 8.83   d. 18.81

e. None of these

θ	$\cos\theta$	$\sin\theta$	$\tan\theta$
28°	0.883	0.469	0.532
62°	0.469	0.883	1.881

Chapter 9 Closure   What have I learned?

Reflection and Synthesis

The activities below offer you a chance to reflect about what you have learned during this chapter. As you work, look for concepts that you feel very comfortable with, ideas that you would like to learn more about, and topics you need more help with. Look for connections between ideas as well as connections with material you learned previously.

① TEAM BRAINSTORM

What have you studied in this chapter? What ideas were important in what you learned? With your team, brainstorm a list. Be as detailed as you can. To help get you started, lists of Learning Log entries, Toolkit entries, and Math Notes boxes are given below.

What topics, ideas, and words that you learned *before* this chapter are connected to the new ideas in this chapter? Again, be as detailed as you can.

How long can you make your list? Challenge yourselves. Be prepared to share your team's ideas with the class.

Learning Log Entries
- Lesson 9.1.1 – Volume of a Three-Dimensional Shape
- Lesson 9.1.2 – Finding Volume
- Lesson 9.1.4 – Volumes of Similar Solids

Toolkit Entries
- Construction Toolkit (Lesson 9.2,1. 9.2.2, and 9.2.3 Resource Pages)

Math Notes
- Lesson 9.1.2 – Polyhedra and Prisms
- Lesson 9.1.3 – Volume and Total Surface Area of a Solid
- Lesson 9.1.5 – The $r:r^2:r^3$ Ratios of Similarity
- Lesson 9.2.2 – Rhombus Facts
- Lesson 9.2.3 – Constructing a Perpendicular Bisector
- Lesson 9.2.4 – Centroid and Medians of a Triangle

② MAKING CONNECTIONS

Below is a list of the vocabulary used in this chapter. Make sure that you are familiar with all of these words and know what they mean. Refer to the glossary or index for any words that you do not yet understand.

base	bisect	centroid
circle	compass	concentric circles
construction	cylinder	density
incenter	inscribed	lateral face
line segment	linear scale factor	mat plan
median	net	oblique
perimeter	perpendicular bisector	polygon
polyhedron	point of concurrency	prism
ratio	rhombus	similar
solid	straightedge	surface area
three-dimensional	volume	

Make a concept map showing all of the connections you can find among the key words and ideas listed above. To show a connection between two words, draw a line between them and explain the connection. A word can be connected to any other word as long as you can justify the connection. For each key word or idea, provide an example or sketch that shows the idea.

While you are making your map, your team may think of related words or ideas that are not listed here. Be sure to include these ideas on your concept map.

Showcase your understanding of the different representations of a three-dimensional solid by describing the advantages and disadvantages of each representation, including how each representation makes it easier or more difficult to find the surface area and volume of the solid.

Showcase your constructions ability by using only a compass and straightedge to construct a line segment that is $\sqrt{5}$ units long. Assume the segment below is one unit long and use it to make your line segment. Show your construction marks, and explain each step clearly and in detail to a student that does not know how to complete this construction.

Copy the angle at right. Explain each step clearly and in detail in constructing its angle bisector.

Your teacher may give you the Chapter 9 Closure Resource Page: Representations of a Solid Graphics Organizer, and/or the Chapter 9 Closure Resource Page: Constructions Graphics Organizer to work on (or you can download these pages from www.cpm.org). A Graphic Organizer is a tool you can use to organize your thoughts, showcase your knowledge, and communicate your ideas clearly.

④ WHAT HAVE I LEARNED?

Most of the problems in this section represent typical problems found in this chapter. They serve as a gauge for you. You can use them to determine which types of problems you can do well and which types of problems require further study and practice. Even if your teacher does not assign this section, it is a good idea to try these problems and find out for yourself what you know and what you still need to work on.

Solve each problem as completely as you can. The table at the end of the closure section has answers to these problems. It also tells you where you can find additional help and practice with problems like these.

CL 9-110. On her paper, Kaye has a line with points A and B on it. Explain how she can use a compass to find a point C so that B is a midpoint of $\overline{AC}$. If you have access to a compass, try this yourself.

CL 9-111. Assume that the solid at right has no hidden cubes.

a. On graph paper, draw the front, right, and top views of this solid.

b. Find the volume and surface area of the cube.

c. Which net(s) below would have the same volume as the solid at right when it is folded to create a box?

FRONT   RIGHT

i.   ii.

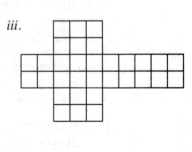

iii.

CL 9-112. The solid from problem CL 9-111 is redrawn at right.

a. If this solid were enlarged by a linear scale factor of 4, what would the volume and surface area of the new solid be?

b. Enrique enlarged the solid at right so that its volume was 1500 cubic units. What was his linear scale factor? Justify your answer.

FRONT   RIGHT

CL 9-113. After constructing a △*ABC*, Pricilla decided to try a little experiment. She chose a point *V* outside of △*ABC* and then constructed rays $\overrightarrow{VA}$, $\overrightarrow{VB}$, and $\overrightarrow{VC}$. Her result is shown at right. Copy this diagram onto your paper.

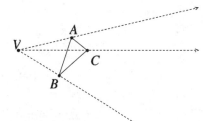

a. Pricilla then used a compass to mark point *A′* so that *VA* = *AA′*. She also constructed points *B′* and *C′* using the same method. For the diagram on your paper, locate *A′*, *B′*, and *C′*.

b. Now connect the new points to form △*A′B′C′*. What is the relationship between △*ABC* and △*A′B′C′*? Explain what happened.

c. If the area of △*ABC* is 19 cm² and its perimeter is 15 cm, find the area and perimeter of △*A′B′C′*.

CL 9-114. A restaurant has a giant fish tank, shown at right, in the shape of an octagonal prism.

2 m

0.8 m

a. Find the volume and surface area of the fish tank if the base is a regular octagon with side length 0.8 m and the height of the prism is 2 m.

b. What is the density of fish if there are 208 fish in the tank?

CL 9-115. Answer the questions about the angles of polygons below, if possible. If it is not possible, explain how you know it is not possible.

a. Find the sum of the interior angles of a 28-gon.

b. If the exterior angle of a regular polygon is 42°, how many sides does the polygon have?

c. Find the measure of each interior angle of a pentagon.

d. Find the measure of each interior angle of a regular decagon.

CL 9-116. Fill in the blanks in each statement below with one of the quadrilaterals listed at right so that the statement is *true*. Use each quadrilateral name only once.

> List:
>
> Kite
>
> Rectangle
>
> Rhombus
>
> Trapezoid

a. If a shape is a square, then it must also be a _____.

b. The diagonals of a _____ must be perpendicular to each other.

c. If the quadrilateral has only one line of symmetry, then it could be a _____.

d. If a quadrilateral has only two sides that are congruent, then the shape could be a _____.

CL 9-117. Copy quadrilateral *DART*, shown at right, onto your paper. If $\overline{DR}$ bisects $\angle ADT$ and if $\angle A \cong \angle T$, prove that $\overline{DA} \cong \overline{DT}$.

CL 9-118. After Myong's cylindrical birthday cake was sliced, she received the slice at right. If her birthday cake originally had a diameter of 14 inches and a height of 6 inches, find the volume of her slice of cake.

CL 9-119. Check your answers using the table at the end of the closure section. Which problems do you feel confident about? Which problems were hard? Use the table to make a list of topics you need help on and a list of topics you need to practice more.

Answers and Support for Closure Activity #4
What Have I Learned?

Note: MN = Math Note, LL = Learning Log

Problem	Solution	Need Help?	More Practice
CL 9-110.	She should match the length of $\overline{AB}$ with her compass. Then, with the point of the compass at point B, she should mark a point on the line on the side of point B opposite point A. Then she should label that point C.	Lesson 9.2.1 Construction Toolkit	Problems 9-79, 9-80, 9-98, and 9-104
CL 9-111.	a. Front Right Top b. $V = 12$ un^3, SA = 42 units^2 c. All three nets will form a box with volume 12 units^3.	Lessons 9.1.1 and 9.1.2 MN: 9.1.3 LL: 9.1.1	Problems 9-7, 9-21, 9-49, 9-56, 9-74, and 9-91
CL 9-112.	a. $V = 12(4)^3 = 768$ units^3, $SA = 42(4)^2 = 672$ units^2 b. Linear scale factor = 5	Lessons 9.1.4 and 9.1.5 MN: 9.1.5	Problems 9-45, 9-46, 9-56, 9-86, and 9-91
CL 9-113.	a. b. $\triangle ABC$ was enlarged (or dilated) to create a similar triangle with a linear scale factor of 2. c. $A = 19(2)^2 = 76$ units^2; $P = 15(2) = 30$ units	Lessons 8.2.1, 8.2.2, and 9.2.1 MN: 3.1.1, 8.2.1, and 9.1.5 Construction Toolkit	Problems 8-71, 8-83, 9-8, 9-20, and 9-33

Problem	Solution	Need Help?	More Practice
CL 9-114.	a. Area of base ≈ 3.09 m^2 Volume ≈ 6.18 m^3 Surface Area ≈ 18.98 m^2 b. density ≈ 33.66 fish/m^3	Lessons 9.1.2 and 9.1.3 MN: 8.3.1 and 9.1.3 LL: 8.1.5 and 9.1.2	Problems 9-26, 9-34, 9-38, 9-40, 9-46, 9-57, 9-69, 9-83, 9-95, and 9-103
CL 9-115.	a. 4680° b. Not possible because 42° does not divide evenly into 360°. c. Not possible because it is not stated that the pentagon is regular. d. 144°	Lessons 8.1.2, 8.1.3, and 8.1.4 MN: 7.1.4 and 8.1.5 LL: 8.1.2, 8.1.3, and 8.1.4	Problems CL 8-138, 9-22, 9-84, 9-95, and 9-105
CL 9-116.	a. Rectangle b. Rhombus c. Kite d. Trapezoid	Lessons 7.3.1 and 7.3.3 MN: 7.2.3, 8.1.2, and 9.2.2	Problems CL 7-156, 8-12, 8-61, and 9-58
CL 9-117.	$\overline{DR}$ bisects $\angle ADT$ — Given $\angle A \cong \angle T$ (Given) $\angle ADR \cong \angle TDR$ (Definition of angle bisector) $\overline{DR} \cong \overline{DR}$ (Reflexive Property) $\triangle ADR \cong \triangle TDR$ — AAS $\cong$ $\overline{DA} \cong \overline{DT}$ — $\cong \triangle s \rightarrow \cong$ parts	Section 3.2 and Lessons 6.1.1 through 6.1.4 MN: 3.2.2, 3.2.4, 6.1.4, 7.1.3, and 7.2.1 LL: 3.2.2	Problems CL 3-123, CL 4-123, CL 5-140, CL 6-101, CL 7-155, CL 8-134, 9-35, 9-92, and 9-96
CL 9-118.	$V \approx 97.49$ cubic inches	Lesson 9.1.3 MN: 8.3.2, 8.3.3, and 9.1.3 LL: 9.1.2	Problems 9-38, 9-40, 9-46, and 9-103

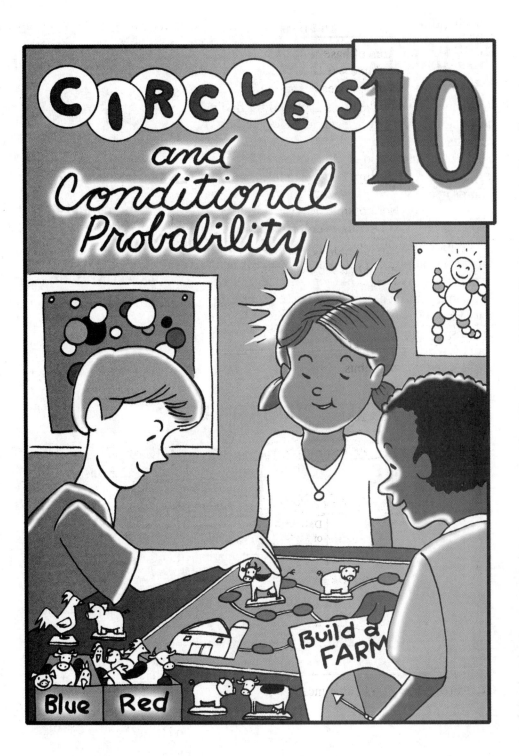

CHAPTER 10

Circles and Conditional Probability

In Chapter 8, you developed a method for finding the area and circumference of a circle, and in Chapter 9 you constructed many shapes using circles as a starting point. In Section 10.1, you will explore the relationships between angles, arcs, and chords in a circle.

The focus of your work turns to probability in Section 10.2. As you analyze probabilities, you will develop an understanding of conditional probability and more formal mathematical definitions of independence. With that you can determine if two categorical variables are associated with each other. To calculate and display probabilities, you will add the additional tool of two-way tables to your existing tools of area models and tree diagrams.

Guiding Question

Mathematically proficient students use appropriate tools strategically.

As you work through this chapter, ask yourself:

What tools do I have available to help me solve this problem?

Chapter Outline

Section 10.1   The relationships between angles, arcs, and line segments in a circle will be investigated to develop "circle tools" that can help solve problems involving circles.

Section 10.2   Area models and two-way tables provide the basis for calculating conditional probabilities and determining whether events are independent.

Section 10.3   Some sample spaces are so large that models cannot easily represent them. Based on the Fundamental Principal of Counting, other formulas for permutations and combinations are developed that can be used to solve more complex problems.

10.1.1 What is the length of the diameter?

Introduction to Chords

In Chapter 8, you learned that the diameter of a circle is the distance across the center of the circle. This length can be easily determined if the entire circle is in front of you and the center is marked, or if you know the length of the radius of the circle. However, what if you only have part of a circle, called an **arc**? Or what if the circle is so large that it is not practical to measure its diameter using standard measurement tools, such as finding the diameter of the Earth's equator?

Today you will consider a situation that demonstrates the need to learn more about the parts of a circle and the relationships between them.

10-1.   THE WORLD'S WIDEST TREE

The baobab tree is a species of tree found in Africa and Australia. It is often referred to as the world's widest tree because it has been known to be up to 45 feet in diameter!

While digging at an archeological site, Rafi found a fragment of a fossilized baobab tree that appears to be wider than any tree on record! However, since he does not have the remains of the entire tree, he cannot simply measure across the tree to find its diameter. He needs your help to determine the length of the radius of this ancient tree. Assume that the shape of the tree's cross-section is a circle.

Tree fragment

a.   Obtain the Lesson 10.1.1 Resource Page from your teacher. On it, locate $\overset{\frown}{AB}$, which represents the curvature of the tree fragment. Trace this arc as neatly as possible on tracing paper. Then decide with your team how to fold the tracing paper to find the center of the tree. (Hint: This will take more than one fold.) Be ready to share with the class how you found the center.

b.   In part (a), you located the center of a circle. Use a ruler to measure the radius of that circle. If 1 cm represents 10 feet of tree, find the approximate length of the radius and diameter of the tree. Does the tree appear to be larger than 45 feet in diameter?

10-2.   PARTS OF A CIRCLE, Part One

A line segment that connects the endpoints of an arc is called a **chord**. Thus, $\overline{AB}$ in the diagram below is an example of a chord.

a.   One way to find the center of a circle when given an arc is to fold it so that the two parts of the arc coincide (lie on top of each other).

If you fold $\overarc{AB}$ so that A lies on B, what is the relationship between the resulting crease and the chord $\overline{AB}$? Explain how you know.

b.   The tree fragment in problem 10-1 was an arc between points A and B. However, the missing part of the tree formed another larger arc of the tree. With your team, find the larger arc formed by the circle and points A and B above. Then propose a way to use the points to name the larger arc to distinguish it from $\overarc{AB}$.

c.   In problem 10-1, the tree fragment formed the shorter arc between two endpoints. The shorter arc between points A and B is called the **minor arc** and is written $\overarc{AB}$. The larger arc is called a **major arc** and is usually written using three points, such as $\overarc{ACB}$. What do you know about $\overline{AB}$ if the minor and major arcs are the same length? Explain how you know.

10-3.   In problem 10-1, folding the arc several times resulted in a point that seemed to be the center of the circle. But how can you prove that the line bisecting an arc (or chord) will pass through the center? To consider this, first assume that the perpendicular bisector does *not* pass through the center. This is an example of a proof by contradiction.

a.   According to our assumption, if the perpendicular bisector does not pass through the center, then the center, C, will be off the line in the circle, as shown at right. Copy this diagram onto your paper.

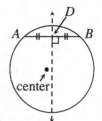

b.   Now consider $\triangle ACD$ and $\triangle BCD$. Are these two triangles congruent? Why or why not?

c.   Explain why your result from part (b) contradicts the original assumption. That is, explain why the center must lie on the perpendicular bisector of $\overline{AB}$.

Core Connections Geometry

10-4.   What if you are given two non-parallel chords in a circle and nothing else? How can you use the chords to find the center of the circle?

   a.   On the Lesson 10.1.1 Resource Page, locate the chords provided for ⊙P and ⊙Q. Work with your team to determine how to find the center of each circle. Then use a compass to draw the circles that contain the given chords. Tracing paper may be helpful.

   b.   Describe how to find the center of a circle without tracing paper. That is, how would you find the center of ⊙P with only a compass and a straightedge? Be prepared to share your description with the rest of the class.

10-5.   Examine the chord $\overline{WX}$ in ⊙Z at right. If $WX = 8$ units and the length of the radius of ⊙Z is 5 units, how far from the center is the chord? Draw the diagram on your paper and show all work.

ETHODS AND MEANINGS

Circle Vocabulary

An **arc** is a part of a circle. Remember that a circle does not contain its interior. A bicycle tire is an example of a circle. The spokes and the space in between them are not part of the circle. The piece of tire between any two spokes of the bicycle wheel is an example of an arc.

Any two points on a circle create two arcs. When these arcs are not the same length, the larger arc is referred to as the **major arc**, while the smaller arc is referred to as the **minor arc**.

To name an arc, an arc symbol is drawn over the endpoints, such as $\overset{\frown}{AB}$. To refer to a major arc, a third point on the arc should be used to identify the arc clearly, such as $\overset{\frown}{ACB}$.

A **chord** is a line segment that has both endpoints on a circle. $\overline{AB}$ in the diagram at right is an example of a chord. When a chord passes through the center of the circle, it is called a **diameter**.

10-6.   A rectangular prism has a cylindrical hole removed, as shown at
right.

a.   If the length of the radius of the cylindrical hole is
0.5 cm, find the volume of the solid.

b.   What could this geometric figure represent? That is, if it
were a model for something that exists in the world, what
might it be? Also, how might you change it to make it a
better model?

10-7.   In the diagram below, $\overline{AD}$ is a diameter of $\odot B$.

a.   If $m\angle A = 35°$, what is $m\angle CBD$?

b.   If $m\angle CBD = 100°$, what is $m\angle A$?

c.   If $m\angle A = x$, what is $m\angle CBD$?

10-8.   Lavinia started a construction at right. Explain what
she is constructing. Then copy her diagram and finish
her construction.

10-9.   A sector is attached to the side of a parallelogram,
as shown in the diagram at right. Find the area and
perimeter of the figure.

10-10. For each recursively defined sequence, list the first five terms and identify the
sequence as arithmetic, geometric, or neither.

a. $a_1 = 17$, $a_{n+1} = -a_n$

b. $a_1 = 32$, $a_{n+1} = -5 + \frac{1}{2}a_n$

c. $a_1 = 81$, $a_{n+1} = a_n$

10-11. On the same set of axes, graph both equations listed below. Then name all points of intersection in the form (x, y). How many times do the graphs intersect?

$$y = 4x - 7$$
$$y = x^2 - 2x + 2$$

10-12. **Multiple Choice:** A penny, nickel, and dime are all flipped once. What is the probability that at least one coin comes up heads?

a. $\frac{1}{3}$ b. $\frac{3}{8}$ c. 1 d. $\frac{7}{8}$

10.1.2 What is the relationship?

Angles and Arcs

In order to learn more about circles, you need to investigate different types of angles and chords that are found in circles. In Lesson 10.1.1, you studied an application with a tree to learn about the chords of a circle. Today you will study a different application that will demonstrate the importance of knowing how to measure the angles and arcs within a circle.

10-13.

ERATOSTHENES' REMARKABLE DISCOVERY

Eratosthenes, who lived in the 3rd century B.C., was able to determine the circumference of the Earth at a time when most people thought the world was flat! Since he was convinced that the Earth was round, he realized that he could use a shadow to help calculate the length of the Earth's radius.

Eratosthenes knew that Alexandria was located about 500 miles north of a town that was closer to the equator, called Syene. When the sun was directly overhead at Syene, a meter stick had no shadow. However, at the same time in Alexandria, a meter stick had a shadow due to the curvature of the Earth. Since the sun is so far away from the Earth, Eratosthenes assumed that the sun's rays were essentially parallel once they entered the Earth's atmosphere and realized that he could therefore use the stick's shadow to help calculate the length of the Earth's radius.

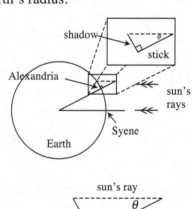

a. Unfortunately, the precise data used by Eratosthenes was lost long ago. However, if Eratosthenes used a meter stick for his experiment today, then the stick's shadow in Alexandria would be 127 mm long. Determine the angle θ that the sunrays made with the meter stick. Remember that a meter stick is 1000 millimeters long.

b. Assuming that the sun's rays are essentially parallel, determine the central angle of the circle if the angle passes through Alexandria and Syene. How did you find your answer?

Problem continues on next page →

Core Connections Geometry

10-13.   *Problem continued from previous page.*

c.
Alexandria

500 miles

Syene

Since the distance along the Earth's surface from Alexandria to Syene is about 500 miles, that is the length of the arc between Alexandria and Syene. Use this information to approximate the circumference of the Earth.

d.   Use your result from part (c) to approximate the length of the radius of the Earth.

10-14.   PARTS OF A CIRCLE, Part Two

In order to find the circumference of the Earth, Eratosthenes used an angle that had its vertex at the center of the circle. Like the angles in polygons that you studied in Chapter 8, this angle is called a **central angle**.

a.   An **arc** is a part of a circle. Every central angle has a corresponding arc. For example, in $\odot T$ at right, $\angle STU$ is a central angle and corresponds to $\overset{\frown}{SU}$. Since the measure of an angle helps us know its part of the whole 360° of a circle, an arc can also be measured in degrees, representing its fraction of an entire circle. Thus, the **measure of an arc** is defined to be equal to the measure of its corresponding central angle.

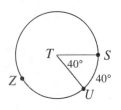

Examine the circle above. What is the measure of $\overset{\frown}{SU}$ (written $m\overset{\frown}{SU}$)? What is $m\overset{\frown}{SZU}$? Show how you got your answer.

b.   When Eratosthenes measured the distance from Syene to Alexandria, he measured the length of an arc. This distance is called **arc length** and is measured with units like centimeters or feet. One way to find arc length is to wrap a string about a part of a circle and then to straighten it out and measure its length. Calculate the arc length of $\overset{\frown}{SU}$ above if the length of the radius of $\odot T$ is 12 inches.

10-15.   INSCRIBED ANGLES

In the diagram at right, ∠BDC is an example of
an **inscribed angle**, because it lies within ⊙A and
its vertex lies on the circle. It corresponds to
central angle ∠BAC because they both intercept
the same arc, $\overset{\frown}{BC}$. (An **intercepted arc** is an arc
with endpoints on each side of the angle.)

inscribed angle

intercepted
arc

Investigate the measure of inscribed angles as you
answer the questions below.

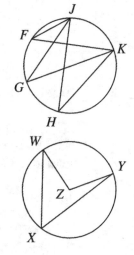

a.   In the circle at right, ∠F, ∠G, and ∠H are
      examples of inscribed angles. Notice that all
      three angles intercept the same arc ($\overset{\frown}{JK}$). Use
      tracing paper to compare their measures. What
      do you notice?

b.   Now compare the measurements of the central
      angle (such as ∠WZY in ⊙Z at right) and an
      inscribed angle (such as ∠WXY). What is the
      relationship of an inscribed angle and its
      corresponding central angle? Use tracing
      paper to test your idea.

10-16.   In problem 10-15, you found that the measure of an inscribed angle was half of
          the measure of its corresponding central angle in the cases you tested. Later
          you will prove that this is always true and since the measure of the central angle
          always equals the measure of its intercepted arc, then the measure of the
          inscribed angle must be half of the measure of its intercepted arc.

          Examine the diagrams below. Find the measures of the indicated angles. If a
          point is labeled C, assume it is the center of the circle.

a.
      118°

b.
      x
      41°

c.
      z
      78°
      y
      x

d.
      x
      56°
      C
      y

e.
      114°
      x
      C
      y

f.
      x
      28°
      y

10-17.   LEARNING LOG

Reflect on what you have learned during this lesson. Write a Learning Log entry describing the relationships between inscribed angles and their intercepted arcs. Be sure to include an example. Title this entry "Inscribed Angles" and include today's date.

ETHODS AND MEANINGS

More Circle Vocabulary

The vertex of a **central angle** is at the center of a circle. An **inscribed angle** has its vertex on the circle with each side intersecting the circle at a different point.

One way to discuss an arc is to consider it as a fraction of 360°, that is, as a part of a full circle. When speaking about an arc using degrees, this is called the **arc measure**. The arc between the endpoints of the sides of a central angle has the same measure (in degrees) as its corresponding central angle.

When you want to know how *far* it is from one point to another as you travel along an arc, you call this the **arc length** and measure it in feet, miles, etc.

For example, point O is the center of $\odot O$ at right, and $\angle AOB$ is a central angle. The sides of the angle intersect the circle at points A and B, so $\angle AOB$ intercepts $\overarc{AB}$. In this case, the measure of $\overarc{AB}$ is 60°, while the measure of the major arc, $m\overarc{ACB}$, is 300° because the sum of the major and minor arcs is 360°. The length of $\overarc{AB}$ is $\frac{60}{360} = \frac{1}{6}$ of the circumference.

10-18.   In $\odot A$ at right, $\overline{CF}$ is a diameter and $m\angle C = 64°$. Find:

a. $m\angle D$

b. $m\overarc{BF}$

c. $m\angle E$

d. $m\overarc{CBF}$

e. $m\angle BAF$

f. $m\angle BAC$

10-19.   Find the area of a regular polygon with 100 sides and with a perimeter of 100 units.

10-20.   For each of the geometric relationships represented below, write and solve an equation for the given variable. For parts (a) and (b), assume that C is the center of the circle. Show all work.

a.

b.

c.

p
6
p − 2

d.

2t + 9°
3t + 1°
5t   8t − 10°

10-21.   On graph paper, plot $\triangle ABC$ if $A(-1, -1)$, $B(1, 9)$, and $C(7, 5)$.

a.   Find the midpoint of $\overline{AB}$ and label it D. Also find the midpoint of $\overline{BC}$ and label it E.

b.   Find the length of the midsegment, $\overline{DE}$. Use it to predict the length of $\overline{AC}$.

c.   Now find the length of $\overline{AC}$ and compare it to your prediction from part (b).

10-22. $ABCDE$ is a regular pentagon inscribed in $\odot O$, meaning that each of its five vertices just touches the circle.

a.   Draw a diagram of $ABCDE$ and $\odot O$ on your paper.

b.   Find $m\angle EDC$. How did you find your answer?

c.   Find $m\angle BOC$. What relationship did you use?

d.   Find $m\overset{\frown}{EBC}$. Is there more than one way to do this?

10-23.   Create mat plans from the following isometric views and find the volume of
          each.

a.

b.

c.   Did you have to make any assumptions about hidden cubes when you
      drew the mat plans? If so, what assumptions did you make in each case
      and why?

d.   What other view would you need to see to be sure how many cubes
      there are? Explain.

10-24.   **Multiple Choice:** Jill's car tires are spinning at a rate of 120 revolutions per
          minute. If her car tires' radii are each 14 inches, how far does she travel in
          5 minutes?

a. 140π in.   b. 8400π in.   c. 3360π in.   d. 16800π in.

10.1.3 What more can I learn about circles?

Chords and Angles

As you investigate more about the parts of a circle, look for connections that you can make to other shapes and relationships you have studied so far in this course.

10-25.   WHAT IF IT'S A SEMICIRCLE?

What is the measure of an angle when it is inscribed in a **semicircle** (an arc with measure 180°)? Consider this as you answer the questions below.

a.   Assume that the diagram at right is not drawn to scale. If $m\overarc{QR} = 180°$, then what is $m\angle P$? Why?

b.   Since you have several tools to use with right triangles, the special relationship you found in part (a) can be useful. For example, $\overline{UV}$ is a diameter of the circle at right. If $TU = 6$ units and $TV = 8$ units, what is the length of the radius of the circle? What is its area?

10-26.   In Lesson 10.1.1, you learned that a chord is a line segment that has its endpoints on a circle. What geometric tools do you have that can help find the length of a chord?

a.   Examine the diagram of chord $\overline{LM}$ in $\odot P$ at right. If the length of the radius of $\odot P$ is 6 units and if $m\overarc{LM} = 150°$, find LM. Be ready to share your method with the class.

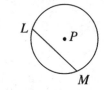

b.   What if you know the length of a chord? How can you use it to reverse the process? Draw a diagram of a circle with radius with length 5 units and chord $\overline{AB}$ with length 6 units. Find $m\overarc{AB}$.

10-27. Timothy asks, "*What if two chords intersect inside a circle? Can triangles help me learn something about these chords?*" Copy his diagram at right in which chords $\overline{AB}$ and $\overline{CD}$ intersect at point E.

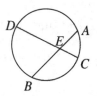

a. Timothy decided to create two triangles ($\triangle BED$ and $\triangle ACE$). Add line segments $\overline{BD}$ and $\overline{AC}$ to your diagram.

b. Compare $\angle B$ and $\angle C$. Which is bigger? How can you tell? Likewise, compare $\angle D$ and $\angle A$. Write down your observations.

c. How are $\triangle BED$ and $\triangle ACE$ related? Justify your answer.

d. If $DE = 8$, $AE = 4$, and $EB = 6$, then what is EC? Show your work.

10-28. A polygon is said to be **inscribed** in a circle when each of is vertices touch the circle. How are the angles of a quadrilateral inscribed in a circle related? Consider this as you answer the questions below.

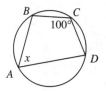

a. For *ABCD* inscribed in the circle at right, solve for x. Explain how you found your answer.

b. Alejandra noticed something. "*I think that the opposite angles of a quadrilateral inscribed in a circle are always supplementary.*" Is she correct? Prove your conclusion.

10-29. Use the relationships in the diagrams to solve for *x*. Justify your solutions.

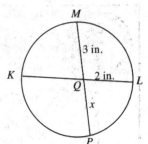

a. $\overline{KL}$ and $\overline{MP}$ intersect at Q and $KL = 8$ inches

b. $\overline{RT}$ is a diameter

c.

10-30. **LEARNING LOG**

Look over your work from today. Consider all the geometric tools you applied to learn more about angles and chords of circles. In a Learning Log entry, describe which connections you made today. Title this entry "Connections with Circles" and include today's date.

⬤ETHODS AND MEANINGS

Inscribed Angle Theorem

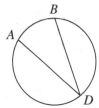

The measure of any inscribed angle is half of the measure of its intercepted arc. Likewise, any intercepted arc is twice the measure of any inscribed angles whose sides pass through the endpoints of the arc.

For example, in the diagram at right:

$$m\angle ADB = \tfrac{1}{2}\,m\widehat{AB} \text{ and } m\widehat{AB} = 2m\angle ADB$$

Proof:

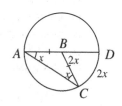

To prove this relationship, consider the relationship between an inscribed angle and its corresponding central angle. In problem 10-7, you used the isosceles triangle $\triangle ABC$ to demonstrate that if one of the sides of the inscribed angle is a diameter of the circle, then the inscribed angle must be half of the measure of the corresponding central angle. Therefore, in the diagram at right, $m\angle DAC = \tfrac{1}{2}\,m\widehat{DC}$.

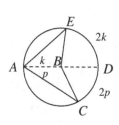

But what if the center of the circle instead lies in the interior of an inscribed angle, such as $\angle EAC$ shown at right? By extending $\overline{AB}$ to construct the diameter $\overline{AD}$, the work above shows that if $m\angle EAD = k$ then $m\widehat{ED} = 2k$ and if $m\angle DAC = p$, then $m\widehat{DC} = 2p$. Since $m\angle EAC = k + p$, then
$m\widehat{EC} = 2k + 2p = 2(k + p) = 2m\angle EAC$.

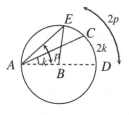

The last possible case to consider is when the center lies outside of the inscribed angle, as shown at right. Again, constructing a diameter $\overline{AD}$ helps show that if $m\angle CAD = k$ then $m\widehat{CD} = 2k$ and if $m\angle EAD = p$, then $m\widehat{ED} = 2p$. Since $m\angle EAC = p - k$, then
$m\widehat{EC} = 2k - 2p = 2(k - p) = 2m\angle EAC$.

Therefore, an arc is always twice the measure of any inscribed angle that intercepts it.

10-31. Assume point B is the center of the circle below. Match each item in the left column with the best description for it in the right column.

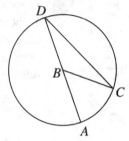

a.	$\overline{AB}$	1.	inscribed angle
b.	$\overline{CD}$	2.	semicircle
c.	$\overset{\frown}{AD}$	3.	radius
d.	$\angle CDA$	4.	minor arc
e.	$\overset{\frown}{AC}$	5.	central angle
f.	$\angle ABC$	6.	chord

10-32. The figure at right shows two concentric circles.

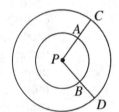

a. What is the relationship between $\overset{\frown}{AB}$ or $\overset{\frown}{CD}$? How do you know?

b. Of $\overset{\frown}{AB}$ or $\overset{\frown}{CD}$, which has greater measure? Which has greater length? Explain.

c. If $m\angle P = 60°$ and $PD = 14$, find the length of $\overset{\frown}{CD}$. Show all work.

10-33. In $\odot Y$ at right, assume that $m\overset{\frown}{PO} = m\overset{\frown}{EK}$. Prove that $\overline{PO} \cong \overline{EK}$. Use the format of your choice.

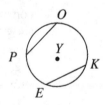

10-34.   While working on the quadrilateral hotline, Jo
          Beth got this call: "*I need help identifying the
          shape of the quadrilateral flowerbed in front of
          my apartment. Because a shrub covers one side,
          I can only see three sides of the flowerbed.
          However, of the three sides I can see, two are
          parallel and all three are congruent. What are
          the possible shapes of my flowerbed?*" Help Jo
          Beth answer the caller's question.

10-35.   Compute the volume of the solid shown at right.

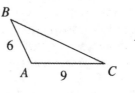

10-36.   For each pair of triangles below, decide if the triangles are similar or not and
          explain how you know. If the triangles are similar, complete the similarity
          statement $\triangle ABC \sim \triangle$ _____.

a.

b.

c.

10-37.   **Multiple Choice:** Which equation below is perpendicular to $y = \frac{-2}{5}x - 7$ and
          passes through the point $(4, -1)$?

a. $2x - 5y = 13$ b. $2x + 5y = 3$ c. $5x - 2y = 22$

d. $5x + 2y = 18$ e.   None of these

10.1.4 What is the relationship?

Tangents and Secants

So far, you have studied the relationships that exist between angles and chords (line segments) in a circle. Today you will extend these ideas to include the study of lines and circles.

10-38. Consider all the ways a circle and a line can intersect. Can you visualize a line and a circle that intersect at exactly one point? What about a line that intersects a circle twice? On your paper, draw a diagram for each of the situations below, if possible. If it is not possible, explain why.

   a. Draw a line and a circle that do not intersect.

   b. Draw a line and a circle that intersect at exactly one point. When this happens, the line is called a **tangent**.

   c. Draw a line and a circle that intersect at exactly two points. A line that intersects a circle twice is called a **secant**.

   d. Draw a line and a circle that intersect three times.

10-39. A line that intersects a circle exactly once is called a **tangent**. What is the relationship of a tangent to a circle?

   To investigate this question, carefully copy the diagram showing line *l* tangent to ⊙*C* at right onto tracing paper. Fold the tracing paper so that the crease is perpendicular to line *l* through point *P*. Your crease should pass through point *C*. What does this tell you about the tangent line?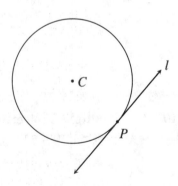

10-40.   Ventura began to think about perpendicularity in a circle. He wondered, "*If a radius is perpendicular to a line at a point on the circle, how do we know if that the line is a secant or a tangent?*" His team decided to tackle his question.

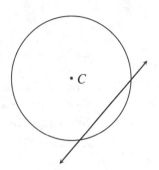

a.   Ho says, "*Let's assume the line perpendicular to the radius is a secant.*" On your paper, draw a diagram, like the one at right, with ⊙C and a secant. Label the points where the secant intersects the circle A and B. Since Ventura's question assumes that the line is perpendicular to a radius, assume that $\overleftrightarrow{AB}$ is perpendicular to $\overline{CA}$ at A.

b.   Ventura adds "*I think △CAB is isosceles.*" Do you agree? Explain how you know.

c.   Sandra chimes in with, "*Then ∠CBA must be a right angle too.*" Ventura quickly adds, "*But that's impossible!*" What do you think? Discuss this with your team and give reasons to support your conclusions.

d.   Explain to Ventura what this contradiction reveals about the line perpendicular to the radius of a circle at a point on the circle.

10-41.   Use the relationships in the diagrams below to answer the following questions. Be sure to name what relationship(s) you used.

a. $\overrightarrow{PQ}$ is tangent to ⊙C at P. If $PQ = 5$ and $CQ = 6$, find CP and $m\angle C$.

b.   In ⊙H , $m\overset{\frown}{DR} = 40°$ and $m\overset{\frown}{GOR} = 210°$. Find $m\overset{\frown}{GD}$, $m\overset{\frown}{OR}$, and $m\angle RGO$.

c. $\overline{AC}$ is a diameter of ⊙E and $\overline{BC} \parallel \overline{ED}$. Find the measure of $\overset{\frown}{CD}$.

d. $\overline{HJ}$ and $\overline{IK}$ intersect at G. If $HG = 9$, $GJ = 8$, and $GK = 6$, find IG.

e. $\overline{AC}$ is a diameter of ⊙E , the area of the circle is 289π units², and $AB = 16$ units. Find BC and $m\overset{\frown}{BC}$.

f.   △ABC is inscribed in the circle at right. Using the measurements provided in the diagram, find $m\overset{\frown}{AB}$.

10-42.   In Chapter 9, it was stated that the intersection of the angle bisectors of a triangle is the center of a circle inscribed in the triangle. You now have enough information to prove this relationship.

a.   Assume that in $\triangle ABC$, $\overline{AG}$ and $\overline{BH}$ are angle bisectors of $\angle CAB$ and $\angle CBA$, respectively. Draw this diagram on your paper. Label the intersection of the angle bisectors P.

b.   You need to show that P is the same distance from sides $\overline{AB}$ and $\overline{AC}$. Draw a perpendicular from P to $\overline{AB}$ and label its intersection D. Similarly, draw a perpendicular from P to $\overline{AC}$ and label its intersection E. How can you prove that $\triangle ADP \cong \triangle AEP$?

c.   Explain why $PE = PD$.

d.   Use similar reasoning to show that P must also be the same distance from $\overline{BC}$. For example, if the perpendicular from P to $\overline{BC}$ intersects $\overline{BC}$ at F, why is $PF = PD$?

e.   Explain why there must be a circle through points D, E, and F with center P and that each side of $\triangle ABC$ must be tangent to this circle, making the circle inscribed in the triangle.

METHODS AND MEANINGS

Intersecting Chords

When two chords in a circle intersect, an interesting relationship between the lengths of the resulting segments occurs. If the ends of the chords are connected as shown in the diagram, similar triangles are formed (see problem 10-27). Then, since corresponding sides of similar triangles have a common ratio, $\frac{a}{d} = \frac{c}{b}$, and so

$$ab = cd.$$

Core Connections Geometry

10-43. If $\overline{QS}$ is a diameter and $\overline{PO}$ is a chord of the circle at right, find the measure of the geometric parts listed below.

    a. $m\angle QSO$

    b. $m\angle QPO$

    c. $m\angle ONS$

    d. $m\overset{\frown}{PS}$

    e. $m\overset{\frown}{PQ}$

    f. $m\angle PQN$

10-44. For each triangle below, solve for the given variables.

    a.

    b.

    c.

10-45. The spinner at right is designed so that if you randomly spin the spinner and land in the shaded sector, you win $1,000,000. Unfortunately, if you land in the unshaded sector, you win nothing. Assume point C is the center of the spinner.

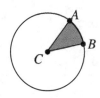

    a.   If $m\angle ACB = 90°$, how many times would you have to spin to reasonably expect to land in the shaded sector at least once? How did you get your answer?

    b.   What if $m\angle ACB = 1°$? How many times would you have to spin to reasonably expect to land in the shaded sector at least once?

    c.   Suppose $P(\text{winning } \$1,000,000) = \frac{1}{5}$ for each spin. What must $m\angle ACB$ equal? Show how you got your answer.

10-46. Calculate the total surface area and volume of the prism at right. Assume that the base is a regular pentagon.

10-47.   Quadrilateral *ABCD* is graphed so that $A(3, 2)$, $B(1, 6)$, $C(5, 8)$, and $D(7, 4)$.

      a.   Graph *ABCD* on graph paper. What shape is *ABCD*? Justify your answer.

      b.   *ABCD* is rotated 180° about the origin to create $A'B'C'D'$. Then $A'B'C'D'$ is reflected across the *x*-axis to form $A''B''C''D''$. Name the coordinates of C' and D''.

10-48.   Polly has a pentagon with angle measures $3x - 26°$, $2x + 70°$, $5x - 10°$, $3x$, and $2x + 56°$. Find the probability that if one vertex is selected at random, then the measure of its angle is more than or equal to 90°.

10-49.   **Multiple Choice:** Which graph below represents $y > -\frac{1}{2}x + 1$?

    a.   b.   c.   d.

10.1.5 How can I solve it?

Problem Solving with Circles

Your work today is focused on consolidating your understanding of the relationships between angles, arcs, chords, and tangents in circles. As you work today, ask yourself the following focus questions:

Is there another way?

What is the relationship?

10-50. On a map, the coordinates of towns *A*, *B*, and *C* are $A(-3, 3)$, $B(5, 7)$, and $C(6, 0)$. City planners have decided to connect the towns with a circular freeway.

a. Graph a map of the towns on graph paper. Once the freeway is built, $\overline{AB}$, $\overline{BC}$, and $\overline{AC}$ will be chords of the circle. Use this information to find the center of the circle.

b. Draw triangle *ABC* and use a compass to draw the circle connecting all three towns on your graph paper. Then, find the length of the radius of the circular freeway.

The circle that you drew **circumscribes** triangle △*ABC*, because △*ABC* is inscribed in the circle. The center of the circle is called the **circumcenter** of the triangle, because it is the center of the circle that circumscribes the triangle.

c. The city planners also intend to locate a new restaurant at the point that is an equal distance from all three towns. Where on the map should that restaurant be located? Justify your conclusion.

10-51. An 8-inch dinner knife is sitting on a circular plate so that its ends are on the edge of the plate. If the minor arc that is intercepted by the knife measures 120°, find the length of the diameter of the plate. Show all work.

10-52. A cylindrical block of cheese has a 6-inch diameter and is 2 inches thick. After a party, only a sector remains that has a central angle of 45°. Find the volume of the cheese that remains. Show all work.

10-53.   Dennis plans to place a circular hot tub in the corner of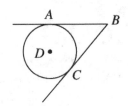
his backyard so that it is tangent to a fence on two
sides, as shown in the diagram at right.

a.   Prove that $\overline{AB} \cong \overline{CB}$.

b.   The switch to turn on the air jets is located at point
B. If the length of the diameter of the hot tub is 6 feet and $AB = 4$ feet,
how long does his arm need to be for him to reach the switch from the
edge of the tub? (Assume that Dennis will be in the tub when he turns the
air jets on and that the switch is level with the top edge of the hot tub.)

METHODS AND MEANINGS

MATH NOTES

Points of Concurrency

You learned that the **centroid** of a
triangle is the point at which the three
medians of a triangle intersect, as shown
at right. When three lines intersect at a
single point, that point is called a **point of
concurrency**. Refer to the Math Notes
box in Lesson 9.2.4.

Centroid

A circle that **circumscribes** a triangle
touches all three vertices of the triangle.
The center of this circle is called the
circumcenter. The circumcenter is
another point of concurrency because it is
located where the perpendicular bisectors
of each side of a triangle meet. See the
example at right.

Circumcenter

A circle that **inscribes** a triangle touches
all three sides of the triangle just once.
The center of this circle is called the
incenter. The incenter is yet another point
of concurrency because it is located where
the three angle bisectors of a triangle meet.

Incenter

Core Connections Geometry

10-54.   In the diagram at right, ⊙M has radius length
of 14 feet and ⊙A has radius length of 8 feet.
$\overline{ER}$ is tangent to both ⊙M and ⊙A. If
$NC = 17$ ft feet, find ER.

10-55.   Use the sectors in circles D and E to
answer the following questions.

a.   What is the ratio of the arc length
to the radius of circle D? Leave
your answer in terms of π.

b.   What is the ratio of the arc length to
the radius of circle E?

c.   The ratio of the arc length to the radius of a circle is called a **radian**. Why
will all sectors with a central angle of 30° have the same radian measure?

10-56.   In the figure at right, find the interior height
(h) of the obtuse triangle. Show all work.

10-57.   A cylinder with volume 500π cm³ is similar to a smaller cylinder. If the scale
factor is $\frac{1}{5}$, what is the volume of the smaller cylinder? Explain your reasoning.

10-58.   A six-year old house, now worth $175,000, has had an annual appreciation of
5%.

a.   What is the multiplier?

b.   What did it cost when new?

c.   Write a function of the form $f(t) = ab^t$, where t is the time in years, that
represents the value of the house since it was new.

10-59. In the figure at right, $\overline{EX}$ is tangent to $\odot O$ at point X. $OE = 20$ cm and $XE = 15$ cm.

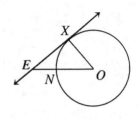

a. What is the area of the circle?

b. What is the area of the sector bounded by $\overline{OX}$ and $\overline{ON}$?

c. Find the area of the region bounded by $\overline{XE}$, $\overline{NE}$, and $\overset{\frown}{NX}$.

10-60. **Multiple Choice:** In the circle at right, $\overline{CD}$ is a diameter. If $AE = 10$, $CE = 4$, and $AB = 16$, what is the length of the radius of the circle?

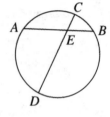

a. 15   b. 16

c. 18   d. 19

e. None of these

10.2.1 What does independence tell me?

Conditional Probability and Independence

When two events can occur, either simultaneously or one after the other, how can you calculate the probability of one of them when you know the other has already happened? You will investigate this question today. Then you will see how finding **conditional probabilities** will help you determine if two events are independent of each other.

10-61. EIGHT THE HARD WAY

Maribelle is playing the board game Eight The Hard Way with her friends. Each player rolls two dice on their turn, and moves according to the sum on the dice. However, if a player rolls two fours (called "eight the hard way"), they instantly win the round of play and a new round is started.

Shayna stepped into the kitchen to get snacks when she heard Maribelle shout *"Woo Hoo! I got an eight!"*

Shayna knows Maribelle got an eight. With your team, help Shayna investigate the probability that Maribelle rolled two fours and won the round of play. In other words calculate the **conditional probability** that Maribelle rolled two fours, given that you know she already rolled a sum of eight.

a. Use an area model to represent all of the possible sums of numbers when rolling two dice.

b. However, since you know that Maribelle rolled a sum of eight, the sample space is changed. Now the sample space is only all the ways a sum of eight can be rolled. On your area model, shade all of the ways a sum of eight can be rolled. How many different ways can a sum of eight be rolled, that is, how many outcomes are in the new sample space?

c. You are interested in the event {eight the hard way}. How many different ways can two fours be rolled?

d. What is the probability of the event {eight the hard way} given that you know Maribelle already rolled a sum of eight?

e. Becca rolls "high" (meaning that she rolled a sum of nine or more). What is the conditional probability that she rolled an odd number, given that you know she rolled high?

10-62.　At Einstein Technical University (ETU), data on engineering majors was collected:

	Engineering majors	Other majors
Live Off Campus	30	170
Live On Campus	6	34

a.　What is the probability of a student living on campus at ETU?

b.　Copy the table and shade the cells with engineering majors. What is the conditional probability of a student living on campus, given that you know a student is an engineering major?

c.　Two events, A and B, are **independent** if knowing that B occurred does not change the probability of event A occurring. That is, two events, A and B, are independent if P(A given B) = P(A). Are the events {live on campus} and {engineering} independent?

d.　Two events are **mutually exclusive** (or **disjoint**) if they cannot both occur at the same time. That is, two events are mutually exclusive if P(A and B) = 0. Are the events {on campus} and {engineering} mutually exclusive?

10-63.   The following data was collected about students in Mr. Rexinger's high school statistics class.

	Wearing jeans	Not wearing jeans
Male	7	7
Female	5	13

a.   Mr. Rexinger is playing a game with his students. He randomly chooses a student from his class roster. If a player guesses the gender of the student correctly, the player gets an early-lunch pass. Madeline is the next player. Which gender should she guess to have the greatest chances of winning the lunch pass? Explain.

b.   Mr. Rexinger tells Madeline that the student is wearing jeans. Should Madeline change her guess? Explain.

c.   In a previous course, you may have studied the **association** of two *numerical* variables by analyzing scatterplots and least squares regression lines. Associations between *categorical* variables are determined by independence – if two variables are independent then they are not associated.

Are the events {female} and {wearing jeans} associated for the students in Mr. Rexinger's class today? Explain using the independence relationship from part (c) of problem 10-62.

d.   Are the events {female} and {wearing jeans} mutually exclusive? Explain.

10-64.   At Digital Technical Institute, the following data was collected:

	Engineering majors	Other majors
Live Off Campus	30	170
Live On Campus	0	40

a.   Are the events {live on campus} and {engineering majors} associated at this institute?

b.   Are the events {live on campus} and {engineering} mutually exclusive at this institute? What outcomes are in the intersection of {live on campus} and {engineering}?

10-65.   LEARNING LOG

Explain in your Learning Log what it means for two
numerical variables to be associated, and give an example.
What does it mean for two *categorical* variables to be
associated? Give an example. Think of a new situation in which two events are
associated mathematically, and explain the difference between mutually
exclusive and independent events in your own words. Title this entry,
"Independent or Mutually Exclusive?" and include today's date.

METHODS AND MEANINGS

Mutually Exclusive

Mutually exclusive events, also called **disjoint** events, can never
both happen at the same time. When one of the events occurs, it
means the other cannot possibly occur. If event B occurs, then you
know that event A cannot occur: $P(A \text{ and } B) = 0$ and the intersection
of {A} and {B} contains no outcomes.

If events A and B are mutually exclusive, the occurrence of B tells
you precisely about the probability of A occurring (A cannot occur). The
probabilities of mutually exclusive events depend on each other. Mutually
exclusive events are never independent (and thus always associated).

For example, suppose natural blondes occur in about 10% of the students at your
school. Being naturally blonde and having naturally black hair are mutually
exclusive – if one occurs, the other cannot possibly occur. If your friend tells
you that a randomly selected person has naturally black hair, the probability they
have naturally blonde hair is 0%. The probability of blonde has changed,
knowing that the person has black hair. The events {blonde hair} and {black
hair} are not independent.

10-66. Natalie has a bag that contains eight marbles. She
        draws out a marble, records its color, and puts it back.

   a.   If Natalie repeats this eight times and does not
        record any red marbles, can she conclude that
        there are not any red marbles in the bag? Explain.

   b.   If she repeats this 100 times and does not record any red marbles, can she
        conclude that there are not any red marbles in the bag? Explain.

   c.   How many times would she have to draw marbles (putting them back each
        time) to be absolutely certain that there are no red marbles in the bag?

10-67. When the net at right is folded, it creates a die with values as
        shown.

   a.   If the die is rolled randomly, what is P(even)? P(1)?

   b.   If the die is rolled randomly 60 times, how many times would you expect
        an odd number to land side-up? Explain how you know.

   c.   Now create your own net so that the resulting die has P(even) = $\frac{1}{3}$,
        P(3) = 0, and P(a number less than 5) = 1.

10-68. In the diagram at right, $\overline{AB}$ is a diameter of $\odot L$. If
        $BC = 5$ and $AC = 12$, use the relationships shown in the
        diagram to solve for the quantities listed below.

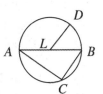

   a. AB b.   length of the radius of $\odot L$

   c. $m\angle ABC$ d. $m\overset{\frown}{AC}$

10-69.   When Erica and Ken explored a cave, they each found
         a gold nugget. Erica's nugget is similar to Ken's
         nugget. They measured the length of two matching
         parts of the nuggets and found that Erica's nugget is
         five times as long as Ken's. When they took their
         nuggets to the metallurgist to be analyzed, they
         learned that it would cost $30 to have the surface area
         and weight of the smaller nugget calculated, and $150
         to have the same analysis done on the larger nugget.

         *"I won't have that kind of money until I sell my nugget, and then I won't need it
         analyzed!"* Erica says.

         *"Wait, Erica. Don't worry. I'm pretty sure we can get all the information we
         need for only $30."*

         a.   Explain how they can get all the information they need for $30.

         b.   If Ken's nugget has a surface area of 20 cm², what is the surface area of
              Erica's nugget?

         c.   If Ken's nugget weighs 5.6 g (about 0.2 oz), what is the weight of Erica's
              nugget?

10-70.   Find *x* if the angles in a quadrilateral are 2*x*, 3*x*, 4*x*, and 5*x*.

10-71.   A graph of an inequality is shown at right. Decide
         if each of the points (*x*, *y*) listed below would make
         the inequality true or not. For each point, explain
         how you know.

         a.   (1, 1)   b.   (−3, 2)

         c.   (−2, 0)   d.   (0, −2)

10-72.   **Multiple Choice:** Which expression below represents
         the length of the hypotenuse of the triangle at right?

         a. $\frac{y}{x}$ b. $\sqrt{x^2 + y^2}$ c. $x + y$

         d. $\sqrt{y^2 - x^2}$ e.   None of these

10.2.2 Is there another way to organize data?

Two Way Tables

In the previous lesson, you were given the counts (or the frequency) of the number of people or objects in a given situation, and then, from this, you computed conditional probabilities. In this lesson, you will extend your understanding of conditional probabilities by starting from probabilities rather than counts. You will see how data or probabilities are often organized into **two-way tables**, and you will continue to investigate the association of two categorical variables.

10-73.   BUILD-A-FARM

In the children's game, Build-a-Farm, each player first spins a spinner. Half of the time the spinner comes up red and half of the time the spinner comes up blue. If the spinner is red, the player reaches into the red box. If the spinner is blue, the player reaches into the blue box. The red box has 10 chicken counters, 10 pig counters, and 10 cow counters, while the blue box has 5 chicken counters, 4 pig counters, and 1 cow counter.

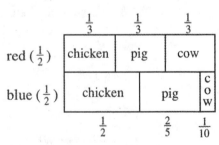

a.   Draw a tree diagram, including probabilities, to represent the sample space for this game.

b.   What is the probability of getting a cow counter in one turn?

c.   Even though the events {spin} and {animal counter} are not independent, a modified area model, as shown at right, is possible for this situation.

Copy the area model and shade the parts of the diagram that correspond to getting a cow counter. Using the diagram, verify that P(cow) is the same as the one that you found in part (b).

Problem continues on next page →

10-73.   *Problem continued from previous page.*

    d.   Let's investigate the conditional probability that a child's spin was red, given that you know the child got a cow counter.

        Since you know that the child got a cow counter, the new sample space is limited to only the outcomes that contain cow – which is the area that you shaded in part (c). Considering only the outcomes that contain cow, what is the conditional probability that a child spun red, knowing that the child got a cow counter?

    e.   Using the method in part (d), find the conditional probability that if you got a pig counter, your spin was blue.

10-74.   FLIP TO SPIN OR ROLL

On the midway at the county fair, there are many popular games to play. One of them is Flip to Spin or Roll. First, the player flips a coin. If a head comes up, the player gets to spin the big wheel, which has ten equal sections: three red, three blue, and four yellow. If the coin shows a tail, the player gets to roll a cube with three red sides, two yellow sides, and one blue side. If the wheel spin lands on blue, or if the blue side of the cube comes up, the player wins a stuffed animal.

    a.   Draw a modified area model to represent the sample space for Flip to Spin or Roll. Note that the rectangles for heads will have different areas than the rectangles for tails.

    b.   Suppose that you know that Tyler won a stuffed animal. Discus this with your team and then shade the appropriate parts of the modified area model to help you figure out the probability that he started off by getting a head. Be prepared to share your ideas with the class.

10-75.   Raul is conducting a survey for the school news blog. He surveyed 200 senior-class students and found that 78 students had access to a car on weekends, 54 students had regular chores assigned at home, and 80 students neither had access to a car, nor had regular chores to do. Raul said he couldn't figure out how to put the data into a table like the one at right.

	car	no car
chores		
no chores		

a.   Copy and complete Raul's table to figure out the number of students in each cell.

b.   This type of table is called a **two-way table** and is often used to organize information and calculate probabilities. Two-way tables often include row and column totals also. If you have not already done so, add row and column totals to your two-way table. Is there an association between car privileges and having regular chores for this group? Explain your answer in the context of the problem.

10-76.   There are 30 students in Mr. Cooper's class; 18 boys and 12 girls. Mr. Cooper chooses a student at random to take the attendance folder to the office. Four of the boys have previously taken the folder to the office, and 3 of the girls have previously taken it.

a.   Create a two-way table to display this data.

b.   If Mr. Cooper randomly selects a student, what is the probability he selects a boy who previously took the folder? Make a new two-table table, and fill in that probability. Then fill in the remaining cells with their respective probabilities. Include row and column totals.

c.   If a student is chosen at random, what is the probability that the student is a girl or is a student that has taken the folder previously? Use the probabilities from the table that you made in part (b).

d.   Shade the cells in your table from part (c) where a student has previously taken the folder. If a student previously took the folder, what is the probability that the student is a girl?

10-77.   If Letitia studies for her math test tonight, she has an
          80% chance of getting an A. If she does not study,
          she only has a 10% chance. Whether she can study or
          not depends on whether she has to work at her
          parents' store. Earlier in the day, her father said there
          is a 50% chance that Letitia would be able to study.

    a.   Draw a modified area model for the situation.

    b.   Find the probability that Letitia gets an A on the
          math test.

    c.   What are the chances that Letitia studied, given that she got an A? Show
          how you shaded the diagram.

    d.   Create a two-way table that shows the probabilities for this situation.
          Include row and column totals. Verify using your table that if she studies,
          Letitia has an 80% chance of getting an A as described in the beginning of
          this problem.

Review & Preview

10-78.   For each diagram below, write an equation to represent the relationship between
          x and y.

    a.   b.   c.   d.

10-79.   For each triangle below, use the information in the diagram to decide if it is a
          right triangle. Justify each conclusion. Assume the diagrams are not drawn to
          scale.

    a.   b.

                        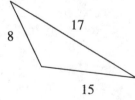

Core Connections Geometry

10-80.   A cement block is the shape of a prism with length 1.5 ft, width 1 ft and height 1 ft. Centered on the top of the block and passing all the way through the block are two 0.25 ft by 0.2 ft rectangular holes.

a.   Draw a diagram of the block.

b.   What is the volume of the block?

10-81.   A spinner is divided into two regions. One region, red, has a central angle of 60°. The other region is blue.

a.   On your paper, sketch a picture of this spinner.

b.   If the spinner is spun twice, what is the probability that both spins land on blue?

c.   If the radius of the spinner is 7 cm, what is the area of the blue region?

d.   A different spinner has three regions: purple, mauve, and green. If the probability of landing on purple is $\frac{1}{4}$ and the probability of landing on mauve is $\frac{2}{3}$, what is the central angle of the green region?

10-82.   After doing well on a test, Althea's teacher placed a gold star on her paper. When Althea examined the star closely, she realized that it was really a regular pentagon surrounded by 5 isosceles triangles, as shown in the diagram at right. If the star has the angle measurements shown in the diagram, find the sum of the angles inside the shaded pentagon. Show all work.

10-83.   Remember that the radian measure of a central angle of a circle is the ratio of the arc length to the radius (see problem 10-55).

a.   What is the radian measure for a 45-degree central angle on a circle with radius 5 cm? What is the radian measure for a 45-degree central angle on a circle with radius 1 cm? Answer in terms of π.

b.   The central angle of a circle has a radian measure of $\frac{\pi}{3}$. What is the measure of the central angle of the sector in degrees?

10-84. **Multiple Choice:** $\triangle ABC$ is a right triangle and is graphed on coordinate axes. If $m\angle B = 90°$ and the slope of $\overline{AB}$ is $-\frac{4}{5}$, what is the slope of BC?

a. $\frac{4}{5}$ b. $\frac{5}{4}$ c. $-\frac{5}{4}$ d. $-\frac{4}{5}$

e. Cannot be determined

10-85. At the University of the Great Plains the following data about engineering majors was collected:

	Engineering major	Other major	
Live Off Campus	800	7200	8000
Live On Campus	120	11,880	12,000
	920	19,080	20,000

a. What is the conditional probability of living on campus, given that you know a student is an engineering major?

b. Compare your answer to part (a) to the probability of living on campus.

c. Are the two events, {living on campus} and {engineering major} associated? Use the probabilities to explain why or why not.

10-86. The spinner at right has three regions: A, B, and C. If it is spun 80 times, how many times would you expect each region to result? Show your work.

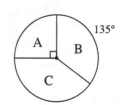

10-87. Review what you know about the angles and arcs of circles below.

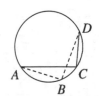

a. A circle is divided into nine congruent sectors. What is the measure of each central angle?

b. In the diagram at right, find $m\widehat{AD}$ and $m\angle C$ if $m\angle B = 97°$.

c. In $\odot C$ at right, $m\angle ACB = 125°$ and $r = 8$ inches. Find $m\widehat{AB}$ and the length of $\widehat{AB}$. Then find the area of the smaller sector.

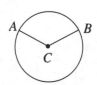

10-88. Examine the diagram at right. Use the given geometric relationships to solve for x, y, and z. Be sure to justify your work by stating the geometric relationship and applicable theorem.

10-89. Solve each equation below for x. Check your work.

a. $\frac{x}{2} = 17$ b. $\frac{x}{4} = \frac{1}{3}$ c. $\frac{x+6}{2} + 2 = \frac{5}{2}$ d. $\frac{4}{x} = \frac{5}{8}$

10-90. Mrs. Cassidy solved the problem $(w-3)(w+5) = 9$ and got $w = 3$ and $w = -5$. Is she correct? If so, show how you know. If not, show how you know and find the correct solution.

10-91. **Multiple Choice:** Which expression represents the area of the trapezoid at right?

a. $\frac{c(a+b)}{4}$ b. $\frac{c(a+b)}{2}$

c. $\frac{bc}{2}$ d. $\frac{a+b+c}{2}$

e. None of these

10.2.3 How can I pull it all together?

Applications of Probability

Probability has uses far beyond its origins in games of chance. Often, probabilities are based on survey data or data taken from a sample population. Today you will learn two new probability rules, and at the end of the lesson you will be given an opportunity to summarize the probability rules that you know.

10-92. In a recent survey of college freshman, 35% of students checked the box next to "Exercise regularly," 33% checked the box next to "Eat five servings of fruits and vegetables a day," and 57% checked the box next to "Neither."

a. Create a two-way table to represent this situation. Include row and column totals.

b. What is the probability that a freshman in this study exercises regularly *and* eats 5 servings of fruits and vegetables each day?

c. What is the probability that a freshman in this study exercises regularly *or* eats 5 servings of fruits and vegetables each day?

d. Do you think that freshmen who eat 5 servings of fruit and vegetables per day are more likely to exercise? In other words, are exercising and eating associated?

e. Compare and contrast a two-way table with an area model.

10-93.   DOUBLE SPIN

Remember Double Spin, the game at the fair from Chapter 4?
The player gets to spin a spinner twice, but only wins if the
same amount comes up both times. The $100 sector is $\frac{1}{8}$ of the
circle. Nick is currently playing the game.

a.   Make an area model to show the sample space of every possible outcome
      for two spins. What is the probability that Nick wins?

b.   When Nick came home from the fair, he told Zack that he had won some
      money in the Double Spin game. Knowing that Nick won some money,
      what are the chances that he won $100?

c.   Make a two-way table that shows the probabilities for the Double Spin
      game. How does your table compare to the area model from part (a)?
      Explain.

d.   A mathematical way to express the conditional probability relationship is:

$$P(A \text{ given } B) = \frac{P(A \text{ and } B)}{P(B)}.$$

      This relationship is called the **Multiplication Rule**. (You will learn why it
      is called that in the next problem.) Verify your answer to part (b) using
      the Multiplication Rule. Be sure to define events A and B.

10-94.   ANOTHER DEFINITION FOR INDEPENDENCE

a.   To learn how the Multiplication Rule got its name, rewrite the
      Multiplication Rule starting with "P(A and B) = ".

b.   Write the relationship between event A and event B for when they are
      independent using symbols.

c.   Substitute the independence relationship from part (b) into the
      Multiplication Rule that you wrote for part (a) to get another definition for
      independence.

10-95.   The Laundry Shop sells washers and dryers. The owner of the store, Mr. McGee, thinks that a customer who purchases a washer is more likely to purchase a dryer than a customer that did not purchase a washer. He analyzes the sales from the last month and finds that a total of 240 customers made purchases. He counts 180 washers that were purchased and 96 dryers that were purchased. Mr. McGee then counts the number of sales that included both a washer and a dryer and finds 72 customers purchased both.

Is there an association between the purchase of washers and dryers? Explain and show your reasoning using the relationships that you have learned in this lesson.

10-96.   SHIFTY SHAUNA

Shauna has a bad relationship with the truth – she doesn't usually tell it! In fact, whenever Shauna is asked a question, she rolls a die. If it comes up 6, she tells the truth. Otherwise, she lies.

a.   If Shauna flips a fair coin and you ask her how it came out, what is the probability that she says "heads" *and* is telling the truth? Choose a method to solve this problem and carefully record your work. Be ready to share your solution method with the class.

b.   Suppose Shauna flips a fair coin and you ask her whether it came up heads or tails. What is the probability that she says "heads"? (Hint: The answer is not $\frac{1}{12}$!)

c.   Suppose Shauna tells you that the coin says heads. What is the probability that she really did flip heads?

d.   Is whether Shauna lies or tells the truth independent of whether the coin lands on heads or tails?

10-97. It is generally assumed that there is no relationship between height and IQ (a measure of intelligence). Thus, the heights for 175 people randomly selected people are independent of their IQ's.

Using this assumption, complete the two-way table below.

	Below average height	Above average height	
Below average IQ			70
Above average IQ			105
	50	125	175

10-98. A spinner has just two colors, red and blue. The probability the spinner will land on blue is x.

a. What is the probability it will land on red?

b. Sketch an area model for spinning this spinner twice.

c. When the spinner is spun twice, what is the probability that it will land on the same color both times?

d. Given that the spinner lands on the same color twice, what is the probability that it landed on blue both times?

10-99. On another spinner, blue occurs a fraction x of the time, while the red and green portions have equal area. There are no other colors on the spinner.

a. Find the probability that the spinner will land on green.

b. Sketch an area diagram for spinning the spinner twice.

c. Shade the region on your area diagram corresponding to getting the same color on the spinner twice.

d. What is the probability that both spins give the same color?

e. If you know that you got the same color twice, what is the probability that the color was blue?

10-100. LEARNING LOG

Title this Learning Log entry, "Probability Rules" and
include today's date. First, consider the Build A Farm
game described in problem 10-73. What are three different
models you can use to find probabilities?

Then summarize the probability rules you know as follows:

- State the Addition Rules. Also state the rule as a union or intersection,
  whichever is appropriate.

- State both versions of the Multiplication Rule (the multiplication and the
  division versions).

- State two different rules that define independence.

- For each rule, create examples from the Build A Farm game.

ETHODS AND MEANINGS

Conditional Probability and Independence

MATH NOTES

When you are calculating a probability, but have been given
additional information about an event that has already occurred,
you are calculating a **conditional probability**. For the conditional
probability P(A given B), you know that event B has occurred, so
event B becomes the sample space of all possible outcomes.
P(A given B) is the fraction of event B's outcomes that also include
event A, which is formally stated as the **Multiplication Rule**:

$$P(A \text{ given } B) = \frac{P(A \text{ and } B)}{P(B)}$$

Two events are **independent** when the outcome of one does not influence the
outcome of the other. Two independent events could both occur, but knowing event
B has occurred does not change the probability of event A occurring, thus
P(A given B) = P(A). When events are not independent, you say that they are
associated. That is, one event influences the other.

If you substitute the definition for independence, P(A given B) = P(A), into the
Multiplication Rule and rearrange the result, you get an alternate definition for
independence: If events A and B are independent, then P(A and B) = P(A) · P(B).
The converse of this statement is also true: If P(A and B) = P(A) · P(B), then A and
B are independent.

10-101. A technology group wants to determine if bringing a laptop on a trip that involves flying is related to people being on business trips. Data for 1000 random passengers at an airport was collected and summarized in the table below.

	Laptop	No laptop
Traveling for business	236	274
Not traveling for business	93	397

a.   What is the probability of traveling with a laptop if someone is traveling for business?

b.   Does it appear that there is an association between bringing a laptop on a trip that involves flying and traveling for business?

10-102. In a certain small town, 65% of the households subscribe to the daily paper, 37% subscribe to the weekly local paper, and 25% subscribe to both papers.

a.   Make a two-way table to represent this data.

b.   If a household is selected at random, what is the probability that it subscribes to at least one of the two papers? Shade these areas in your table.

c.   Charlie's neighbor subscribes to a paper. What is the probability that he receives the daily paper?

10-103. The Sunshine Orange Juice Company wants its product in a one-quart container (1 quart equals 107.75 cubic inches). The manufacturer for their containers makes cylindrical cans that have a base that is 5 inches in diameter. What will be the height of the one-quart container?

10-104. The radian measure of a central angle of 90° is $\frac{\pi}{2}$. What must the radian measure of a central angle of 180° be? How can you tell without actually computing the radian measure?

10-105. The mat plan for a three-dimensional solid is shown at right.

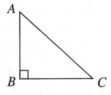

a. On graph paper, draw *all* of views of this solid. (There are six views.) Compare the views. Are any the same?

b. Find the volume and surface area of the solid. Explain your method.

c. Do the views you drew in part (a) help calculate volume or surface area? Explain.

10-106. For the triangle at right, find each trigonometric ratio below. The first one is done for you.

a. $\tan C = \frac{AB}{BC}$

b. $\sin C$

c. $\tan A$

d. $\cos C$

e. $\cos A$

f. $\sin A$

10-107. Review circle relationships as you answer the questions below.

a. On your paper, draw a diagram of $\odot B$ with $\widehat{AC}$. If $m\widehat{AC} = 80°$ and the length of the radius of $\odot B$ is 10, find the length of chord $\overline{AC}$.

b. Now draw a diagram of a circle with two chords, $\overline{EF}$ and $\overline{GH}$, that intersect at point K. If $EF = 15$, $EK = 6$, and $HK = 3$, what is GK?

10.3.1 What if the sample space is very large?

The Fundamental Principle of Counting

Phone numbers in the U.S. are composed of a three-digit area code followed by seven digits. License plates in some states are made up of three letters followed by a three-digit number. Postal ZIP codes are made up of five digits, and another four digits are often added. To win the lottery in one state you need to select the correct five numbers from all the possible choices of five numbers out of 56. Consider these questions:

- How likely is it that you could win the lottery?

- Are there enough phone numbers for the dramatic increase in cell phones, tablets, and e-readers for books, many of which use unseen phone numbers to download information?

- Jay wants to know the probability of randomly getting JAY on his license plates so he can avoid paying the extra amount for a personalized license plate.

The sample spaces for these questions are very large. Imagine trying to draw a tree diagram! Tree diagrams with three or four branches, branching two or three times, are messy enough. You need a way to count possibilities without having to draw a complete diagram. In this and the next two lessons, you and your team will develop some strategies that will allow you to account for all possibilities without having to make a complete list or draw a complete tree diagram. As you work on the problems in this lesson, discuss the following questions with your team:

What decisions am I making when I make a systematic list?

How many decisions do I need to make?

How many ways are there to make each decision?

How can I use the patterns in a tree diagram to find the total number of branches?

10-108. Nick came across the following problem: If a 4-digit number is randomly selected from all of the 4-digit numbers that use the digits 1, 2, 3, 4, 5, 6, and 7, with repeated digits allowed, what is the probability that the selected number is 2763? Nick knew that he had to figure out how many numbers were possible, in order to know the size of his sample space.

a. Nick started to make a systematic list of the possibilities, but after the first few he gave up. What is the difficulty in trying to create a list?

b. Next he started a tree diagram. What problem did he encounter with the tree?

c. Nick decided he needed a shortcut strategy for organizing this problem; otherwise he was going to be up all night. He started by asking himself, *"How many decisions (about the digits) do I need to make?"* With your team discuss his first question and then consider his next question, *"How many choices do I have for each decision (each digit)?"*

d. Audrey was at her house working on the same problem. She was thinking of a tree diagram, when she asked herself, *"How many branch points will this tree have?"* and *"How many branches at each point?"* What are the answers to her questions? How are these questions related to the one that Nick was pondering?

e. At the same moment, they text messaged each other that they were stuck. When they talked, they realized they were on the same track. The problem asks for four-digit numbers, so there are four decisions. Simultaneously they said, *"We need a **decision chart**."* They wrote the following on their papers:

$$\underline{\qquad} \quad \underline{\qquad} \quad \underline{\qquad} \quad \underline{\qquad}$$
1st digit   2nd digit   3rd digit   4th digit

How many choices are there for each decision? How many four digit numbers are there?

f. What is the probability that the randomly selected number will be 2763?

10-109. How many four-digit numbers could you make with the digits 1, 2, 3, 4, 5, 6, and 7 if you could not use any digit more than once in the four-digit number? Make a decision chart and explain the similarities and differences between this situation and the one described in problem 10-108.

10-110.   The basis for a decision chart is the **Fundamental Principle of Counting**. Read the Math Notes box at the end of this lesson to help you understand the Fundamental Principle of Counting. Then use a decision chart to answer each question below.

   a.   A game contains nine discs, each with one of the numbers 1, 2, 3, 4, 5, 6, 7, 8, or 9 on it. How many different three-digit numbers can be formed by choosing any three discs, without replacing the discs?

   b.   A new lotto game called Quick Spin has three wheels, each with the numbers 1, 2, 3, 4, 5, 6, 7, 8, and 9 equally spaced around the rim. Each wheel is spun once, and the numbers the arrows point to are recorded in order. How many three-digit numbers are possible?

   c.   Explain the similarities and differences between part (a) and part (b).

10-111.   Marcos is selecting classes for next year. He plans to take English, physics, government, pre-calculus, Spanish, and journalism. His school has a six-period day, so he will have one of these classes each period.

   a.   How many different schedules are possible?

   b.   How many schedules are possible with first-period pre-calculus?

   c.   What is the probability that Marcos will get first-period pre-calculus?

   d.   What is the probability that Marcos will get both first-period pre-calculus *and* second-period physics?

10-112. **CAN MY CALCULATOR FIND IT FASTER?**

a. How many possible ways can the letters in the word MATH be arranged?

b. On your calculator, find the **factorial** function, $n!$ or $!$. On many scientific calculators, it can be found by pressing the PRB key. On many graphing calculators, it is a function in the math menu and probability submenu.

   Find the value of 7 factorial (written 7!), then 6!, then 5!, 4!, ... , 1!

c. How do you think your calculator computes 5!

d. Explain why 4! gives the correct solution to the possible number of ways to arrange the letters M A T H.

e. What happens when you try to find 70! with your calculator? Why?

10-113. Remembering what $n!$ means can help you do some messy calculations quickly, as well as help you do problems that might be too large for your calculator's memory.

For instance, if you wanted to calculate $\frac{9!}{6!}$, you could use the $n!$ button on your calculator and find that 9! = 362,880 and 6! = 720, so $\frac{9!}{6!} = \frac{362880}{720} = 504$.

You could also use a simplification technique. Since
$9! = 9 \cdot 8 \cdot 7 \cdot 6 \cdot 5 \cdot 4 \cdot 3 \cdot 2 \cdot 1$ and $6! = 6 \cdot 5 \cdot 4 \cdot 3 \cdot 2 \cdot 1$, you can
rewrite $\frac{9!}{6!} = \frac{9 \cdot 8 \cdot 7 \cdot 6 \cdot 5 \cdot 4 \cdot 3 \cdot 2 \cdot 1}{6 \cdot 5 \cdot 4 \cdot 3 \cdot 2 \cdot 1} = 9 \cdot 8 \cdot 7 = 504$.

Use this simplification technique to simplify each of the following problems before computing the result.

a. $\frac{10!}{8!}$ b. $\frac{70!}{68!}$ c. $\frac{7!}{4!3!}$ d. $\frac{20!}{18!2!}$

METHODS AND MEANINGS

MATH NOTES

Fundamental Principle of Counting

The **Fundamental Principle of Counting** is a method for counting the number of outcomes (the size of the sample space) of a probabilistic situation, often where the order of the outcomes matters. If event {A} has *m* outcomes, and event {B} has *n* outcomes after event {A} has occurred, then the event {A} followed by event {B} has *m* ● *n* outcomes.

For a sequence of events, a tree diagram could be used to count the number of outcomes, but if the number of outcomes is large a **decision chart** is more useful.

For example, how many three-letter arrangements could be made by lining up any three blocks, chosen from a set of 26 alphabet blocks, if the first letter must be a vowel? There are three decisions (three blocks to be chosen), with 5 choices for the first letter (a vowel), 25 for the second, and 24 for the third. According to the Fundamental Principle of Counting, the total number of possibilities is:

$$\underset{\text{1st decision}}{\underline{5}} \cdot \underset{\text{2nd decision}}{\underline{25}} \cdot \underset{\text{3rd decision}}{\underline{24}} = 3000 .$$

This decision chart is a way to represent a tree with 5 branches for the first alphabet block, followed by 25 branches for each of those branches; each of those 125 branches would then have 24 branches representing the possibilities for the third alphabet block.

10-114.   A Scrabble® player has four tiles with the letters A, N, P, and S.

   a.   How many arrangements of these letters are possible?

   b.   Draw a tree diagram that shows how to get the arrangements and explain how a decision chart represents the tree.

   c.   What is the probability of a two-year-old randomly making a word using the four letters?

10-115. Five students are running for Junior class president. They must give speeches before the election committee. They draw straws to see who will go first, second, etc. In how many different orders could they give their speeches?

10-116. Parents keep telling their teens to "turn down the music" or "turn off the computer" when studying. But teens insist that these "distractions" actually help them study better! In order to put this argument to rest, a psychologist studied whether subjects were able to memorize 20 index cards while listening to loud music or studying in silence. The sixty subjects had these results:

	Able to memorize	Not able to memorize
Loud music	9	36
Silence	3	12

a. What is the probability that a randomly chosen subject is able to memorize the index cards?

b. What is the probability that a music listener memorizes the index cards?

c. According to the data from this study, is the ability to memorize independent of listening to loud music?

10-117. Marty and Gerri played Pick a Tile, in which the player reaches into two bags. One bag contains square tiles and the other circular tiles. The bag with squares contains three yellow, one blue, and two red squares. The bag with circles has one yellow and two red circles. In order to win the game (and a large stuffed animal), a player must choose one blue square and one red circle.

a. Complete the two-way table below.

CIRCLES

	red	yellow	
yellow			$\frac{3}{6}$
red			
blue			
	$\frac{2}{3}$	1	

SQUARES

b. What is the probability of a player choosing the wining blue-red combination?

c. When Marty pulled her hand out of the bag, Gerri squealed with delight because she thought she saw something blue. If it was something blue, what is the probability that Marty won a stuffed animal?

10-118. The *sum* of the lengths of the edges of a cube is 1200 cm. Find the surface area and the volume of the cube.

10-119. The circle at right is inscribed in a regular hexagon. Find the area of the shaded region.

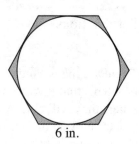

6 in.

10-120. **Multiple Choice:** Examine $\odot L$ at right. Which of the mathematical statements below is not necessarily true?

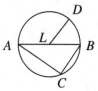

a. $LD = AL$

b. $m\angle DLB = m\widehat{DB}$

c. $\overline{LD} \parallel \overline{CB}$

d. $m\widehat{BC} = 2m\angle BAC$

e. $2AL = AB$

10.3.2 How can I count arrangements?

Permutations

There are many kinds of counting problems. In this lesson you will learn to recognize problems that involve arrangements. In some cases outcomes will be repeated, but in others they will not. A list of **permutations** includes different arrangements of distinct objects chosen from a set of objects. In other words, permutations are arrangements of elements without using any element more than once, and without repetition. As you work on the problems in this lesson discuss the following questions with your team:

> When I make a decision chart, how many choices do I have after I make the first choice? The second? The third? …

> Can I use the same choice again?

> Can this situation be represented as a permutation?

> What patterns can I find in these problems?

10-121.   Jasper finally managed to save enough money to open a savings account at the credit union. When he went in to open the account, the accounts manager told him that he needed to select a four-digit PIN (personal identification number). She also said that he could not repeat a digit, but that he could use any of the digits 0, 1, 2, …, 9 for any place in his four-digit PIN.

   a.   How many different PIN's are possible?

   b.   Notice that the decision chart for this problem looks like the beginning of 10!, but it does not go all the way down to 1. Factorials can be used to represent this problem, but you must compensate for the factors that you do not use, so you can write $\frac{10!}{6!}$. Discuss with your team how this method gives the same result as your decision chart.

10-122. With your team, discuss how you could use factorials to represent each of the
following situations. Then find the solutions. Four of the five problems
involve permutations, and one does not. As you work, discuss with your team
which problems fit the definition for permutations and why or why not. Write
your answers both as factorials and as whole numbers.

a. Fifty-two contestants entered a contest for a
new school logo design. In how many
different ways can the judges pick the best
logo and the runners-up one, two, and three?

b. The volleyball team is sponsoring a mixed-
doubles sand court volleyball tournament and sixteen pairs have signed up
for the chance to win one of the seven trophies and cash prizes. In how
many different ways can the teams finish in the top seven slots?

c. Carmen is getting a new locker at school, and the first thing she must do is
decide on a new locker combination. The three-number locker
combination can be picked from the numbers 0 through 35. How many
different locker combinations could she create if none of the numbers can
be repeated?

d. How many three-digit locker combinations could Carmen make up if zero
could only be the second or third number and none of the numbers can be
repeated?

e. How many locker combinations can Carmen have if she can use any of the
numbers 0 through 35 and she can repeat numbers? Is this still a
permutation? Explain why you think that it is or is not.

10-123. Problems about the order of teams or winners, and questions about how many numbers you could make without repeating any digits, are called **permutations**.

a. Below is a list of all of the license plate letter triples that can be made with the letters A, B, and C.

AAA	BBB	CCC	AAB	ABA
BAA	AAC	ACA	CAA	ABB
BAB	BBA	ACC	CAC	CCA
ABC	ACB	CAB	BAC	CBA
BCA	BCC	CBC	CCB	CBB
BCB	BBC			

How is this list different from all the arrangements a child can make on a line on the refrigerator door with three magnetic letters A, B, and C. Make the list of arrangements the child can make with the refrigerator magnets. Why are the lists different? Which one is a permutation?

b. Imagine a group of 8 candidates: one will become president, one vice president, and one secretary of the school senate. Now imagine a different group of 8 applicants, three of whom will be selected to be on the spirit committee. How will the lists of three possible people selected from the 8 people differ? Which list would be longer? Which is a permutation?

c. Consider these two situations. Decide if they are permutations. Why or why not?

- The possible 4-digit numbers you could write if you could choose any digit from the numbers 2, 3, 4, 5, 6, 7, 8, and you could use digits several times.

- All the 4-digit numbers you could make using seven square tiles numbered 2, 3, 4, 5, 6, 7, and 8.

d. What are the important characteristics that a counting problem has to have in order to classify it as a permutation problem? Discuss this with your team and then write a *general* method for counting the number of arrangements in any problem that could be identified as a permutations problem.

10-124.   **WHAT IS THE FORMULA?**

a.   In part (a) of problem 10-122 you calculated how many ways judges could pick the logo contest winner and three runners up from 52 contestants. The answer can be written using factorials as $\frac{52!}{48!}$. Explain where these numbers came from.

b.   The logo contest situation can be thought of as finding the number of possible arrangements of 52 elements arranged 4 at a time. Reexamine your answers to parts (b) and (c) of problem 10-122 and use your answers to write a general formula to calculate the number of possible arrangements of n objects arranged r at a time. Begin your formula with $_nP_r =$.

c.   Use your formula from part (b) above to calculate:

   i. $_7P_4$ ii. $_{52}P_4$ iii. $_{16}P_7$

10-125.   **ANAGRAMS**

a.   How many distinct ways can the letters in the word MASH be arranged?

b.   How many distinct ways can the letters in the word SASH be arranged? Use a tree diagram if it helps.

c.   How many distinct ways can the letters in the word SASS be arranged?

d.   Express your answers to parts (b) and (c) using fractions with factorials. The numerators should both be 4!.

e.   How can you use fractions with factorials to account for repeated letters when counting the number of arrangements?

10-126.   Sasha wonders how many distinct ways she can arrange the letters in her name. She thinks the answer is $\frac{5!}{4!} = 5$. What is her mistake? What is the correct answer, written using factorials?

METHODS AND MEANINGS

$n!$ and Permutations

A **factorial** is shorthand for the product of a list of consecutive, descending whole numbers from the largest down to 1:

$$n! = n(n-1)(n-2) \dots (3)(2)(1)$$

For example, 4 factorial or $4! = 4 \bullet 3 \bullet 2 \bullet 1 = 24$ and $6! = 6 \bullet 5 \bullet 4 \bullet 3 \bullet 2 \bullet 1 = 720$.

A **permutation** is an arrangement of items in which the order of selection matters and items cannot be selected more than once. The number of permutations that can be made by selecting r items from a set of n items can be represented with tree diagrams or decision charts, or calculated $_nP_r = \frac{n!}{(n-r)!} = n(n-1)(n-2)\dots(n-r+1)$.

For example, eight people are running a race. In how many different ways can they come in first, second, and third? The result can be represented $_8P_3$, which means the number of ways to choose *and* arrange three different (not repeated) things from a set of eight.

$$_8P_3 = \frac{8!}{(8-3)!} = \frac{8!}{5!} = \frac{8 \cdot 7 \cdot 6 \cdot 5 \cdot 4 \cdot 3 \cdot 2 \cdot 1}{5 \cdot 4 \cdot 3 \cdot 2 \cdot 1} = 8 \cdot 7 \cdot 6 = 336$$

10-127. For the homecoming football game the cheerleaders at High Tech High printed each letter of the name of the school's mascot, WIZARDS, on a large card. Each card has one letter on it, and each cheerleader is supposed to hold up one card. At the end of the first quarter, they realize that someone has mixed up the cards.

    a. How many ways are there to arrange the cards?

    b. If they had not noticed the mix up, what would be the probability that the cards would have correctly spelled out the mascot?

Core Connections Geometry

10-128.   Twelve horses raced in the CPM Derby.

a.   How many ways could the horses finish in the top three places?

b.   If you have not already done so, write your answer to part (a) as a fraction with factorials.

10-129.   An engineer is designing the operator panel for a water treatment plant. The operator will be able to see four LED lights in a row that indicate the condition of the water treatment system. LEDs can be red, yellow, green, or off. How many different conditions can be signaled with the LEDs?

10-130.   An insurance company wants to charge a higher premium to drivers of red cars because they believe that they get more speeding tickets. A research company collected the following data to investigate their claim. Use the data below to decide if the insurance company should be charging a higher premium to drivers of red cars.

Total: 20,000 cars with 507 speeding tickets

Red Cars: 348 red cars with 9 speeding tickets.

10-131.   A survey of local car dealers revealed that 64% of all cars sold last month had a Green Fang system, 28% had alarm systems, and 22% had both Green Fang and alarm systems.

a.   What is the probability one of these cars selected at random had neither Green Fang nor an alarm system?

b.   What is the probability that a car had Green Fang and was not protected by an alarm system?

c.   Are having Green Fang and an alarm system disjoint (mutually exclusive) events?

d.   Use the alternative definition of independence (see the Math Notes box in Lesson 10.2.3) to determine if having Green Fang is associated with having an alarm.

10-132.   In the past, many states had license plates
           composed of three letters followed by three
           digits (0 to 9). Recently, many states have
           responded to the increased number of cars
           by adding one digit (1 to 9) ahead of the
           three letters. How many more license plates
           of the second type are possible? What is the
           probability of being randomly assigned a
           license plate containing ALG 2?

10-133.   Describe the solid represented by each net below.

    a.   b.   c.

10.3.3 How many groups are possible?

Combinations

In the previous lesson you learned a method for counting arrangements, including permutations. In this lesson you will consider questions such as how many five-card poker hands are possible, how many spirit committees can be selected from the Junior class, or your chances of winning the lottery.

In a five-card poker hand, the *arrangement* of the cards does *not* matter. Since all the spirit committee members have equal status, the *order* in which they are selected does *not* matter. If you have a winning lottery ticket, you will not care about the order in which the numbers are drawn. In these situations, you need to count the **combinations**. As you work with your team on the problems in this lesson, use the following questions to help focus your discussion:

Does the particular arrangement matter?

What are the relationships among these situations?

10-134. Five members of the Spirit Club have volunteered for the club governing board. These members are Al, Barbara, Carl, Dale, and Ernie. The club members will select three of the five as board members for the next year. One way to do this would be to elect a governing committee of three in which all members would have the same title. A second way would be to select a president, vice-president, and secretary.

a. How many different lineups of officers are possible? This means a president, vice-president, and a secretary are chosen. Thus, Al as president, Barbara as vice-president, and Carl as secretary would be a different possibility from Al as president, Barbara as secretary, and Carl as vice-president.

b. How many different three-member committees are possible? In this case, it is a good idea to make a list of all the possibilities, which are called **combinations**.

c. Felicia decides that she wants to volunteer as well.

    i. How many different possibilities for officers are possible now?

    ii. How many different governing committees are possible now? Again, make the list of all of the possibilities, or combinations.

Problem continues on next page →

10-134. *Problem continued from previous page.*

    d.   Since there are more volunteers, the spirit club has decided to appoint another committee member.

        i.   If they add a treasurer to the list of officers, how many different ways are there to select the four officers are possible?

        ii.   If they choose a governing committee of four, how many possibilities are there?

10-135. Compare the results you got for each set of numbers in problem 10-134 when the roles were determined (permutations) and when there were no specific roles (combinations).

    a.   How do the number of combinations and permutations compare in each situation?

    b.   Work with your team to develop a conjecture about the mathematical relationship between permutations and combinations chosen from the same sized groups. Be prepared to share your thinking with the class.

    c.   Test your conjecture by calculating the number of permutations and combinations of 2 items chosen from 6. Does it work?

    d.   How can you generalize your conjecture so that it can be applied to permutations and combinations of r items chosen from n? Write a formula relating permutations (written $_nP_r$) and combinations (written $_nC_r$).

10-136. Now you will use your calculator to test the formula you wrote in problem 10-135.

    a.   Try 4 items chosen from 20. Does your formula work?

    b.   With your team, find a way to justify the logic of your formula. How can you convince someone that it has to be correct for all numbers?

10-137. In one state lottery, there are 56 numbers from which a player can choose six.

    a.   Does the order in which the numbers are chosen matter?

    b.   Find the number of possible combinations for a set of 6 winning lottery numbers.

    c.   What is the probability of selecting the six winning numbers?

10-138.   In the game of poker called Five-Card Draw, each player is dealt five cards
           from a standard deck of 52 cards. While players tend to arrange the cards in
           their hands, the order in which they get them does not matter. How many five-
           card poker hands are possible? Use the methods you developed in today's
           investigation to answer this question.

METHODS AND MEANINGS

Combinations

When selecting committees, it matters who is selected but not
the **order** of selection or any **arrangement** of the groups.
Selections of committees, or of lists of groups without regard to the
order within the group, are called **combinations**. Note that
combinations do not include repeated elements.

For example: Eight people are eligible to receive $500 scholarships, but
only three will be selected. How many different ways are there to select a
group of three?

This is a problem of counting combinations. $_8C_3$ represents the number of ways
to choose three from a set of eight. This is sometimes read as "eight *choose* three."

To compute the number of combinations, first calculate the number of
permutations and then divide by the number of ways to arrange each permutation.

$$_8C_3 = \frac{_8P_3}{3!} = \frac{8!}{5!3!} = 56$$

In general: Number of ways to choose $= \dfrac{\text{\# of ways to choose and arrange}}{\text{\# of ways to arrange}}$

$$_nC_r = \frac{_nP_r}{r!} = \frac{n!}{(n-r)!r!}$$

Review & Preview

10-139.   How many different batting orders can be made from the
           nine starting players on a baseball team? Write the
           answer using factorials and as a number.

10-140.   What do you think $0!$ is equal to?

a.   Try it on your calculator to see what you get.

b.   What does $_8P_8$ mean? What *should* $_8P_8$ be equal to? Write $_8P_8$ using the factorial formula. Why is it necessary for $0!$ to equal 1?

c.   Do you remember how to show that $2^0 = 1$? You can use a sequence of powers of two like this: $\frac{2^4}{2} = 2^3$, $\frac{2^3}{2} = 2^2$, $\frac{2^2}{2} = 2^1$, so $\frac{2^1}{2} = 2^0$. Since $\frac{2^1}{2} = 1$ you also know that $2^0 = 1$.

You can construct a similar pattern for $0!$, starting with $\frac{5!}{5} = 4!$ and then $\frac{4!}{4} = 3!$. Continue the pattern and make an argument to justify that $0! = 1$.

10-141.   For the each of the following, write down a factorial expression and then compute the value. Use the $_nC_r$ and $_nP_r$ functions on your calculator to make the computation.

a. $_{10}P_8$ b. $_{10}C_8$ c. $_6C_1$

10-142.   Of the 63 drinks at Joe's Java and Juice Hut, 42 contain coffee and 21 contain dairy products. If Alexei randomly chooses a drink, what is the probability of getting a drink with both coffee and a dairy product? What is the probability of getting neither coffee nor a dairy product? Assume that choosing a coffee drink is independent of choosing a dairy-product drink. See if you can answer these questions without making a two-way table first.

10-143.   Akio coaches the girls volleyball team. He needs to select players for the six different starting positions from his roster of 16 players. On Akio's teams, each position has its own special responsibility: setter, front left-side and middle hitters, back right- and left-side passers, and libero.

a.   If he chooses randomly, how many ways can Akio form his starting lineup?

b.   How many of those teams have Sidney playing in the libero position?

c.   If Akio chooses starting teams randomly, what is the probability (in percent) that Sidney gets chosen as the starting libero?

d.   If Akio just randomly chooses six players to start, without regard to who plays which position, what is the probability that Sidney gets chosen?

10-144.   If $f(n) = n!$, evaluate each of the following ratios.

    a. $\frac{f(5)}{f(3)}$ b. $\frac{f(6)}{f(4)}$ c. $\frac{f(9)}{f(7)f(2)}$

10-145.   Consider the following anagrams.

    a.   How many distinct ways can the letters in the word ITEMS be arranged?

    b.   How many distinct ways can the letters in the word STEMS be arranged?

    c.   How many distinct ways can the letters in the word SEEMS be arranged?

    d.   What makes these counts different?

10.3.4 What kind of counting problem is this?

Categorizing Counting Problems

One of the biggest challenges in solving problems that involve counting techniques is deciding which method of counting to use. Selecting a counting method depends on whether different arrangements of elements will be considered to be different outcomes and on whether elements can be repeated in an outcome. As you work with your team on the Ice Cream Shop problem, starting a list of possibilities will be a useful strategy. The list may be too long to complete, but starting it might help you decide which counting technique to use.

10-146.   THE ICE-CREAM SHOP

Friday was the seventh day of the heat wave with temperatures over 95°, and DJ's Gourmet Ice-Cream Shop had only five flavors left: chocolate fudge, French vanilla, maple nut, lemon custard, and blueberry delight. Some customers ordered their ice cream in cones and some in a dish, but everyone ordered three scoops, the maximum DJ was allowing to ensure that the inventory would last.

On Saturday the temperature hit 100°. DJ still had five flavors and both cones and dishes, but he decided to allow no more than one scoop of a particular flavor per customer in order to keep a balanced variety on hand. On Friday, the customers had more choices than on Saturday because they could order a cone (which most people eat from the top down) or a dish (where scoops can be eaten in any order) and they could have three different flavors or more than one scoop of their favorite.

DJ's advertises that it has **Over 100 Choices!** When DJ's customers complained that he did not have 100 flavors, he responded, "*But I still offer more than 100 choices!*" Was that true on both Friday and Saturday?

Your Task: There are four counting problems here, two for Friday and two for Saturday. Describe each situation and show how to calculate the number of choices customers have once they decide on a cone or a dish.

Discussion Points

What are some possible outcomes for this situation? Can I start a list?

Does the arrangement or order of the scoops matter?

Can the choices be repeated?

Does the description of the outcomes for this situation fit any
of the counting formulas I know?

Could this situation involve several different counting situations?

Further Guidance

10-147. It is useful to organize the information in a large 2×2 chart with columns for
Friday and Saturday and rows for dishes and cones. With your team, set up a
2×2 chart or obtain the Lesson 10.3.4 Resource Page from your teacher and
use it to organize the different possibilities. Describe each problem in relation
to whether it involves arrangements or repeats elements, and make a prediction
about which situation has the greatest number of choices and which has the
least.

10-148. Use what you have learned about the Fundamental Principal of Counting,
permutations, and combinations to solve three of the four problems.

10-149. The fourth problem is more cumbersome because the order of the scoops does
not matter and all of the scoops could be different, two could be the same and
one different, or all could be the same. This problem has a number of
subproblems, and for at least one of them you may need to make a list. Work
with your team to identify and solve each subproblem.

—————— *Further Guidance* ——————
section ends here.

10-150. Charlie and his nephew, Jake, who is a bottomless hunger pit, went to the state fair. Charlie had promised he would buy Jake three snacks, one when they arrived, one mid-afternoon, and one when they were about to leave. As they were arriving, Jake was trying to negotiate to get all of the snacks all at once. At the food stand the menu included seven items:

Corn Dogs   Popcorn

Root Beer   Orange Soda

Sno Cones   Cotton Candy

Candied Apples

Jake has a dilemma. He likes everything on the menu so much that he would not mind having any three items or even any two or three of the same thing. Uncle Charlie thinks variety is good so he wants Jake to choose three different things.

Your Task: With your team, categorize the alternatives for Jake and Charlie in terms of arrangements and repetition. Then describe and justify the solution method you would use to count the number of possibilities for each situation. Finally, figure out how many possible ways there are for Jake to choose his snacks for each situation.

10-151. When Jake and Charlie disagree, Jake has a two-thirds chance of getting his way. Draw an area model or tree diagram and calculate the probability that Charlie prevails and Jake has to order three different items and have his snacks spread out.

10-152. LEARNING LOG

Summarize the differences between combinations and permutations, anagrams, and other counting problems that involve the Fundamental Principle of Counting. Make your explanation clear and thorough enough that a student who is just transferring into your class could understand counting techniques. Include information about whether arrangements are important and whether elements can be repeated and give examples that illustrate the different possibilities. Title this entry, "Counting Problems and Strategies" and label it with today's date.

10-153.   From a batch of 500 light bulbs, how many ways can three be tested to see if they are defective?

10-154.   Mr. K wants to bring a variety of language textbooks to the classroom in which he teaches French. From his library at home, he found some that would be appropriate for the classroom: 4 Russian texts, 7 German texts, 1 Japanese text, 2 Italian texts, and 3 Danish texts. If he decides to bring one book of each language to the classroom, and put them in alphabetical order by language on his bookshelf (Danish, German, Italian, and so forth), how many different ways can Mr. K arrange the new language books?

10-155.   Joaquin is getting a new locker at school and the first thing he must do is decide on a new combination. The three number locker combination can be selected from the numbers 0 through 21.

   a.   How many different locker combinations can Joaquin choose if none of the numbers can be repeated?

   b.   With your understanding of permutations, combinations, and factorials, decide if the name "combination lock" is appropriate.

   c.   How many mathematical combinations are possible?

   d.   How many choices would there be if you could repeat a number, but not use the same number twice in a row?

10-156.   This problem is a checkpoint for finding angles in and areas of regular polygons. It will be referred to as Checkpoint 10.

   a.   What is the measure of each interior angle of a regular 20-gon?

   b.   Each angle of a regular polygon measures 157.5°. How many sides does this polygon have?

   c.   Find the area of a regular octagon with sides 5 cm.

   Check your answers by referring to the Checkpoint 10 materials located at the back of your book.

   If you needed help solving these problems correctly, then you need more practice. Review the Checkpoint 10 materials and try the practice problems. Also, consider getting help outside of class time. From this point on, you will be expected to do problems like these quickly and easily.

10-157.   The first four factors of 7! are 7, 6, 5, and 4 or 7, $(7-1)$, $(7-2)$, and $(7-3)$.

   a.   Show the first four factors of 12! in the same way the factors of 7! are shown above.

   b.   What are the first six factors of $n!$?

   c.   What is $_nP_6$?

10-158.   Here is another way to think about the question: *"What is 0! ?"*

   a.   How many ways are there to choose all five items from a group of five items? What happens when you substitute into the factorial formula to compute $_5C_5$? Since you know (logically) what the result has to be, use this to explain what 0! must be equal to.

   b.   On the other hand, how many ways are there to choose *nothing* from a group of five items? And what happens when you try to use the factorial formula to compute $_5C_0$?

10-159.   A European high-speed passenger train is made up of two first-class passenger cars, five second-class cars, and a restaurant car. How many ways can the train be made up?

Core Connections Geometry

10.3.5 What are my chances of winning?

Some Challenging Probability Problems

In this lesson, you will have the opportunity to apply what you have learned about probability and counting principles to solve some interesting (and very challenging) problems. As you work with your team on one of the following problems, you may get stuck at some point along the way. Below are discussion questions that can help you to get started again.

What subproblems do I need to solve?

What simpler problem would help us to understand this problem?

How would I start a tree or a list?

Does order matter? Are the outcomes combinations, permutations, or something else?

Are these separate groups of outcomes? Are the probabilities independent? Should I add or do I need to multiply?

Would it be easier to consider what is *not* an outcome?

10-160. THE CANDY DISH

A bowl contains three candies: two red and one green. Work with a partner and decide who is player A and who is player B. Then take turns choosing a candy from the bowl without looking. Player A takes one and holds on to it, then player B takes one. If the colors match, player A gets a point; if they differ, player B gets a point. Is this a fair game?

a. First try the game experimentally. Then show your analysis of the probabilities.

b. Now put four candies in the bowl, three of one color and one of another. Will this game be fair? Again, check experimentally then give your analysis using probabilities.

c. Are there other ways to put different numbers of two colors of candy in the bowl that would lead to a fair game while keeping the rest of the rules the same as in the previous two problems? Try a number of different possibilities (up to at least a total of 20 candies). Analyze each one using probability, make some hypotheses, and report any patterns you see in the results, conclusions, or generalizations that you can justify mathematically.

Problem continues on next page →

10-160.   *Problem continued from previous page.*

Your Task: Prepare a report or poster that shows:

- The number and variety of cases you investigated and analyzed.

- Your organization of the data, your analyses, and your general conclusions.

- The extent to which you can mathematically generalize your observations and justify your generalizations.

10-161.   CASINO DICE GAME

To play this game, you roll two dice. If your total on the first roll is 7 or 11 points, you win. If your total is 2, 3, or 12 points, you lose. If you get any other number (4, 5, 6, 8, 9, or 10), that number becomes your point. You then continue to roll until your point comes up again or until a 7 comes up. If your point comes up before you roll a 7, you win. If 7 comes up first, you lose. You ignore any outcomes that are not your point or 7.

a.   In pairs, play the game ten times. Record how many wins and losses your team has. Combine your information with other teams working on the problem. Are the results fairly even or were there many more wins or losses?

b.   The game you have been playing is the basic dice game played in casinos worldwide. What is the probability of winning?

Your Task: To calculate the probability of winning, you will need to identify and solve several subproblems. Prepare a report that shows each of the subproblems clearly, as well as how you solved each one. Your report should also show the exact probability of winning as a fraction as well as a decimal approximation.

10-162.   An extra challenge: Most casinos allow bettors to bet against the dice roller. In this case, the bettor wins whenever the roller would lose *except when the roller gets a 12 on the first roll*. When 12 comes up, the bettor does not win or lose and he or she just waits for the next roll. What is the probability of winning a bet against the roller? Which is the better bet, for or against? By how much?

10-163. Start with a list of the ways to get each sum 2, 3, ..., 12. For the remaining parts of this work, it will help to keep answers in fraction form.

    a.   Find the probability of winning on the first roll.

    b.   Find the probability of losing on the first roll.

    c.   Find the probability of the game ending on the first roll.

10-164. Now consider the other ways to win by rolling the point before rolling a 7.

    a.   Find the probability of rolling a 4.

    b.   Find the probability of rolling a 4 before a 7. (Note that you are only interested in 4's and 7's for this problem.)

    c.   Find the probability of rolling a 4 and then rolling another 4 before a 7. In other words, what is the probability of getting the outcome in part (a) and then the outcome in part (b)?

    d.   Find the probability of rolling a 5.

    e.   Find the probability of rolling a 5 before a 7. (You only care about 5's and 7's here.)

    f.   Find the probability of rolling a 5 and another 5 before a 7.

    g.   Find the probabilities for winning when your first roll is 6, 8, 9, or 10. Look for symmetry as you do this.

10-165. Make a list of the all the ways to win.

    a.   What is the probability of winning?

    b.   If you won the game, what is the probability that you won by throwing 7 or 11 on the first throw?

    c.   What is the probability of losing this game?

    d.   Is it a fair game? Is it close to fair? Explain why casinos can allow betting on this game without expecting to lose money.

Further Guidance
section ends here.

10-166.   TRIANGLES BY CHANCE

Obtain three dice from your teacher. You may also want some string, linguini, a compass, or some other building material.

a.   Roll the three dice and use the numbers on the dice to represent the lengths of sides of a triangle. Build (or draw) the triangle. Record the three numbers in a table according to the type of triangle formed (scalene, isosceles, equilateral, or no triangle). For example, if 3, 3, and 5 came up on the dice, you would record 3, 3, 5 under the heading isosceles since a triangle with sides of length 3, 3, and 5 is isosceles.

b.   Repeat this ten times, and then combine your information with the other teams working on this problem. Examine the data and discuss the results.

c.   Based on your discussion, make an estimate for the probability of each outcome. Then calculate the theoretical probabilities.

Your Task: Complete a team report or poster that includes:

- Initial estimates of probabilities with your team justification for each one.

- The subproblems you solved, including how you counted the possible outcomes.

- The theoretical probability for each case.

Further Guidance

10-167.   First you will need to calculate the size of the sample space for rolling three dice.

a.   How many ways come up so that the result is an equilateral triangle?

b.   How many ways can the dice come up so that the result is an isosceles triangle?

c.   How many ways can the dice come up so that the result is a scalene triangle?

d.   How many outcomes lead to no triangle?

e.   Use your results from parts (a) through (d) to compute the probabilities for each outcome.

————————   *Further Guidance*   ————————
section ends here.

10-168. POKER

In the basic game of five-card-draw poker, five cards are dealt to each player from a standard deck of 52 cards. Players place bets based on their estimate of their chances of winning. They then draw any number of cards (up to five) to see if they can improve their hands, and they make another round of placing bets.

The winning poker hands (assuming no wild cards) are described below, in order from best to worst. Poker is a game that has been played for many centuries. Players had established the order of winning hands centuries before mathematicians developed the counting techniques, which verified that the order was mostly correct based on the probability of getting the hand.

(Note: In the list below, J stands for Jack, Q stands for Queen, K stands for King, A stands for Ace, and X stands for any card.)

1. Royal flush: 10-J-Q-K-A, all the same suit.

2. Straight flush: such as, 7-8-9-10-J, any five in a row, all the same suit (A can be used before 2 or after K).

3. Four of a kind: 2-2-2-2-X, four of a number or face card, and any other card.

4. Full house: 7-7-7-A-A-, three of one kind and two of another.

5. Flush: any five cards of the same suit, not all consecutive.

6. Straight: 3-4-5-6-7, any five in a row, a mixture of 2 or more suits.

7. Three of a kind: 8-8-8-J-A, three of a number or face card, the other two different.

8. Two pair: 9-9-5-5-2, pairs of two different numbers or face cards, with one other number or face card.

9. Two of a kind: A-A-7-8-J, any pair with three random others that do not match.

10. Bust: no matches, no runs of five in a row, different suits.

Your Task: Calculate the number of five-card hands that can be selected from a deck of 52 cards, and then, for the first six of the above hands, calculate the number of ways the hand can be dealt, and the probability that a player will be dealt that hand. Prepare a team report or poster that describes your work on both the counting problems and the probabilities.

10-169. The most difficult Poker hand to get is a royal flush. To calculate the probability of getting a royal flush, you first need to determine the size of the sample space. How many five-card hands are possible if there are 52 cards to choose from? Then decide how many ways there are to make a royal flush.

a.   What is the probability of getting a royal flush?

b.   How many straight flushes are there that are all spades? Making a list will help you decide. Then how many straight flushes are there altogether?

c.   What is the probability of getting a straight flush that is not a royal flush?

10-170. Flushes are five cards of one suit.

a.   How many flushes are possible?

b.   What is the probability of getting a flush?

10-171. Straights are five cards in a row, such as 4-5-6-7-8 of any suit.

a.   How many straights are possible that include 2 or more suits? In other words, how many straights are possible that are not also straight flushes or royal flushes?

b.   What is the probability of getting a straight?

10-172. How many ways are there to draw four cards that are the same number? Making a list will help. And how many ways are there to get the fifth card? What do you need to do to get the total number of five-card hands that contain four of a kind?

a. What is the probability of getting four of a kind?

b. Now consider a full house. First, think of listing the number of ways to get exactly three cards that are the same number. Once you know the three cards, how many ways are there to get the other two cards in your hand the same? What should you do with these two results to get the number of full houses possible?

c. What is the probability of getting a full house?

d. Recall your result for the number of ways to get three of a kind and figure out how many ways there are to get two cards that are different from the rest of the deck. Use this information to calculate the number of five-card hands with three matching numbers.

e. What is the probability of getting three of a kind?

f. Use a similar method for calculating the number of ways to get one pair and the probability of getting another pair.

g. Think about how you calculated the number of full houses and about how you calculated the number of hands with four of a kind. Then calculate the number of hands with two pairs.

h. What is the probability of drawing a hand that is a "bust?" How can you use the probabilities you have already calculated?

*Further Guidance
section ends here.*

METHODS AND MEANINGS

Definition of 0!

The use of the combinations formula when $r = n$ (when the number to be chosen is the same as the total number in the group) leads to a dilemma, as illustrated in the following example.

Suppose the Spirit Club has a total of three faithful members. Only one three-member governance committee is possible. If you apply the formula for combinations, you get $_3C_3 = \frac{_3P_3}{3!} = \frac{3!}{(3-3)!3!} = \frac{3!}{0!3!} = 1$. Does this make sense?

To resolve this question and make the formulas useful for all cases, mathematicians decided on this definition: $0! = 1$.

10-173.   From a new shipment of 100 video games, how many ways can three games be tested to see if they are defective?

10-174.   Which is greater: $(5-2)!$ or $(5-3)!$? Justify your answer.

10-175.   Write an equivalent expression for each of the following situations that does not include the factorial (!) symbol.

   a.   The first five factors of $(n-3)!$

   b.   The first five factors of $(n+2)!$

   c. $\frac{n!}{(n-3)!}$

   d. $\frac{(n+2)!}{(n-2)!}$

658

Core Connections Geometry

10-176.   Of the students who choose to live on campus at Coastal College, 10% are
          seniors. The most desirable dorm rooms are in the newly constructed
          OceanView dorm, and 60% of the seniors live there, while 20% of the rest of
          the students live there.

          a.   Represent these probabilities in a two-way table.

          b.   What is the probability that a randomly selected resident of the OceanView
                dorm is a senior?

          c.   Use the alternative definition of independence (see the Math Notes box in
                Lesson 10.2.3) to determine if being a senior is associated with living in
                the Ocean View dorm.

10-177.   At 10:00 a.m. a radioactive material weighed 2 grams but at 6:00 p.m. it only
          weighed 0.45 grams. What were the approximate hourly multiplier and the
          hourly percent of decrease?

10-178.   A triangular prism has a volume of 600 cubic cm. The base is a right triangle
          with a hypotenuse of length 17 cm and one leg with length 15 cm.

          a.   Draw the figure.

          b.   Find the height of the prism.

          c.   Find the surface area of the prism.

          d.   Find all three angles of the triangle in the base of the prism.

10-179.   A pizza parlor has 12 toppings other than cheese.
          How many different pizzas can they create with five
          or fewer toppings? List all subproblems and
          calculate the solution.

10-180. Mike was asked to make his popular ten-layer dip for the tailgate party at the big football game. The ten layers are: three layers of mashed avocado, two layers of cheddar cheese, and one layer each of refried beans, sour cream, sliced olives, chopped tomatoes, and green onions. How many ways can Mike make the ten layers in a glass serving pan?

10-181. Write an equation and use it to solve this problem.

Jill has a 9-inch tall cylinder that she is using to catch water leaking from a pipe. The water level in the cylinder is currently 2 inches deep and is increasing at a rate of $\frac{1}{4}$-inch per hour. How long will it be before the water overflows?

10-182. Determine whether or not the two triangles in each pair below are similar. If so, write a flowchart to show your reasoning. If not, explain why not.

a.

b.
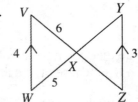

10-183. For each mat plan, create an isometric view of the solid.

a.

b.

10-184. Calculate the total surface area and volume of the prism at right. The bases are equilateral triangles.

10 cm

8 cm

Chapter 10 Closure What have I learned?

Reflection and Synthesis

The activities below offer you a chance to reflect about what you have learned during this chapter. As you work, look for concepts that you feel very comfortable with, ideas that you would like to learn more about, and topics you need more help with. Look for connections between ideas as well as connections with material you learned previously.

① **TEAM BRAINSTORM**

What have you studied in this chapter? What ideas were important in what you learned? With your team, brainstorm a list. Be as detailed as you can. To help get you started, lists of Learning Log entries and Math Notes boxes are below.

What topics, ideas, and words that you learned *before* this chapter are connected to the new ideas in this chapter? Again, be as detailed as you can.

How long can you make your list? Challenge yourselves. Be prepared to share your team's ideas with the class.

Learning Log Entries
- Lesson 10.1.2 – Inscribed Angles
- Lesson 10.1.3 – Connections with Circles
- Lesson 10.2.1 – Independent or Mutually Exclusive?
- Lesson 10.2.3 – Probability Rules
- Lesson 10.3.4 – Counting Problems and Strategies

Math Notes
- Lesson 10.1.1 – Circle Vocabulary
- Lesson 10.1.2 – More Circle Vocabulary
- Lesson 10.1.3 – Inscribed Angle Theorem
- Lesson 10.1.4 – Intersecting Chords
- Lesson 10.1.5 – Points of Concurrency
- Lesson 10.2.1 – Mutually Exclusive
- Lesson 10.2.3 – Conditional Probability and Independence
- Lesson 10.3.1 – Fundamental Principle of Counting
- Lesson 10.3.2 – $n!$ and Permutations
- Lesson 10.3.3 – Combinations
- Lesson 10.3.5 – Definition of 0!

MAKING CONNECTIONS

Below is a list of the vocabulary used in this chapter. Make sure that you are familiar with all of these words and know what they mean. Refer to the glossary or index for any words that you do not yet understand.

arc length	arc measure	association
center	center-radius form	central angle
chord	circle	circumcenter
circumference	circumscribed	combination
conditional probability	decision chart	diameter
factorial	Fundamental Principle of Counting	
independent events	inscribed	Inscribed Angle Theorem
intercepted arc	major arc	minor arc
Multiplication Rule	mutually exclusive	permutation
perpendicular	probability	radius
sample space	secant	semicircle
similar	tangent	two-way table
$x^2 + y^2 = r^2$	zero factorial	

Make a concept map showing all of the connections you can find among the key words and ideas listed above. To show a connection between two words, draw a line between them and explain the connection. A word can be connected to any other word as long as you can justify the connection.

While you are making your map, your team may think of related words or ideas that are not listed here. Be sure to include these ideas on your concept map.

③ PORTFOLIO: EVIDENCE OF MATHEMATICAL PROFICIENCY

Showcase your new knowledge of circles by describing all the new circle tools you have developed (such as lengths of two intersecting chords are related, and what is special about an angle inscribed in a semicircle). Be sure to include diagrams.

Choose one or two problems from Lesson 10.1.5 that you feel best showcases your understanding of circles and carefully copy your work, modifying and expanding it if needed. Make sure your explanation is clear and in detail. Remember you are not only showcasing your understanding of the mathematics, but you are also showcasing your ability to communicate your justifications.

Showcase your understanding of counting methods by copying one of the solutions from Lesson 10.3.5, modifying and expanding it as needed. Again, make sure your explanation is clear and detailed.

Core Connections Geometry

WHAT HAVE I LEARNED?

Most of the problems in this section represent typical problems found in this chapter. They serve as a gauge for you. You can use them to determine which types of problems you can do well and which types of problems require further study and practice. Even if your teacher does not assign this section, it is a good idea to try these problems and find out for yourself what you know and what you still need to work on.

Solve each problem as completely as you can. The table at the end of the closure section has answers to these problems. It also tells you where you can find additional help and practice with problems like these.

CL 10-185.   Copy the diagram at right onto your paper. Assume $\overline{AD}$ is tangent to $\odot C$ at D. Assume each part is a separate problem.

a.   If $AD = 9$ cm and $AB = 15$ cm, what is the area of $\odot C$?

b.   If the length of the radius of $\odot C$ is 10 cm and the $m\overset{\frown}{ED} = 30°$, what are $m\overset{\frown}{EB}$ and AD?

c.   If $m\overset{\frown}{EB} = 86°$ and $BC = 7$ cm, find EB.

CL 10-186.   A circle has two intersecting chords as shown in the diagram at right. Find the value of x.

CL 10-187. Eight friends go to the movies to celebrate their win in academic facts competition. They want to sit together in a row with a student on each aisle. (Assume the row is 8 seats wide including 2 aisle seats.)

a. If Kristen wants to sit in an aisle seat, how many ways can they all sit in the row?

b. If they sit down randomly, what is the probability they end up with five boys on the left and three girls on the right?

c. They decide to arrange themselves randomly by using the first letter of their last names. But two of the students' last names begin with K, and three begin with S. How many ways can they arrange themselves by using the first letter of their last name?

CL 10-188. At East College, 7776 students are in the freshman class, 6750 are sophomores, 6750 are juniors, and the rest are seniors. About 18% of students in each class are in the performing arts.

a. If there are 27,000 undergraduates at the school, what is the probability of being a senior in the performing arts?

b. Is being in a performing art independent of your class standing?

c. If a student is in the performing arts, what is the probability that he or she is a senior?

CL 10-189. Beethoven wrote nine symphonies and Mozart wrote 27 piano concertos.

a. If the local radio station KALG wants to play two pieces, a Beethoven symphony and then a Mozart concerto, in how many ways can this be done?

b. The station manager has decided that on each successive night (seven days a week), a Beethoven symphony will be played, followed by a Mozart concerto, followed by a Schubert string quartet (there are 15 of those). How long could this policy be continued before exactly the same program would have to be repeated?

CL 10-190. Antonio and Giancarlo are playing a board game that uses three spinners, which are shown in the diagrams at right. On each turn the player has to spin the first spinner. The first spinner determines which of the other two spinners the player also has to spin. The second spin determines how far the player gets to move his marker.

Spinner #1

a. What is the probability that Giancarlo will get to move his marker 4 or 6 spaces? Use a two-way table as needed.

Spinner #2

b. What is the probability he will have to stay put?

c. What is the probability that he will get to move?

Spinner #3

d. Antonio moved his marker 2 spaces. What is the probability that he spun S2 on the first spinner?

e. Explain your method for finding the probability in part (d) so that a student who was absent for today's work would understand conditional probability.

CL 10-191. Consider the solid represented by the mat plan at right.

a. Draw the front, right, and top view of this solid on graph paper.

b. Find the volume and surface area of this solid.

3	1	0
0	1	1
0	2	3

Right

Front

c. If this solid is enlarged by a linear scale factor of 3.5, what will be its new volume and surface area?

CL 10-192. Consider the descriptions of the different shapes below. Which shapes *must* be a parallelogram? If a shape does not have to be a parallelogram, what other shapes could it be?

a. A quadrilateral with two pairs of parallel sides.

b. A quadrilateral with two pairs of congruent sides.

c. A quadrilateral with one pair of sides that is both congruent and parallel.

d. A quadrilateral with two diagonals that are perpendicular.

e. A quadrilateral with four congruent sides.

CL 10-193. In $\odot C$ at right, $\overline{AB} \cong \overline{DE}$.
Prove that $\angle ACB \cong \angle DCE$.

CL 10-194. Find the measure of x in each diagram below.
Assume each polygon is regular.

a.   b.   c.

CL 10-195. Check your answers using the table at the end of the closure section. Which
problems do you feel confident about? Which problems were hard? Use the
table to make a list of topics you need help on and a list of topics you need
to practice more.

Answers and Support for Closure Activity #4
What Have I Learned?

Note: MN = Math Note, LL = Learning Log

Problem	Solution	Need Help?	More Practice
CL 10-185.	a. 36π cm^2 b. $m\widehat{EB} = 150°$, $AD = 20\tan 15° \approx 5.36$ cm c. $14\sin 43° \approx 9.55$ cm	Lesson 8.3.2 and Section 10.1 MN: 5.1.2, 8.3.2, 10.1.1, 10.1.2, and 10.1.3 LL: 5.1.2, 8.3.2, 10.1.2, and 10.1.3	Problems 10-7, 10-18, 10-43, 10-54, 10-59, 10-68, 10-87, and 10-119
CL 10-186.	$4(x+5) = 10x$ $x = \frac{20}{6} \approx 3.33$	Lesson 10.1.3 MN: 10.1.4 LL: 10.1.3	Problems 10-60, 10-78(c), and 10-107
CL 10-187.	a. $2 \cdot 7! = 10080$ b. $\frac{{}_5P_5 \cdot {}_3P_3}{{}_8P_8} = \frac{720}{40320} \approx 1.8\%$ c. This is an anagram. $\frac{8!}{2!3!} = 3360$	Section 10.3 MN: 10.3.1 and 10.3.2 LL: 10.2.3 and 10.3.4	Problems 10-114, 10-115, 10-127, 10-128, 10-132, 10-139, 10-145, and 10-154

Core Connections Geometry

Problem	Solution	Need Help?	More Practice
CL 10-188.	a. About 18% of the 5724 seniors are in the performing arts, so P(senior and performing arts) = $\frac{(0.18)(5724)}{27,000} \approx \frac{1030}{27,000} \approx 3.8\%$. b. They are independent. The probability of being in a performing art is always 18%; it does not change knowing the class standing of a student. Or, make a two-way table and check if P(A given B) = P(A), for example, P(art given soph) = $\frac{1215}{6750}$ which equals P(art) = $\frac{1400+1215+1215+1030}{27,000}$. c. Since they are independent, P(senior given performing arts) = P(senior) = $\frac{5724}{27000} = 21.2\%$.	Section 10.2 MN: 10.2.1 and 10.2.3 LL: 10.2.1 and 10.2.3	Problems 10-85, 10-101, 10-116, and 10-130
CL 10-189.	a. 243 b. 3645 ways, 9.98 years	Section 10.3 MN: 10.3.1 and 10.3.2 LL: 10.2.3 and 10.3.4	Problems 10-114, 10-115, 10-127, 10-128, 10-132, 10-139, 10-145, and 10-154
CL 10-190.	a. Since the spinners are independent of each other, we can find entries in a two-way table by using P(A and B) = P(A) · P(B). See table below. $\frac{2}{12}+\frac{2}{12}+\frac{2}{15}+\frac{1}{12} \approx 63.3\%$	Section 10.2 MN: 10.2.3 LL: 10.2.1 and 10.2.3	Problems 10-102, 10-117, 10-131, 10-142, and 10-176

	0 spaces	2 spaces	4 spaces	6 spaces	
Spinner 2	$\frac{1}{4}\cdot\frac{2}{3}=\frac{2}{12}$	$\frac{2}{12}$	$\frac{2}{12}$	$\frac{2}{12}$	$\frac{2}{3}$
Spinner 3	0	$\frac{7}{20}\cdot\frac{1}{3}=\frac{7}{60}$	$\frac{2}{15}$	$\frac{1}{12}$	$\frac{1}{3}$

$\frac{2}{12}+0=\frac{2}{12}$

b. P(0 spaces) = $\frac{2}{12} \approx 16.7\%$

c. $1-\frac{2}{12} \approx 83.3\%$

d. P(Spinner 2 given 2 spaces) = $\frac{\frac{2}{12}}{\frac{2}{12}+\frac{7}{60}} \approx 58.8\%$

e. Answers will vary.

Problem	Solution	Need Help?	More Practice
CL 10-191.	a. Front Right Top b. $V = 11$ units^3, SA $= 42$ units^2 c. $V = 11(3.5)^3 = 471.625$ units^3, $42(3.5)^2 = 514.5$ units^2	Lessons 9.1.1 and 9.1.2 MN: 9.1.3 LL: 9.1.1	Problems CL 9-111, 10-23, 10-105, and 10-183
CL 10-192.	Must be a parallelogram: (a), (c), and (e) (b) could be a kite (d) could be a kite	Lessons 7.3.1 and 7.3.3 MN: 7.2.3 and 8.1.2	Problems CL 7-156, CL 9-116, and 10-34
CL 10-193.	*C* is the center of circle Given $\overline{AC} \cong \overline{BC} \cong \overline{DC} \cong \overline{EC}$ All radii of a circle are equal. $\overline{AB} \cong \overline{DE}$ Given $\triangle BCA \cong \triangle DCE$ SSS $\cong$ $\angle ACB \cong \angle ECD$ $\cong \triangle s \rightarrow \cong$ parts	Section 3.2 and Lessons 6.1.1 through 6.1.4 MN: 3.2.2, 3.2.4, 6.1.4, and 7.1.3 LL: 3.2.2	Problems CL 3-123, CL 4-123, CL 5-140, CL 6-101, CL 7-155, CL 8-134, CL 9-117, 10-30, 10-36, and 10-47
CL 10-194.	a. $60°$ b. $135°$ c. $36°$	Lessons 8.1.2, 8.1.3, and 8.1.4 Checkpoint 10 MN: 7.1.4 and 8.1.5 LL: 8.1.2, 8.1.3, and 8.1.4	Problems CL 8-138, CL 9-115, 10-22, 10-82, and 10-156

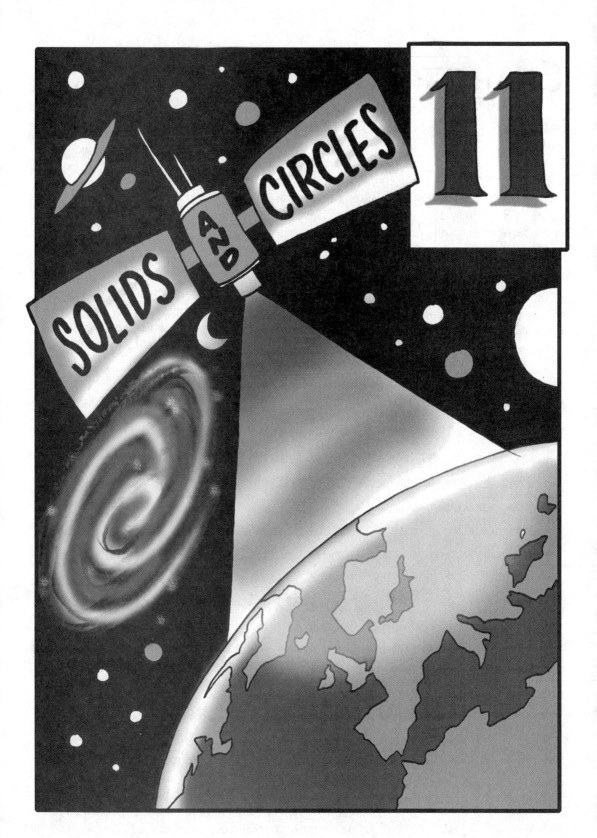

SOLIDS AND CIRCLES

11

CHAPTER 11   Solids and Circles

In Chapter 9, you looked at how to find the volume and surface area of three-dimensional solids formed with blocks. You extended these concepts to include prisms and cylinders. In this chapter, you will complete your study of three-dimensional solids to include pyramids, cones, and spheres. You will learn how to identify the cross-sections of a solid and will investigate a special group of solids known as Platonic Solids.

As the word *geometry* literally means the "measurement of the Earth," it is only fitting that Section 11.2 focuses on developing the geometric tools that are used to learn more about the Earth. For example, by studying the height at which satellites orbit the Earth, you will get a chance to develop tools to work with the angle and arc measures that occur when two lines that are tangent to the same circle intersect each other.

Guiding Question

Mathematically proficient students will make sense of problems and persevere in solving them.

As you work through this chapter ask yourself:

What information do I need, what do I already know, and how can I use this information to solve the problem?

In this chapter, you will learn:

> How to find the volume and surface area of a pyramid, a cone, and a sphere.

> About the properties of special polyhedra (Platonic Solids).

> How to find the cross-section of a solid.

> How to find the measure of angles and arcs that are formed by tangents and secants.

> About the relationships between the lengths of segments created when tangents or secants intersect outside a circle.

Chapter Outline

 Section 11.1   In this section, you will learn how regular polygons can be used to form three-dimensional solids called "polyhedra." You will extend your knowledge of finding volume and surface area to include other solids, such as pyramids, cones, and spheres.

 Section 11.2   By studying the coordinate system of latitude and longitude lines that help refer to locations on the Earth, you will learn about great circles and how to find the distance between two points on a sphere. You will also investigate the geometric relationships created when tangents and secants intersect a circle.

670   *Core Connections Geometry*

11.1.1 How can I build it?

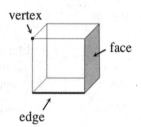

. . . .

Platonic Solids

In Chapter 9, you explored three-dimensional solids such as prisms and cylinders. You developed methods to measure their sizes using volume and surface area and learned to represent three-dimensional solids using mat plans and two-dimensional (front, right, and top) views.

But what other types of three-dimensional solids can you learn about? During Section 11.1, you and your team will examine new types of solids made from regular polygons in order to expand your understanding of three-dimensional shapes.

11-1.   EXAMINING A CUBE

In Chapter 9, you studied the volume and surface area of three-dimensional solids, such as prisms and cylinders. A **cube** is a special type of rectangular prism because each face is a square.

a.   What are some examples of cubes you remember seeing?

b.   Find the volume and surface area of a cube with an edge length of 10 units.

c.   Remember that a "flat side" of a prism is called a **face**, as shown in the diagram above. Notice that the line segment where two faces meet is called an **edge**, while the point where the edges meet is called a **vertex**. How many faces does a cube have? How many edges? How many vertices? (Vertices is plural for vertex.)

d.   Confirm with your team that a cube has three square faces that meet at each vertex. Is it possible to have a solid where only two square faces and no other faces meet at a vertex? Could a solid have four or more square faces at a vertex? Explain.

11-2.   OTHER REGULAR POLYHEDRA

A three-dimensional solid made up of
flat, polygonal faces is called a
polyhedron (*poly* is the Greek root for
"many," while *hedron* is the Greek root
for "faces"). A cube, like the one you
studied in problem 11-1, is an example
of a **regular polyhedron** because all of
the faces are congruent, regular polygons
and the same number of faces meet at
each vertex. In fact, you found that a
cube is the *only* regular polyhedron with
square faces.

But what if the faces are equilateral triangles? Or what if the faces are other
regular polygons such as pentagons or hexagons?

Your Task: With your team, determine what other regular polyhedra are
possible. First, obtain building materials from your teacher. Then work
together to build regular polyhedra by testing how the different types of regular
polygons can meet at a vertex. For example, what type of solid is formed when
three equilateral triangle faces meet at each vertex? Four? Five? Six? Do
similar tests for regular pentagons and hexagons. For each regular polyhedron,
describe its shape and count its faces. Be ready to discuss your results with the
class.

Discussion Points

- What is this task asking you to do?

- How should you start?

- How can your team organize the task among the members
  to complete the task efficiently?

Further Guidance

11-3.   For help in testing the various ways that congruent, regular polygons can build regular polyhedra, follow the directions below.

a.   Start by focusing on equilateral triangles. Attach three equilateral triangles so that they are adjacent and share a common vertex, as shown at right. Then fold and attach the three triangles so that they completely surround the common vertex. Complete the solid with as many equilateral triangles as needed so that each vertex is the intersection of three triangles. How would you describe this shape?

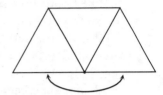

Fold so that these edges meet.

b.   Now repeat your test to determine what solids are possible when 4, 5, or more equilateral triangles meet at each vertex. If a regular polyhedron is possible, describe it and state the number of faces it has. If a regular polyhedron is not possible, explain why not.

c.   What if the faces are regular pentagons? Try building a regular polyhedron so that each vertex is the intersection of three regular pentagons. What if four regular pentagons meet at a vertex? Explain what happens in each case.

d.   End your investigation by considering regular hexagons. Place three or more regular hexagons at a common vertex and explain what solids are formed. If no solid is possible, explain why.

11-4.   POLYHEDRA VOCABULARY

The regular polyhedra you discovered in
problem 11-2 (along with the cube from
problem 11-1) are sometimes referred to as
Plato's Solids (or **Platonic Solids**) because
the knowledge about them spread about
2300 years ago during the time of Plato, a
Greek philosopher and mathematician.

In addition, polyhedra are classified by the
number of faces they have. For example, a
cube is a solid with six faces, so it can be
called a regular hexahedron (because *hexa*
is the Greek root meaning "six" and *hedron*
is the Greek root for "face").

Plato (490 – 430 B.C.)

Examine the table of names below. Then return to your results from problem
11-2 and determine the name for each regular polyhedron you discovered.

4 faces	Tetrahedron	**9 faces**	Nonahedron
5 faces	Pentahedron	**10 faces**	Decahedron
6 faces	Hexahedron	**11 faces**	Undecahedron
7 faces	Heptahedron	**12 faces**	Dodecahedron
8 faces	Octahedron	**20 faces**	Icosahedron

11-5.   Find the surface area of each of Plato's Solids you built in problem 11-2 (the
regular tetrahedron, octahedron, dodecahedron, and icosahedron) if the length
of each edge is 2 inches. Show all work and be prepared to share your method
with the class.

11-6.   DUAL POLYHEDRA

Ivan wonders, *"What happens when the centers of adjacent faces of a regular polyhedron are connected?"* These connections form the edges of a solid, which can be called a **dual polyhedron**.

To investigate dual polyhedra, first predict the results for each regular polyhedron with your team using spatial visualization. Then use a dynamic geometry tool to test your prediction of what solid is formed when the centers of adjacent faces of a Platonic Solid are connected. Be sure to test all five Platonic Solids (tetrahedron, cube, octahedron, dodecahedron, and icosahedron) and record the results.

11-7.   Reflect on what you learned about Plato's Solids during this lesson. What connections did you make to previous material? Write an entry in your Learning Log explaining what is special about this group of solids. Name and describe each Platonic Solid. Title this entry "Plato's Solids" and include today's date.

11-8.   Draw a hexagon on your paper.

a.   Do all hexagons have an interior angle sum of 720°?

b.   Does every hexagon have an interior angle measuring 120°? Explain your reasoning.

c.   Does every hexagon have 6 sides? Explain your reasoning.

11-9.   The mascot for Sacramento High School is the DRAGONS.

a.   How many ways can the cheerleaders rearrange the letters in the school mascot?

b.   How many ways can the letters be rearranged if the first and last letters are correctly placed?

11-10.   The **lateral surface** of a cylinder is the surface connecting the bases. For example, the label from a soup can would represent the lateral surface of a cylindrical can. If the radius of a cylinder is 4 cm and the height is 15 cm, find the lateral surface area of the cylinder. Note: It may help you to think of "unrolling" a soup can label and finding the area of the label.

11-11.   For each of the relationships represented in the diagrams below, write and solve an equation for x and/or y. Justify your method. In part (a), assume that C is the center of the circle.

a.

b.

c.

d.

11-12.   Garland is having trouble with the copy machine. He is trying to copy a triangle with an area of 36 square units and a perimeter of 42 units.

a.   After he pressed the button to copy, Garland noticed the copier's zoom factor (the linear scale factor) was set to 200%. What is the area and perimeter of the resulting triangle?

b.   Now Garland takes the result from part (a) and accidentally shrinks it by a linear scale factor of $\frac{1}{3}$! What is the area and perimeter of the resulting triangle?

11-13. Three flags are shown below on flagpoles. For each flag, determine what shape appears if the flag is spun very quickly about its pole. If you do not know the name of the shape, describe it.

a.
← pole

b.
↑
pole

c.
↑
pole

11-14. **Multiple Choice:** $\triangle ABC$ has a right angle at B. If $m\angle A = 42°$ and $BC = 7$ mm, what is the approximate length of AC?

a. 9.4 mm   b. 10.5 mm   c. 7.8 mm   d. 4.7 mm

11-15. Draw a tetrahedron on your paper.

a. How many faces does the tetrahedron have?

b. How many edges does it have?

c. How many vertices does it have?

11-16. If $n > 3$, write a shorter, equivalent expression for $n \cdot (n-1) \cdot (n-2) \cdot (n-3)$.

11-17. Mia found the volume of a rectangular prism to be 840 mm³. As she was telling her father about it, she remembered that the base had a length of 10 mm and a width of 12 mm, but she could not remember the height. *"Maybe there's a way you can find it by going backwards,"* her father suggested. Can you help Mia find the height of her prism? Explain your solution.

11-18.   For each geometric relationship below, determine whether *a* or *b* is larger, or if
         they are equal. Assume that the diagrams are not drawn to scale. If there is not
         enough information, explain what information is missing.

a.   b.   c.

                                                              6   4

                                                           area of the   area of the
                                                           triangle is *a*. square is *b*.

11-19.   Examine the diagram of the triangle at right.

   a.   Write an equation representing the relationship
         between x, y, and r.

   b.   Write an expression for $\sin\theta$. What is $\sin\theta$ if $r = 1$?

   c.   Write an expression for $\cos\theta$. What is $\cos\theta$ if $r = 1$?

11-20.   In a circle, chord $\overline{AB}$ has length 10 units, while $m\overarc{AB} = 60°$. What is the area of
         the circle? Draw a diagram and show all work.

11-21.   **Multiple Choice:** Assume that the coordinates of $\triangle ABC$ are $A(5, 1)$, $B(3, 7)$, and
         $C(2, 2)$. If $\triangle ABC$ is rotated 90° clockwise (↻) about the origin, the coordinates
         of the image of B would be:

   a.   (–3, 7)   b.   (–7, 3)   c.   (7, –3)   d.   (7, 3)

11.1.2 How can I measure it?

Pyramids

In Lesson 11.1.1, you explored Plato's five special solids: the tetrahedron, the octahedron, the cube (also known as the hexahedron), the dodecahedron, and the icosahedron. You discovered why these are the only regular polyhedra and developed a method to find their surface area.

Today you will examine the tetrahedron from a new perspective: as a member of the **pyramid** family. As you work today with your team, you will discover ways to classify pyramids by their shape and will develop new tools of measurement.

11-22.   A **pyramid** is a polyhedron with a polygonal base formed by connecting each point of the base to a single given point (the **apex**) that is above or below the flat surface containing the base. Each triangular lateral face of a pyramid is formed by the segments from the apex to the endpoints of a side of the base and the side itself. A tetrahedron is a special pyramid because any face can act as its base.

Obtain the four Lesson 11.1.2 Resource Pages, a pair of scissors, and either tape or glue from your teacher. Have each member of your team build one of the solids. When assembling each solid, be sure to have the printed side of the net on the exterior of the pyramid for reference later. Then answer the questions below.

a.   Sketch each pyramid onto your paper. What is the same about each pyramid? What is different? With your team, list as many qualities as you can.

b.   A tetrahedron can also be called a **triangular-based pyramid**, because its base is always a triangle. Choose similar, appropriate names for the other pyramids that your team constructed.

c.   Find the surface area of pyramids B and D. Use a ruler to find the dimensions of the edges in centimeters.

d.   Compare pyramids B and C. Which do you think has more volume? Justify your reasoning.

11-23. THE TRANSAMERICA BUILDING

The TransAmerica building in San Francisco is built of concrete and is shaped like a square-based pyramid. The building is periodically power-washed using one gallon of cleaning solution for every 250 square meters of surface. As the new building manager, you need to order the cleaning supplies for this large task. The problem is that you do not know the height of each triangular face of the building; you only know the vertical height of the building from the base to the top vertex.

Your Task: Determine the amount of cleaning solution needed to wash the TransAmerica building if an edge of the square base is 96 meters and the height of the building is 220 meters. Include a sketch in your solution.

11-24. Read the Math Notes box for this lesson, which introduces new vocabulary terms such as **slant height** and **lateral surface area**. Explain the difference between the slant height and the height of a pyramid. How can you use one to find the other?

ETHODS AND MEANINGS

Pyramid Vocabulary

If a face of a pyramid (defined in problem 11-22) or prism is not a base, it is called a **lateral face**.

The **lateral surface area** of a pyramid or prism is the sum of the areas of all faces of the pyramid or prism, not including the base(s). The area of the exterior of the TransAmerica building that needs cleaning (from problem 11-23) is an example of lateral surface area, since the exterior of the base of the pyramid cannot be cleaned.

The **total surface area** of a pyramid or prism is the sum of the areas of all faces, including the bases.

Sometimes saying the word "height" for a pyramid can be confusing, since it could refer to the height of one of the triangular faces or it could refer to the overall height of the pyramid. Therefore, the height of each lateral face is called a **slant height** to distinguish it from the **height** of the pyramid itself. See the diagram at right.

11-25. A pyramid has a volume of 108 cubic inches and a base area of 27 square inches. Find its height.

11-26. Connie and Nora went into Ready Scoop to get ice cream cones, but Nora cannot make up her mind. They have 23 flavors and she wants 3 scoops.

a. If Nora is very particular about the order of the scoops, how many choices does she have if all of the scoops are different?

b. Nora changes her mind. She wants a dish, not a cone, but she still wants three different flavors. How many ways can she order?

c. Connie says, *"I still want a cone with dark chocolate on the bottom and then any other two scoops."* How many cones are possible with dark chocolate on the bottom?

d. Vlad came in as they were leaving and saw Connie's cone. He said, *"Oh, that's what I want, a cone with chocolate on the bottom, and then two other flavors that are not chocolate."* The clerk, said, *"Okay, but we have four kinds of chocolate."* Vlad replied, *"Any kind of chocolate will do."* How many different cones could fill Vlad's order?

11-27. Examine $\triangle ABC$, $\triangle ABD$, and $\triangle ABE$ in the diagram at right. If $\overline{CE} \parallel \overline{AB}$, explain what you know about the areas of the three triangles. Justify your statements.

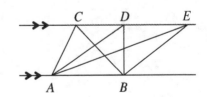

11-28. Solve each equation below, if possible. Show all work.

a. $\frac{3}{5} = \frac{2x}{3} - 8$

b. $\frac{9x}{5000} + \frac{2}{1000} = \frac{28}{5000}$

c. $\frac{2x}{3} + \frac{x}{2} = \frac{2x}{3}$

d. $\frac{3}{2}(2x - 5) = \frac{1}{6}$

11-29.   Prove that when two lines that are tangent to the same circle intersect, the lengths between the point of intersection and the points of tangency are equal. That is, in the diagram at right, if $\overleftrightarrow{AB}$ is tangent to $\odot P$ at B, and $\overleftrightarrow{AC}$ is tangent to $\odot P$ at C, prove that $AB = AC$. Use either a flowchart or a two-column proof.

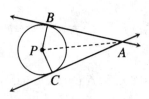

11-30.   On graph paper, plot the points $A(4, 1)$ and $B(10, 9)$.

a.   Find the distance between points A and B. That is, find AB.

b.   If point C is at $(10, 1)$, find $m\angle CAB$. Show all work.

11-31.   Find the missing terms in this geometric sequence.

$$2, \_\_\_, \_\_\_, \_\_\_, 162$$

11-32.   **Multiple Choice:** Which net below *cannot* create a regular octahedron when folded, like the one at right?

a.

b.

c.

d.

e.   None of these

11.1.3 What is the volume?

Volume of a Pyramid

Today, as you continue your focus on pyramids, look for and utilize connections to other geometry concepts. The models of pyramids that you constructed in Lesson 11.1.2 will be useful as you develop a method for finding the volume of a pyramid.

11-33.   GOING CAMPING

As Soraya shopped for a tent, she came across two models that she liked best, shown at right. However, she does not know which one to pick! They are both made by the same company and appear to have the same quality. She has come to you for help in making her decision.

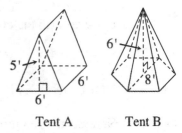

Tent A   Tent B

While she says that her drawings are not to scale, below are her notes about the tents:

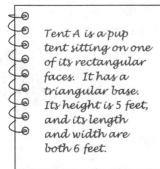

Tent A is a pup tent sitting on one of its rectangular faces. It has a triangular base. Its height is 5 feet, and its length and width are both 6 feet.

Tent B is a 6-foot-tall teepee. Its base is a regular hexagon, and the greatest diagonal across the floor measures 8 feet.

JAKE'S SPORTING GOODS

With your team, discuss the following questions in any order. Be prepared to share your discussion with the class.

- What are the shapes of the two tents?

- Without doing any calculations, which tent do you think Soraya should buy and why?

- What types of measurement might be useful to determine which tent is better?

- What do you still need to know to answer her question?

11-34.   COMPARING SOLIDS

To analyze Tent B from problem 11-33, you need to know how to find the
volume of a pyramid. But how can you find that volume?

To start, consider a simpler pyramid with a square base, such as pyramid B that
your team built in Lesson 11.1.2. To develop a method to find the volume of a
pyramid, first consider what solids(s) you could compare it to. For example,
when finding the area of a triangle, you compared it to the area of a rectangle
and figured out that the area of a triangle is always half the area of a rectangle
with the same base and height. To what solids(s) can you compare the volume
of pyramid B? Discuss this with your team and be prepared to share your
thinking with the class.

11-35.   VOLUME OF A PYRAMID

6 cm

6 cm

6 cm

Soraya thinks that pyramid B could be compared to a
cube, like the one shown at right, since the base edges
and heights of both are 6 cm.

a.   First estimate. What proportion of the cube is
      pyramid B? Discuss this with your team.

b.   Soraya remembers comparing pyramids B and C in
      Lesson 11.1.2. She decided to compare the volumes
      by thinking of it as a stack of slices. When thinking
      of it this way, what is the shape of each layer?
      Note: The name for the shape of a layer of a three-
      dimensional solid is called a **cross-section**.

c.   Soraya then slid all of the layers of the pyramid
      so that the top vertex was directly above one of
      the corners of the base, like Pyramid C from
      problem 11-22.

      When the top vertex of a pyramid is directly above (or below) the center of
      the base, the pyramid is called a **right pyramid**, while all other pyramids
      are referred to as **oblique pyramids**.

      When Soraya slid the layers to create an oblique pyramid, she did not add
      or take away any foam layers. How does the volume of her oblique
      pyramid compare with the right pyramid in part (b) above?

d.   Test your estimate from part (a) by using as many copies of pyramid C as
      you need to assemble a cube. Was your estimate accurate? Now explain
      how to find the volume of a pyramid.

Core Connections Geometry

11-36.   In problem 11-35, you may have noticed that the special square-based pyramid had one-third the volume of the cube. It turns out that this relationship between a pyramid and a prism with the same base area and height works for all other pyramids as well.

   a.   Write an expression for the volume of a pyramid with base area B and height h.

   b.   Use your expression from part (a) to find the volume of a pyramid with base area of 34 square units and height of 9 units.

11-37.   Now return to problem 11-33 and help Soraya decide which tent to buy for her backpacking trip. To make this decision, compare the volumes, base areas, and surface areas of both tents. Be ready to share your decision with the class.

Tent A   Tent B

11-38.   THREE-DIMENSIONAL SOLIDS TOOLKIT

Obtain the Lesson 11.1.3A Resource Pages ("Three-Dimensional Solids Toolkit") from your teacher. On the Resource Page, write everything you know about finding the volume and surface area of all of the solids that you have studied so far. In later lessons, you will continue to add information to this toolkit, so be sure to keep this resource page in a safe place. At this point, your Toolkit should include:

Prisms   Cylinders   Pyramids

METHODS AND **M**EANINGS

Cross-Sections of Three-Dimensional Solids

The intersection of a three-dimensional solid and a plane is called a **cross-section** of the solid. The result is a two-dimensional diagram that represents the flat surface of a slice of the solid.

One way to visualize a cross-section is to imagine the solid sliced into thin slices like a ream of paper. Since a solid can be sliced in any direction and at any angle, you need to know the direction of the slice to find the correct cross-section.

A horizontal cross-section is a circle.

A cylinder

A vertical cross-section is a rectangle.

For example, the cylinder at right has several different cross-sections depending on the direction of the slice. When this cylinder is sliced vertically, the resulting cross-section is a rectangle, while the cross-section is a circle when the cylinder is sliced horizontally.

Review & Preview

11-39. Review the information about cross-sections in the Math Notes box for this lesson. Then answer the questions below.

a. Draw a cube on your paper. Is it possible to slice a cube and get a cross-section that is not a quadrilateral? Explain how.

b. Barbara has a solid on her desk. If she slices it horizontally at any level, the cross-section is a triangle. If she slices it vertically in any direction, the cross-section is a triangle. What could her shape be? Draw a possible shape.

11-40. Find the volume and surface area of a square-based right pyramid if the base edge has length 6 units and the height of the pyramid is 4 units. Assume the diagram at right is not to scale.

11-41.   Twelve students will be chosen at random from the 900 students at Rolling Meadows High School to serve as the Judicial Board for minor student infractions.

a.   How many different Judicial Boards are possible?

b.   Mariko hopes to be on the board. How many possible boards include her?

c.   What is the probability (in percent) that Mariko is chosen for the board?

11-42.   The solid at right is a regular octahedron.

a.   Trace the shape on your paper. How many faces does it have? How many edges? Vertices?

b.   If an octahedron is sliced horizontally, what shape is the resulting cross-section?

11-43.   Assume that the prisms at right are similar.

a.   Solve for x and y.

b.   What is the ratio of the corresponding sides of Solid B to Solid A?

c.   If the base area of Solid A is 27 square units, find the base area of Solid B.

Solid A   Solid B

11-44.   Find the area and circumference of $\odot C$ at right. Show all work.

11-45.   **Multiple Choice:** The volume of the square-based pyramid with base edge 9 units and height 48 units is:

a.   324 units^3 b.   1296 units^3

c.   3888 units^3 d.   not enough information

11-46.   Examine the Venn diagram at right. In which region should the figure below be placed? Show all work to justify your conclusion.

These shapes have an area more than 15 units².

These shapes have perimeter more than 20 units.

A B C

D

6

4

30°

11-47.   While volunteering for a food sale, Aimee studied a cylindrical can of soup. She noticed that it had a diameter of 3 inches and a height of 4.5 inches.

a.   Find the volume of the soup can.

b.   If Aimee needs to fill a cylindrical pot that has a diameter of 14 inches and a height of 10 inches, how many cans of soup will she need?

c.   What is the area of the soup can label?

11-48.   In the diagram at right, assume that $m\angle ECB = m\angle EAD$ and point E is the midpoint of $\overline{AC}$. Prove that $\overline{AD} \cong \overline{CB}$.

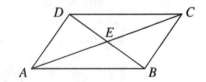

D   C
        E
A   B

11-49.   Next June, Joanna is taking a vacation to do some sightseeing and visit relatives. She will make four stops while she is gone. They might include Baltimore, Pittsburgh, Washington D.C., Philadelphia, New York City, and the New Jersey shore. Joanna is not sure in what order to visit these places.

a.   In how many ways can she organize her drive from place to place?

b.   How many of these trips will include the New Jersey Shore?

11-50.   A snack cracker company conducted a taste test for the three different types of crackers it makes. It surveyed 250 people in each age group in the table below. Participants chose their favorite type of cracker. Use the results to answer the questions.

Age	Cracker A	Cracker B	Cracker C
Under 20	152	54	44
20 to 39	107	85	58
40 to 59	78	101	71
60 and over	34	68	148

   a.   Calculate the probability that a participant chose cracker A or was under 20 years old. Show how you used the Addition Rule.

   b.   What is the probability that a participant did not choose cracker A and was over 20 years old? Show how you used a complement to answer this problem.

   c.   What is the probability that a participant was 20 years old or older. Show how you used a complement to answer this problem.

   d.   A randomly-selected participant says he is 15 years old. What is the probability that he chose cracker A?

11-51.   Write and solve an equation from the geometric relationships provided in the diagrams below.

   a.

   b.

   c.

   d.

11-52.   **Multiple Choice:** Calculate the volume of the rectangle-based pyramid at right.

   a.   84 units^3 b.   648 units^3 c.   882 units^3

   d.   1764 units^3 e.   None of these

11.1.4 What if it is a cone?

Surface Area and Volume of a Cone

Today you will continue to use what you know about the volume and surface area of prisms and pyramids and will extend your understanding to include a new three-dimensional shape: a cone. As you work with your team, look for connections to previous course material.

11-53. Review what you learned in Lesson 11.1.3 by finding the volume of each pyramid below. Assume that the pyramid in part (a) corresponds to a rectangular-based prism and that the base of the pyramid and prism in part (b) is a regular hexagon.

a.

b.

c.

11-54. While finding the volumes of the pyramids in problem 11-53, Jamal asked, *"But what if it is a cone? How would you find its volume?"* Note that a **cone** is somewhat like a pyramid, but it has a circular base. Every point on the perimeter of the circular base connects to a point above the base called the apex.

a. Discuss Jamal's question with your team. How might you use what you learned about the volume of pyramids to reason about the volume of a cone?

b. Lekili said, *"Remember when we found the area of a circle by finding what happens to the area of a regular polygon and the number of sides increase? I think we can use that approach here."* What do you think Lekili means? Explain how this can help find a method to compute the volume of a cone.

c. Use your ideas from part (b) to write an expression for the volume of a cone with radius of length r and height h.

d. Use your expression from part (c) to find the volume of a cone at right. Show all work.

Core Connections Geometry

11-55. **HAPPY BIRTHDAY!**

Your class has decided to throw your principal a surprise
birthday party tomorrow. The whole class is working together
to create party decorations, and your team has been assigned the
job of producing party hats. Each party hat will be created out
of special decorative paper and will be in the shape of a cone.

Your Task: Use the sample party hat provided by your teacher to determine the
size and shape of the paper that forms the hat. Then determine the amount of
paper (in square inches) needed to produce one party hat and figure out the total
amount of paper you will need for each person in your class to have a party hat.

11-56. The Math Club has decided to sell giant waffle ice-
cream cones at the Spring Fair. Lekili bought a cone,
but then he got distracted. When he returned to the
cone, the ice cream had melted, filling the cone to the
very top!

If the diameter of the base of the cone is 4 inches and
the slant height is 6 inches, find the volume of the ice
cream and the area of the waffle that made the cone.

11-57. **THREE-DIMENSIONAL SOLIDS TOOLKIT**

Add details to your Lesson 11.1.3A Resource Pages
("Three-Dimensional Solids Toolkit") for finding the
volume and surface area of cones.

$\mathcal{M}$ETHODS AND MEANINGS

Volume of a Pyramid

MATH NOTES

In general, the volume of a
pyramid is one-third of the
volume of the prism with the
same base area and height. Thus:

$$V = \tfrac{1}{3}(\text{base area})(\text{height})$$

height

base area

11-58. Find the volume and total surface area of each solid below. Show all work.

a.

7"

12"

25"

b.

12 m

10 m

11-59. Each of the *petit fours* (tiny bite-sized layered cakes) at Pauline's Pastries are made with three layers of filling. The pastry chef made one *petit four* for each possible choice of three different fillings of the eight that were available. The assistant iced them all with chocolate icing before marking which petit four contained which fillings. Since they are eaten in one bite, the order of the fillings does not matter.

a. How many *petit fours* did the chef make?

b. How many have raspberry, custard, and one other filling?

c. What is the probability (in percent) of getting a *petit four* that has apricot filling?

11-60. You roll three different-colored dice and use the numbers on the dice to determine the lengths of the sides of a triangle. For example, 3-3-5 would be an isosceles triangle with base 5. What is the probability of building a right triangle?

11-61. Examine the diagram of the cone at right.

a. How could you slice the cone so that the cross-section is a triangle?

b. What cross-section do you get if you slice the cone horizontally?

c. Lois is thinking of a shape. She says that no matter how you slice it, the cross-section will always be a circle. What shape is she thinking of? Draw and describe this shape on your paper.

11-62. For each triangle below, decide if it is similar to the triangle at right. If it is similar, justify your conclusion and complete the similarity statement $\triangle ABC \sim \triangle$_____. If the triangle is not similar, explain how you know. Assume that the diagrams are not drawn to scale.

a.   b. c.

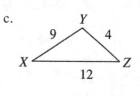

11-63. On graph paper, graph the following system of inequalities. Be sure that your shaded region represents all of the points that make both inequalities true.

$$y < \tfrac{2}{3}x - 2$$
$$y \geq -5x - 2$$

11-64. Examine the diagram at right. State the relationship between each pair of angles listed below (such as vertical angles) and state whether the angles are congruent, supplementary, or neither.

a. $\angle e$ and $\angle a$

b. $\angle t$ and $\angle u$

c. $\angle v$ and $\angle x$

d. $\angle g$ and $\angle v$

11-65. **Multiple Choice:** In the diagram at right, the value of y is:

a. $\sin \theta$ b. $\cos \theta$ c. $\tan \theta$

d. x e. None of these

11.1.5 What is the relationship?

Surface Area and Volume of a Sphere

This lesson will complete your Three-Dimensional Solids Toolkit. You will learn about a new shape that you encounter often in your daily life: a sphere. You will also make connections between a cylinder, cone, and sphere of the same radius and height.

As you work with your team, keep the following focus questions in mind:

What's the relationship?

What other tools or information do I need?

11-66.   Alonzo was blowing bubbles to amuse his little sister. He wondered, *"Why are bubbles always perfectly round?"*

    a.   Discuss Alonzo's question with the class. Why are free-floating bubbles always shaped like a perfectly round ball?

    b.   The shape of a bubble is called a **sphere**. What other objects can you remember seeing that are shaped like a sphere?

    c.   What shapes are related to spheres? How are they related?

11-67.   GEOGRAPHY LESSON, Part One

Alonzo learned in his geography class that about 70% of the Earth's surface is covered in water. *"That's amazing!"* he thought. This information only made him think of new questions, such as *"What is the area of land covered in water?"*, *"What percent of the Earth's surface is the United States?"*, and *"What is the volume of the entire Earth?"*

Discuss Alonzo's questions with your team. Decide:

- What facts about the Earth would be helpful to know?

- What do you still need to learn to answer Alonzo's questions?

11-68.   In order to answer his questions, Alonzo decided to get out his set of plastic geometry models. He has a sphere, cone, and cylinder that each has the same radius and height.

a.   Draw an example diagram of each shape.

b.   If the radius of the sphere is r, what is the height of the cylinder? How do you know?

c.   Alonzo's models are hollow and are designed to hold water. Alonzo was pouring water between the shapes, comparing their volumes. He discovered that when he poured the water in the cone and the sphere into the cylinder, the water filled up the cylinder without going over! Determine what the volume of the sphere must be if the radius of the sphere is r units. Show all work.

11-69.   Now that Alonzo knows that spheres, cylinders, and cones with the same height and radius are related, he decides to examine the surface area of each one. As he paints the exterior of each shape, he notices that the lateral surface area of the cylinder and the surface area of the sphere take exactly the same amount of paint! If the radius of the sphere and cylinder is r, what is the surface area of the sphere?

11-70.   GEOGRAPHY LESSON, Part Two

Now that you have strategies for finding the volume and surface area of a sphere, return to problem 11-67 and help Alonzo answer his questions. That is, determine:

• The area of the Earth's surface that is covered in water.

• The percent of the Earth's surface that lies in the United States.

• The volume of the entire Earth.

Remember that in Chapter 10, you determined that the radius of the Earth is about 4,000 miles. Alonzo did some research and discovered that the land area of the United States is approximately 3,537,438 square miles.

11-71.   THREE-DIMENSIONAL SOLIDS TOOLKIT

Retrieve the Three-Dimensional Solids Toolkit. Complete
the entry for a sphere. That is, write everything you know
about finding the volume and surface area of spheres. Be
sure you include the relationships between the volumes of a
cone, cylinder, and sphere with the same radius and height.

METHODS AND MEANINGS

MATH NOTES

Volume and Lateral Surface of a Cone

The general formula for the volume of a
cone (defined in problem 11-54) is the same as
the formula for the volume of a pyramid:

Volume = $\frac{1}{3}$(Base Area)(Height)

In the case of the cone, the Base Area = πr^2 where r
is the length of the radius of the circular base. So if
h is the height of the cone then the volume is:

$V = \frac{1}{3}$(Base Area)(Height) $= \frac{1}{3}\pi r^2 h$.

To find the lateral surface area of a cone, imagine
unrolling the lateral surface of the cone to create a
sector. The radius of the sector would be the slant
height, l, of the cone, and the arc length would be
the circumference of the base of the cone, $2\pi r$.

Therefore, the area of the sector (the lateral surface area of the cone) is:

$LA = \frac{2\pi r}{2\pi l}\pi l^2 = \pi r l$

11-72.   As Shannon peeled her orange for lunch, she realized that it was very close to
being a sphere. If her orange has a diameter of 8 centimeters, what is its
approximate surface area (the area of the orange peel)? What is the approximate
volume of the orange? Show all work.

11-73.   How many committees of three juniors and three seniors can be formed from the student government class of eight juniors and 10 seniors?

11-74.   Pauline's Pastries is making special *petit fours* (as in problem 11-59). The chef is making *petit fours* with three or four fillings. For Valentine's Day they have twelve fillings available and they make one *petit four* for each of the possible three or four different fillings.

   a.   How many *petit fours* did they make?

   b.   What is the probability of getting a *petit four* that has both raspberry and custard?

11-75.   Martha was playing with a hollow plastic cone that had a diameter of 12 inches and a height of 5 inches. Her brother Matt snatched the cone, cut two inches off the top, and placed the cut piece upside down in the lower portion of the cone as shown at right. How many cubic inches of water would fit inside the space of her redesigned cone?

original view

original view upside-down

11-76.   Review what you know about polyhedra as you answer the questions below. Refer to the table in problem 11-4 if you need help.

   a.   Find the total surface area of a regular icosahedron if the area of each face is 45 mm^2. Explain your method.

   b.   The total surface area of a regular dodecahedron is 108 cm^2. What is the area of each face?

   c.   A regular tetrahedron has an edge length of 6 inches. What is its total surface area? Show all work.

11-77.   Hokiri's ladder has two legs that are each 8 feet long. When the ladder is opened safely and locked for use, the legs are 4 feet apart on the ground. What is the angle that is formed at the top of the ladder where the legs meet?

8 feet

8 feet

4 feet

11-78.   Find the area of the region that represents the solution of the inequality $x^2 + y^2 \le 72$.

11-79.   Solve each system of equations below. Write the solution in the form (x, y). Show all work.

a. $y + 3x = 14$
     $y - 3x = 6$

b. $y = 6 - 3x$
     $2x + y = 7$

11.2.1 Where is this location?

Coordinates on a Sphere

As you learned in Chapter 1, the word *geometry* literally means "measurement of the Earth." In fact, so far in this course, you have used your geometric tools to learn more about Earth. For example, in Lesson 11.1.5, you learned that the United States only makes up 1.8% of the Earth's surface. Also, in Lesson 10.1.1, you learned how Eratosthenes used shadows to estimate the Earth's radius.

Today, you will examine other earthly questions that can be answered using geometry. Since you can approximate the shape of the earth as a sphere, you will be able to use many of the tools you have used previously. As you work with your team, consider the following focus questions:

What strategy or tool can I use?

Is there another way?

Does this strategy always work?

11-80.   YOU ARE HERE

The reference lines connecting the north and south poles of the earth are called lines of **longitude**, as shown in the diagram at right. These lines have been used for hundreds of years to help navigators determine how many degrees east or west they have traveled. While these reference markings are referred to as "lines," they are technically circles that wrap around the Earth.

Lines of Longitude

Lines of longitude extend north and south, while lines of **latitude** circle east and west, as shown in the diagrams below. These lines help to mark off arc measures on the planet's surface. In the diagrams at right, the lines of latitude are marked every 15° while the lines of longitude are marked every 30°. The most famous line of latitude is the **equator**, which separates the Earth into two **hemispheres** (half a sphere).

Equator

Problem continues on next page →

11-80.   *Problem continued from previous page.*

Another name for these lines of longitude is **meridians**, which is Latin from *medius* (which means "middle") and *diem* (which means "day"). The word meridian also used to refer to noon, since it was the time the sun was directly overhead. In the morning, it was "ante meridian" or before noon. This is where the abbreviation **a.m.** comes from. Likewise, **p.m.** is short for "post meridian," which means after noon.

a.   The equator is an example of a **great circle**, which means that it is a circle that lies on the sphere and has the same diameter as the sphere. Compare the equator with the other lines of latitude. What do you notice?

Lines of Latitude   **Lines of Longitude**

b.   Is it possible for two great circles on the same sphere to intersect? If so, draw an example on your paper. If not, explain why not.

c.   On the sphere provided by your teacher, carefully draw circles to represent the lines of latitude (every 30°) and longitude (every 30°) on the Earth. Highlight the equator by making it darker or a different color than the other lines of latitude. Also choose one line of longitude to represent 0° (called the **prime meridian**, which passes through Greenwich, England, on the eastern edge of London) and highlight it as well.

d.   Norman is exactly 1 mile north of Sula. If they both travel due west, will their paths cross? Why or why not? Assume that people can travel over water and all types of terrain.

e.   Erin is exactly 1 mile east of Wilber. If they both travel due south at the same rate, will their paths cross? Why or why not?

11-81.   DEAR PEN PAL

Brianna, who lives in New Orleans, has been writing
to her pen pal in Jacksonville, Florida. *"Gosh,"* she
wonders, *"How far away is my friend?"*

a.   On your spherical model of the globe from
problem 11-80, locate Brianna's home. (New
Orleans, LA, is approximately 90° west of the prime meridian and 30°
north of the equator.) Mark it with a pushpin.

b.   Now, with a second pushpin, mark the location of Brianna's friend, if
Jacksonville is 82° west of the prime meridian and 30° north of the
equator. Use a rubber band to locate the circle with the smallest radius
that passes through these two locations.

c.   What is the measure of the arc connecting these two cities? Show how
you know.

d.   Brianna thinks that if she knew the
circumference of the circle marked with the
rubber band, then she could use the arc
measure to approximate the distance between
the two cities. The shaded circle in the
diagram at right represents the cross-section of
the earth 30° above the equator. If the radius
of the earth is approximately 4000 miles, find
the circumference of the shaded circle.

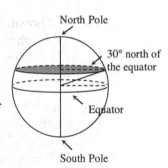

e.   Use what you found in part (d) to find the
distance between New Orleans and Jacksonville.

11-82.   Obtain a Lesson 11.2.1 Resource Page from your teacher. On it, mark and label
the following locations:

a.   London, England, which is on the prime meridian and is approximately
51° north of the equator.

b.   Narsarssuaq, Greenland, which is approximately 45° west of the prime
meridian and 61° north of the equator.

c.   Quito, Ecuador, which is on the equator and is approximately 79° west of
the prime meridian.

d.   Cairo, Egypt, which is approximately 31° east of the prime meridian and
30° north of the equator.

e.   Buenos Aires, Argentina, which is approximately 58° west of the prime
meridian and 35° south of the equator.

11-83.   **EXTENSION**

a.   If a polar bear travels 1 mile south from the North Pole, travels one mile east, and then travels one mile north, where does it end up? Explain what happens and why.

b.   Is there another location the polar bear could have started from so that it still ends up where it started after following the same directions? Explain.

11-84.   The moon is an average distance of 238,900 miles away from the Earth. While that seems very far, how far is it?

a.   Compare that distance with the circumference of the Earth's equator. Assume that the Earth's radius is 4000 miles. How many times greater than the Earth's circumference is the distance to the moon?

b.   One way to estimate the distance between the Earth and the sun is to consider the triangle formed by the sun, Earth, and moon when the moon appears to be half-full. (See the diagram at right.) When the moon appears from earth to be half-full, it can be assumed that the moon forms a 90° angle with the sun and the Earth.

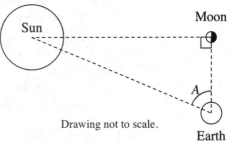

Drawing not to scale.

Using special equipment, Ray found the measure of angle A to be 89.85°. If the moon is 238,900 miles away from the Earth, then how far is the sun from the Earth?

11-85.   The length of chord $\overline{AB}$ in $\odot D$ is 9 mm. If the $m\overset{\frown}{AB} = 32°$, find the length of $\overset{\frown}{AB}$. Draw a diagram.

11-86.   On your paper, draw a diagram of a square-based pyramid if the side length of the base is 9 cm and the height of the pyramid is 12 cm.

a.   Find the volume of the pyramid.

b.   If a smaller pyramid is similar to the pyramid in part (a), but has a linear scale factor of $\frac{1}{3}$, find its volume.

Core Connections Geometry

11-87.   In the card game called "Twenty-One," two cards are dealt from a randomly shuffled deck of playing cards. The player's goal is to get the sum of his or her cards to be as close (or equal) to 21 as possible, without going over 21. To establish the sample space for this problem, you need to think of choosing two from a set of 52.

a.   How many ways are there to be dealt two cards?

b.   The tens, jacks, queens, and kings all have a value of 10 points. There are four of each in a standard deck. What is the probability of being dealt two ten-valued cards?

c.   If you did not already do so, write your solution to part (b) in the form $\frac{{}_aC_b}{{}_dC_e}$.

d.   What is the probability (as a percent) of being dealt two face cards? (Face cards are Kings, Queens, and Jacks, that is, the cards that have faces.) Also write your answer as $\frac{{}_aC_b}{{}_dC_e}$.

e.   In "Twenty-One" an Ace can count as 1 point or 11 points. The deal is called "soft" when the Ace is counted as 11 points. What is the probability of being dealt a "soft 21," that is, a card worth ten points and an Ace?

11-88.   Mr. McGee, the owner of The Laundry Shop (from problem 10-88) has a different question that he wants to answer with data and probability. He wants to estimate the probability that a customer who comes into his store will buy a washer or dryer. He collected the following data during one week: 177 customers came to his store, 88 purchased washers, 64 purchased dryers, and 69 did not make a purchase.

a.   Using this data, what is the probability that the next customer who comes to his store will purchase a washer or a dryer?

b.   Mr. McGee promises his salespeople a bonus if they can increase the probability that the customers who buy washers also buy dryers. For the week's data above, what is the probability that if a customer bought a washer, he or she also bought a dryer?

11-89.   In the picture of a globe at right, the lines of latitude are concentric circles. Where else might you encounter concentric circles?

11-90.   **Multiple Choice:** The volume of a solid is V. If the solid is enlarged proportionally so that its side lengths increase by a factor of 9, what is the volume of the enlarged solid?

a. $9V$ b. $\frac{81}{4}V$ c. $81V$ d. $729V$

11.2.2 What is the relationship?

Tangents and Arcs

Today, you will develop new geometric tools as you continue to study the Earth and its measure.

11-91. EYE IN THE SKY

Did you know that as of 2012, there were approximately 3000 operating satellites orbiting the Earth performing various functions such as taking photographs of the planet? One way that scientists learn more about the Earth is to carefully examine photographs that are taken by an orbiting satellite. Everyday citizens also use imagery from these satellites in applications such as maps on cell phones.

Satellite

However, how much of the Earth can a satellite see? What does this depend upon? In other words, what information would you need to know in order to figure out how much of the planet is in view of a satellite in space? Discuss this with your team and be ready to share your ideas with the rest of the class.

11-92. Locate Satellites A, B, and C on the Lesson 11.2.2 Resource Page (or on a computer if you are using the technology tool.)

a. Draw an angle from Satellite A that shows the portion of the Earth's equator that is visible from the satellite. What is the relationship of the sides of the angle and the circle that represents the equator of the Earth?

b. Draw quadrilateral *ADEF* that connects Satellite A, the points of tangency, and the center of the Earth (point *E*). If the measure of the angle at Satellite A is 90°, what is the measure of the equator's arc that is in view? Explain how you know.

c. What is the relationship of *AD* and *AF*? Prove the relationship using congruent triangles.

d. If $m\angle A = 90°$ and the radius of the Earth is 4000 miles, how far above the surface of the planet is Satellite A?

11-93.   What if the satellite is placed higher in orbit? Consider this as you answer the
          questions below.

    a.   Using a different colored line, draw the viewing angle from Satellite B.
          Label the points of tangency *G* and *H*. Will Satellite B see more or less of
          the Earth's equator than Satellite A?

    b.   If $m\angle B = 60°$, find the length of the equator in view of Satellite B.
          Assume that the radius of the Earth is 4000 miles.

    c.   Use a third color to draw the viewing angle from Satellite C. Label the
          points of tangency *J* and *K*. If $m\angle C = 45°$, find the $m\overset{\frown}{JK}$ and $m\overset{\frown}{JZK}$.

    d.   Is it possible for a satellite to see 50% of the Earth's equator? Why or why
          not?

11-94.   CONSTRUCTING A TANGENT TO A CIRCLE THROUGH A POINT

          In problems 11-92 and 11-93, you drew tangents to a circle through a given
          point. You may have done this by "eye-balling" a point on the circle.
          However, how can the point of tangency be found using geometric
          construction? Do the following to find the answer to this question.

    a.   On a blank piece of paper, use a compass to construct a circle *E*. Then
          mark and label a point outside the circle *A*.

    b.   Tyler remembers that a line tangent to a circle at a point must be
          perpendicular to the radius of the circle at that same point. *"How can we
          find a point that makes a right triangle with the center of the circle and the
          location of Satellite A?"*

          Shana said *"Maybe a different circle will*
          help. If $\overline{EA}$ is a diameter of a circle, then
          any other points on that circle must form a
          right triangle with points E and A." She
          drew the diagram at right. Is Shana correct?
          Discuss Shana's idea with your team.

    c.   With your compass and straightedge, construct $\overline{EA}$ and mark its midpoint,
          M. Then construct the circle through *A* with center *M*. Label one of the
          points where $\odot M$ intersects $\odot E$ point *B*.

    d.   Construct $\overleftrightarrow{AB}$. Prove that $\overleftrightarrow{AB}$ is tangent to $\odot E$ at *B*.

11-95.   HOW ARE THEY RELATED?

In problems 11-92 and 11-93, you found the
measures of angles and arcs formed by two
tangents to a circle that intersect each other.

a.   Copy the diagram at right onto your paper.
Using intuition, describe how the measure
of the angle formed by the tangents ($m\angle A$) seems to be related to the
measures of the major and minor arcs formed by the points of tangency
($\overset{\frown}{BD}$ and $\overset{\frown}{BZD}$).

b.   If $m\angle A = x$, find $m\overset{\frown}{BD}$ and $m\overset{\frown}{BZD}$ in terms of x. Compare the measure of
the angle with the measure of the major and minor arcs. What do you
notice?

c.   LEARNING LOG

Write an entry in your Learning Log describing the
relationship between the angles and arcs formed by
two intersecting tangents to a circle. Also record
what you found out about the lengths of the tangents
from the point of tangency to their point of intersection. Title this entry
"Tangents and Arcs" and include today's date.

11-96.   While making his lunch, Alexander sliced off a portion of his grapefruit. If the area of the cross-section of the slice (shaded at right) was 3 in.^{2}, and if the diameter of the grapefruit was 5 inches long, find the distance between the center of the grapefruit and the slice. Assume the grapefruit is a sphere.

11-97.   The approximate surface areas of the seven Earth continents are shown in the table at right. If the radius of the Earth's moon is approximately 1080 miles, how would its surface area compare with the size of the continents?

Continent	Area (sq. miles)
Asia	17,212,048.1
Africa	11,608,161.4
North America	9,365,294.0
South America	6,879,954.4
Antarctica	5,100,023.4
Europe	3,837,083.3
Australia/Oceania	2,967,967.3

11-98.   A bag contains four red pens, six green pens, and two blue pens. If three pens are chosen at random, what is the probability that one of each color is picked?

11-99.   Find the area of the regular decagon if the length of each side is 20 units.

11-100.   The solid at right is an example of a **truncated pyramid**. It is formed by slicing and removing the top of a pyramid so that the slice is parallel to the base of the pyramid. If the original height of the square-based pyramid at right was 12 cm, find the volume of this truncated pyramid. (Hint: You may find your results from problem 11-86 useful.)

11-101.   Examine the triangles at right. Are they similar? Are they congruent? Explain how you know. Then write an appropriate similarity or congruence statement.

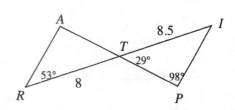

11-102. This problem is a checkpoint for computing volumes and surface areas of prisms and cylinders. It will be referred to as Checkpoint 11.

Compute the volume and surface area of each solid.

a.

b.

c.

Check your answers by referring to the Checkpoint 11 materials located at the back of your book.

If you needed help solving these problems correctly, then you need more practice. Review the Checkpoint 11 materials and try the practice problems. Also, consider getting help outside of class time. From this point on, you will be expected to do problems like these quickly and easily.

11-103. **Multiple Choice:** Which shape below has the *least* area?

a. A circle with radius 5 units.

b. A square with side length 9 units.

c. A trapezoid with bases of length 8 and 10 units and height of 9 units.

d. A rhombus with side length 9 units and height of 8 units.

11.2.3 What is the measure?

Secant and Tangent Relationships

In Lesson 11.2.2, you studied the angles and arcs formed by tangents when a satellite orbits the Earth, as shown in the diagram at right. Today, you will consider a related question: What if the sides of the angle intersect the circle more than once? What are the relationships between the angles and arcs formed when this happens? And what can you learn about the lengths of the segments created by the points of intersection?

Satellite

As you work with your team, carefully record your team's conjectures. And while you work, keep the following questions in mind:

What patterns do I see?

Is this relationship always true?

11-104. Review what you learned in Lesson 11.2.2 by solving for the given variables in the diagrams below. Show all work.

a. (68°, *x*, *y*)   b. (*x*, 152°, *y*)   c. (*x*, 8)

11-105. While a tangent is a line that intersects a circle (such as $\odot C$ in the diagram at right) at exactly one point, a **secant** is a line that intersects a circle twice. $\overleftrightarrow{PR}$ is an example of a secant, while $\overleftrightarrow{QS}$ is an example of a tangent.

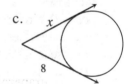

a.   What happens to the measure of the angles and arcs when a secant intersects the circle at the point of tangency? Namely, how are the angles located at point P in the diagram above related to $m\overarc{PR}$ and $m\overarc{PTR}$? First make an educated guess. Then test your ideas out using a dynamic geometry tool. Write a conjecture and be ready to share it with the class.

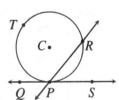

Problem continues on next page →

11-105. *Problem continued from previous page.*

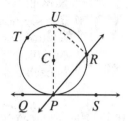

b.   Uri wants to prove his conjecture from part (a) for a non-special secant (meaning that $\overrightarrow{PR}$ is not a diameter). He decided to extend a diameter from point P and to create an inscribed angle that intercepts $\overset{\frown}{PR}$. With your team, examine Uri's diagram carefully and consider all the relationships you can identify that could be useful. To get you started, use the list below.

       i.   What is $m\angle URP$?

      ii.   How is $m\angle RUP$ related to $m\overset{\frown}{PR}$?

    iii.   What is the sum of the angles in $\triangle PRU$?

    iv.   How are $\angle UPR$ and $\angle RPS$ related?

c.   Using the relationships you explored in part (b), prove that if $m\angle RPS = x$ in the diagram from part (b), then $m\overset{\frown}{PR} = 2x$. Remember to justify each step.

11-106.   Uri now has this challenge for you: *What happens when secants and tangents intersect outside a circle?* To consider this, you need to examine two separate cases: One is when a secant and tangent intersect outside a circle (case *i* below). The other is when two secants intersect outside a circle (case *ii* below). As with your earlier investigations,

- First make a prediction about the relationship between the measures of x, a, and b for each case.

- Then use your dynamic geometry tool to test your conjectures.

- For each case, write an algebraic statement (equation) that relates x, a, and b. Be ready to share each equation with the rest of the class.

i.   *ii.*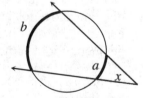

11-107.   Now prove your conjectures from problem 11-106. For each diagram, add a line segment that will help to create an inscribed angle. Then use angle relationships (such as the sum of the angles of a triangle must be 180°) to then find the measures of all the angles in terms of x, a, and b. Be sure to show that in each case, $x = \frac{b-a}{2}$. Remember to justify each statement.

i.

ii.

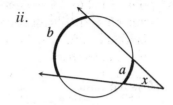

11-108.   Camille is interested in the lengths of segments that are created by the points of intersection. She remembers proving in Lesson 11.2.2 that the lengths of the tangents between their intersection and the points of tangency are equal, as shown in the diagram at right. She figures that there must be some relationships in the lengths created by the intersections of secants, too.

a.   The first case she wants to consider is when a tangent and secant intersect outside a circle, as shown in the figure at right. Copy this diagram onto your paper.

b.   *"To find a relationship, I think we need to add some line segments to create some inscribed angles and triangles,"* Camille tells her team. She decides to add the line segments shown at right. Show why the angles marked x and y must be congruent.

c.   *"If some of these triangles are similar, I can use that to find a relationship between these side lengths,"* Camille explains. Help her prove that $\triangle PQT \sim \triangle PTR$.

d.   Use the fact that $\triangle PQT \sim \triangle PTR$ to write a proportion using a, b, and c. Simplify this equation as much as possible to find an equation that helps you understand the relationship between a, b, and c.

e.   Use the same process to find the relationship between the lengths created when two secants intersect outside a circle. Two extra segments have been added to the diagram to help create similar triangles. Be ready to justify your relationship.

11-109. Use all your circle relationships to solve for the variables in each of the diagrams below.

a.

168°

b.

c.

218°

d. C is the center

e.

f.

11-110. Solve for the variables in each of the diagrams below. Assume point C is the center of the circle in part (b).

a.

b.

c.

11-111. In part (c) of problem 11-110, you used the relationship between the segment lengths formed by intersecting chords to find a missing length. But how are the arc measures of two random intersecting chords related? Examine the diagram at right.

a. Solve for a, b, and c using what you know about inscribed angles and the sum of the angles of a triangle.

b. Compare the result for c with 88° and 72°. Is there a relationship?

11-112. Dr. G, the principal at Westside High School Academy, is worried that the students who win academic awards might also be the ones more likely to win awards in the Fine Arts. He would like to spread out the awards more. Does Dr. G have anything to worry about? Out of the 768 students, 128 won academic awards of some sort, and 48 won Fine Arts awards. 8 won both kinds of awards.

11-113. On your paper, draw a diagram of a square-based right pyramid. If the base has side length 6 units and the height of the pyramid is 10 units, find the total surface area. Show all your work.

11-114. Perhaps you think the Earth is big? Consider the sun!

a. Assume that the radius of the Earth 4000 miles. The sun is approximately 109 times as wide. Find the sun's radius.

b. The distance between the Earth and the moon is 238,900 miles. Compare this distance with the radius of the sun you found in part (a).

c. If the sun were hollow, how many Earths would fill the inside of it?

11-115. A cube has an edge length of 16 units. Draw a diagram of the cube and find its volume and surface area.

11-116. **Multiple Choice:** Which of the following cannot be the measure of an exterior angle of a regular polygon?

a. 18°   b. 24°   c. 28°   d. 40°

11-117. Solve for the variables in each of the diagrams below. Assume that point C is the center of the circle in part (b).

a.

b.

c.

11-118. Which has greater volume: a cylinder with radius 38 units and height 71 units or a rectangular prism with dimensions 34, 84, and 99 units? Show all work and support your reasoning.

11-119. Jean Luc's favorite Asian restaurant has six dishes on its lunch menu. He wants to get their three-item combo for lunch. The server reminds Jean Luc that he can choose two or three servings of the same dish if he wants. How many different ways could he order lunch?

11-120. Copy the diagram at right onto your paper. Use the process from problem 11-111 to find the measure of x. Show all work.

11-121. Find the equation of an exponential function that passes through the points $(1, 6)$ and $(5, 30.375)$.

11-122. A solar eclipse occurs when the moon passes between the Earth and the sun and is perfectly aligned so that it blocks the Earth's view of the sun.

Note: This diagram is not to scale.

How do scientists figure out what areas of the Earth will see an eclipse? To find out, copy the diagram above onto your paper. Then use tangents representing the sun's rays to visually show the portion of the Earth's equator that will see the total eclipse. You do not need to calculate this area, just show it on the diagram.

11-123. **Multiple Choice:** The Mona Lisa, by Leonardo da Vinci, is arguably the most famous painting in existence. The rectangular artwork, which hangs in the Musée du Louvre, measures 77 cm by 53 cm. When the museum created a billboard with an enlarged version of the portrait for advertisement, they used a linear scale factor of 20. What was the area of the billboard?

   a. 4081 cm^2 b. 32,638,000 cm^2

   c. 81,620 cm^2 d. 1,632,400 cm^2

   e. None of these

Chapter 11 Closure   What have I learned?

• •

Reflection and Synthesis

The activities below offer you a chance to reflect
about what you have learned during this chapter. As
you work, look for concepts that you feel very
comfortable with, ideas that you would like to learn
more about, and topics you need more help with.
Look for connections between ideas as well as
connections with material you learned previously.

①   TEAM BRAINSTORM

What have you studied in this chapter? What ideas were important in what you
learned? With your team, brainstorm a list. Be as detailed as you can. To help
get you started, lists of Learning Log entries, Toolkit Entries, and Math Notes
boxes are below.

What topics, ideas, and words that you learned *before* this chapter are connected
to the new ideas in this chapter? Again, be as detailed as you can.

Next consider the Standards for Mathematical Practice that follow Activity ③:
Portfolio. What Mathematical Practices did you use in this chapter? When did
you use them? Give specific examples.

How long can you make your lists? Challenge yourselves. Be prepared to
share your team's ideas with the class.

Learning Log Entries

- Lesson 11.1.1 – Plato's Solids
- Lesson 11.2.2 – Tangents and Arcs

Toolkit Entries

- Three-Dimensional Solids Toolkit (Lesson 11.1.3A
  Resource Pages, problems 11-38, 11-57, and 11-71)

Math Notes

- Lesson 11.1.2 – Pyramid Vocabulary
- Lesson 11.1.3 – Cross-Sections of Three-Dimensional Solids
- Lesson 11.1.4 – Volume of a Pyramid
- Lesson 11.1.5 – Volume and Lateral Surface of a Cone
- Lesson 11.2.2 – Volume and Surface Area of a Sphere
- Lesson 11.2.3 – Intersecting Tangents

②   MAKING CONNECTIONS

Below is a list of the vocabulary used in this chapter. Make sure that you are familiar with all of these words and know what they mean. Refer to the glossary or index for any words that you do not yet understand.

apex	arc	base
circle	cone	cross-section
cube	cylinder	diameter
edge	equator	face
great circle	height	hemisphere
lateral face	latitude	longitude
meridian	oblique	octahedron
platonic solid	polyhedron	pyramid
radius	secant	slant height
sphere	surface area	tangent
tetrahedron	volume	

Make a concept map showing all of the connections you can find among the key words and ideas listed above. To show a connection between two words, draw a line between them and explain the connection. A word can be connected to any other word as long as you can justify the connection. For each key word or idea, provide an example or sketch that shows the idea.

While you are making your map, your team may think of related words or ideas that are not listed here. Be sure to include these ideas on your concept map.

PORTFOLIO: EVIDENCE OF MATHEMATICAL PROFICIENCY

Showcase your ability to work with solids by solving the
following problem. Make sure your explanation is clear
and in detail. Remember you are not only showcasing
your understanding of the mathematics, but you are also
showcasing your ability to communicate your
justifications.

The Germany Historical Society has just acquired a castle on the Rhine River
and wishes to turn it into a museum. But for it to be inviting to guests, they
must heat the castle and place a new layer of plaster around the outside. If one
commercial heater can heat about 16,000 cubic feet, how many heaters will the
Society need to purchase? How many square feet of plaster will they need
(ignoring the windows)? The Society has modeled the castle with the following
diagram:

Next, consider the Standards for Mathematical Practice that follow. What
Mathematical Practices did you use in this chapter? When did you use them?
Give specific examples.

BECOMING MATHEMATICALLY PROFICIENT
The Common Core State Standards For Mathematical Practice

This book focuses on helping you use some very specific Mathematical Practices. The Mathematical Practices describe ways in which mathematically proficient students engage with mathematics everyday.

Make sense of problems and persevere in solving them:

Making sense of problems and persevering in solving them means that you can solve problems that are full of different kinds of mathematics. These types of problems are not routine, simple, or typical. Instead, they combine lots of math ideas and everyday situations. You have to stick with challenging problems, try different strategies, use multiple representations, and use a different method to check your results.

Reason abstractly and quantitatively:

Throughout this course, everyday situations are used to introduce you to new math ideas. Seeing mathematical ideas within a context helps you make sense of the ideas. Once you learn about a math idea in a practical way, you can **reason abstractly** by thinking about the concept more generally, representing it with symbols, and manipulating the symbols. **Reasoning quantitatively** is using numbers and symbols to represent an everyday situation, taking into account the units involved, and considering the meaning of the quantities as you compute them.

Construct viable arguments and critique the reasoning of others:

To **construct a viable argument** is to present your solution steps in a logical sequence and to justify your steps with conclusions, relying on number sense, facts and definitions, and previously established results. You communicate clearly, consider the real-life context, and provide clarification when others ask. In this course, you regularly share information, opinions, and expertise with your study team. You **critique the reasoning of others** when you analyze the approach of others, build on each other's ideas, compare the effectiveness of two strategies, and decide what makes sense and under what conditions.

Model with mathematics:

When you **model with mathematics**, you take a complex situation and use mathematics to represent it, often by making assumptions and approximations to simplify the situation. Modeling allows you to analyze and describe the situation and to make predictions. For example, to find the density of your body, you might model your body with a more familiar shape, say, a cylinder of the same diameter and height. Although a model may not be perfect, it can still be very useful for describing data and making predictions. When you interpret the results, you may need to go back and improve your model by revising your assumptions and approximations.

Use appropriate tools strategically:

To **use appropriate tools strategically** means that you analyze the task and decide which tools may help you model the situation or find a solution. Some of the tools available to you include diagrams, graph paper, calculators, computer software, databases, and websites. You understand the limitations of various tools. A result can be checked or estimated by strategically choosing a different tool.

Attend to precision:

To **attend to precision** means that when solving problems, you need to pay close attention to the details. For example, you need to be aware of the units, or how many digits your answer requires, or how to choose a scale and label your graph. You may need to convert the units to be consistent. At times, you need to go back and check whether a numerical solution makes sense in the context of the problem.

You need to **attend to precision** when you communicate your ideas to others. Using the appropriate vocabulary and mathematical language can help make your ideas and reasoning more understandable to others.

Look for and make use of structure:

Looking for and making use of structure is a guiding principal of this course. When you are involved in analyzing the structure and in the actual development of mathematical concepts, you gain a deeper, more conceptual understanding than when you are simply told what the structure is and how to do problems. You often use this practice to bring closure to an investigation.

There are many concepts that you learn by looking at the underlying structure of a mathematical idea and thinking about how it connects to other ideas you have already learned. For example, geometry theorems are developed from the structure of translations.

Look for and express regularity in repeated reasoning:

To **look for and express regularity in repeated reasoning** means that when you are investigating a new mathematical concept, you notice if calculations are repeated in a pattern. Then you look for a way to generalize the method for use in other situations, or you look for shortcuts. For example, the investigations with simple shapes can be applied to more complex shapes using repeated reasoning.

④   WHAT HAVE I LEARNED?

Most of the problems in this section
represent typical problems found in
this chapter. They serve as a gauge
for you. You can use them to
determine which types of problems
you can do well and which types of
problems require further study and
practice. Even if your teacher does
not assign this section, it is a good
idea to try these problems and find out
for yourself what you know and what
you still need to work on.

Solve each problem as completely as you can. The table at the end of the
closure section has answers to these problems. It also tells you where you
can find additional help and practice with problems like these.

CL 11-124.   Use all your circle relationships to solve for the variables in each of the
diagrams below.

a.

b.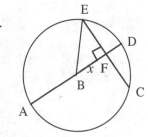

$EC = 8$ and $AB = 5$

c. $\overline{MN} \cong \overline{PQ}$, $MN = 7x + 13$,
     and $PQ = 10x - 8$.

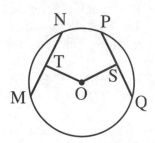

CL 11-125.   On graph paper, draw $\triangle ABC$ if $A(2,4)$, $B(9,5)$, and $C(4,10)$.

a.   Verify that $D(3,7)$ is a midpoint of $\overline{AC}$.

b.   Find the equation of the line through points D and B.

c.   Is $\overline{BD}$ a height of $\triangle ABC$? Use slope to show that $\overline{BD}$ is perpendicular to $\overline{AC}$.

CL 11-126.   Four brown dogs and two white dogs are in a large doghouse. Someone tells you that exactly two dogs are asleep.

a.   What is the probability that the two dogs are brown?

b.   What is the probability that the two dogs are both white?

c.   What is the probability that one dog is white and the other is brown?

d.   If someone also told you the two sleeping dogs were the same color, what is the probability they are brown?

CL 11-127.   In the game Tic Tac Toe, players can choose to put their marker in any square that is not already occupied. The rows can be labeled **Top**, **Middle**, **Bottom**, and the columns **Left**, **Inner**, **Right**, as shown in the diagram below. For example, the first three moves might be MI, BR, then TL.

	Left	Inner	Right
Top	✓		
Middle		✓	
Bottom			✓

a.   How many different ways are there to make the first three moves in Tic Tac Toe? In this case, you are not concerned with which player made the move, just what the first three moves were.

b.   If you have not done so already, write your answer to part (a) as a fraction with factorials.

CL 11-128.   Find the volume and surface area of a right pyramid if its height is 7 mm and its base is a regular pentagon with perimeter 20 mm.

CL 11-129. According to the U.S. Census Bureau, in 2010 pet ownership in the U.S. was distributed as shown in the table below (out of every 1000 households).

Household income	Number with primarily dogs	Number with primarily cats	Number with primarily birds	Number with primarily horses	Number with no pets
under $20,000	64	63	69	3	70
$20,000 to $34,999	66	59	7	3	41
$35,000 to $54,999	77	66	8	4	38
$55,000 to $84,999	82	68	7	4	31
$85,000 and over	97	77	9	5	42

a. What is the probability of having no pets?

b. What is the probability of having a pet?

c. If a person is selected at random, what is the probability the person earns under $35,000 *and* owns a dog?

d. What is the probability the person earns under $35,000 *or* owns a dog?

e. Use another method for determining the probability of earning under $35,000 *or* owning a dog to verify your result for part (d).

f. What is the probability that a randomly-selected person who earns under $35,000 owns a dog?

CL 11-130. Examine the triangles below. Based on the markings and measurements provided in the diagrams, which are similar to $\triangle ABC$ at right? Which are congruent? Are there any that you cannot determine? Justify your conclusion and, if appropriate, write a similarity or congruence statement. Note: The diagrams are not drawn to scale.

a.   b.   c.

CL 11-131. Talila is planning on giving her geometry teacher a gift. She has two containers to choose from:

> • A cylinder tube with diameter 6 inches and height 10 inches.
>
> • A rectangular box with dimensions 5 inches by 6 inches by 9 inches.

a. Assuming that her gift can fit in either box, which will require the least amount of wrapping paper?

b. She plans to tie two loops of ribbon about the package as shown at right. Which package will require the least amount of ribbon? Ignore any ties or bows.

CL 11-132. A big warehouse carrying tents has a miniature model that is similar to the full-sized tent. The tent is a triangular-based prism and the miniature model has dimensions shown in the diagram at right.

a. How much fabric does the small tent use? That is, what is its surface area?

b. What is the volume of the small model?

c. If the volume of the full-sized model is 72 ft^3, how tall is the full-sized tent?

d. How much fabric does the full-sized tent use?

CL 11-133. Check your answers using the table at the end of the closure section. Which problems do you feel confident about? Which problems were hard? Use the table to make a list of topics you need help on and a list of topics you need to practice more.

Answers and Support for Closure Activity #4
What Have I Learned?

Note: MN = Math Note, LL = Learning Log

Problem	Solution	Need Help?	More Practice
CL 11-124.	a. $x = 3.5$ b. $x = 3$ c. $x = 7$	Section 10.1 MN: 10.1.2, 10.1.3, and 10.1.4 LL: 10.1.2 and 10.1.3	Problems CL 10-185, CL 10-186, 11-44, 11-110, 11-111, 11-117, and 11-120
CL 11-125.	a. Typical response: The distance between A and D ($\sqrt{10}$) equals the distance between B and D (also $\sqrt{10}$). b. $y = -\frac{1}{3}x + 8$ c. Yes, the slope of $\overline{BD}$ is $-\frac{1}{3}$ while the slope of $\overline{AC}$ is 3. Since the slopes are opposite reciprocals, $\overline{BD}$ is perpendicular to $\overline{AC}$.	Lessons 2.3.2 and 7.3.2 Checkpoint 3 MN: 1.2.6, 2.3.2, and 7.3.3 LL: 2.3.2 and 7.3.2	Problems CL 2-121, CL 3-116, CL 5-147, CL 7-151, and CL 7-153
CL 11-126.	a. $\frac{_4C_2}{_6C_2} = \frac{6}{15} = 40\%$, or $\frac{_4P_2}{_6P_2} = \frac{4 \cdot 3}{6 \cdot 5} = 40\%$ b. $\frac{_2C_2}{_6C_2} = \frac{1}{15} \approx 6.7\%$ or $\frac{_2P_2}{_6P_2} = \frac{2}{30} \approx 6.7\%$ c. $1 - (\frac{6}{15} + \frac{1}{15}) = \frac{8}{15} \approx 53.3\%$ d. P(brown given same color) = $\frac{\frac{6}{15}}{\frac{6}{15} + \frac{1}{15}} = \frac{6}{7}$	Lesson 10.3.3 MN: 10.3.3 LL: 10.3.4	Problems 10-153, 10-155, 10-173, 11-26, 11-41, 11-59, and 11-87
CL 11-127.	a. $_9P_3 = 504$ b. $_9P_3 = \frac{9!}{(9-3)!} = \frac{9!}{6!}$	Lesson 10.3.2 MN: 10.3.2 LL: 10.3.4	Problems 10-128, 10-143, 10-155, 11-9, 11-26, 11-49, 11-60

Problem	Solution	Need Help?	More Practice
CL 11-128.	$V \approx 64.23$ mm.^{3}, SA = 102.75 mm^2	Lessons 8.1.5, 11.1.2, and 11.1.3 MN: 8.3.1, 11.1.2, and 11.1.4 LL: 8.1.4 and 8.1.5 Three-Dimensional Solids Toolkit	Problems CL 9-114, 10-46, 11-25, 11-40, 11-52, 11-86, 11-100, and 11-113
CL 11-129.	a. $\frac{222}{1000} = 22.2\%$ b. $1 - \frac{222}{1000} = \frac{778}{1000} = 77.8\%$ c. $\frac{130}{1000} = 13\%$ d. See solution to part (e) below e. Either sum the appropriate cells: $\frac{64+63+69+3+70+66+59+7+3+41+77+82+97}{1000} = 70.1\%$ or use the Addition Rule: $\frac{445}{1000} + \frac{386}{1000} - \frac{130}{1000} = \frac{701}{1000} = 70.1\%$ f. P(dog given < \$35,000) = $\frac{64+66}{64+63+69+3+70+66+59+7+3+14} = 29.2\%$	Section 10.2 MN: 10.2.1 and 10.2.3 LL: 10.2.1 and 10.2.3	Problems CL 10-188, 11-50, and 11-88
CL 11-130.	a. $\triangle ABC \sim \triangle RTS$ AA~) b. $\triangle ABC \sim \triangle MPK$ (AAS $\cong$) c. Cannot be determined because there are two possible triangles when SSA is given.	Section 3.2 MN: 3.1.4, 3.2.1, and 3.2.5 LL: 3.1.2 and 3.2.4	Problems CL 3-122, CL 4-123, CL 5-140, 11-62, and 11-101

Problem	Solution	Need Help?	More Practice
CL 11-131.	a. The cylinder needs less paper ($SA = 78\pi$ in.^{2}). b. The prism requires less ribbon (80 in.).	Lessons 9.1.2 and 9.1.3 Checkpoint 11 MN: 9.1.2 and 9.1.3 Three-Dimensional Solids Toolkit	Problems 11-10, 11-47, 11-58, and 11-102
CL 11-132.	a. $SA \approx 31.0$ ft^2 b. $V \approx 9$ ft^3 c. linear scale factor = 2, height = 6 ft d. $SA \approx 124$ ft^2	Lessons 9.1.4 and 9.1.5 MN: 9.1.3 and 9.1.5 LL: 9.1.1, 9.1.2, and 9.1.4 Three-Dimensional Solids Toolkit	Problems CL 9-112, CL 10-191, 11-12, 11-43, 11-86, 11-90, and 11-123

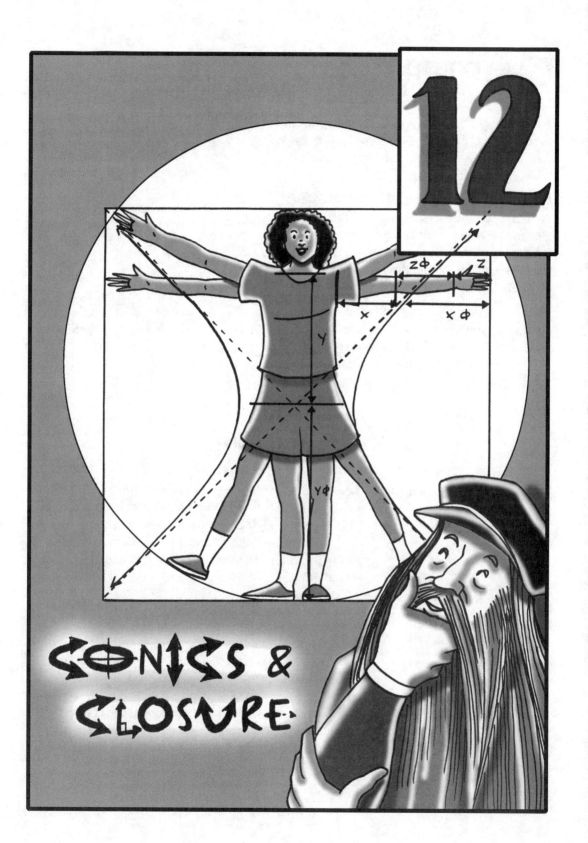

CHAPTER 12 Conics and Closure

As this course draws to a close, it is appropriate to reflect on what you have learned so far as you continue to see connections between topics in both algebra and geometry.

For example, in Section 12.1, you will extend your geometric understanding of circles to write algebraic equations for circles. Then you will look at the cross-sections of a cone, called conic sections and learn about the geometric properties of parabolas.

Then in Section 12.2, four activities offer a chance for you to apply your geometric tools in new ways. You will find new connections between familiar geometric ideas and learn more special properties of familiar shapes.

Guiding Question

Mathematically proficient students look for and make use of structure.

As you work through this chapter, ask yourself:

How can I connect these ideas to previous topics, and can I make it simpler or make a generalization?

Chapter Outline

Section 12.1 You will start with what you know geometrically about a circle, and extend it to write an algebraic equation for a circle. By studying the different cross-sections of a cone (the conic sections), and a parabola in particular, you will further discover how geometry and algebra can each define a shape.

Section 12.2 As you complete the course closure activities in this section, you will apply the mathematics you have learned throughout this course. For example, you will discover a special ratio that seems to occur in nature and art, find new relationships that exist in basic polyhedra, learn about a shape created when the midpoints of the sides of a quadrilateral are connected, and determine where a goat should be tethered to a barn so that it has the lowest probability of eating a poisoned weed.

12.1.1 What is the equation?

The Equation of a Circle

During Chapters 7 through 10, you studied circles *geometrically*, that is, based on the geometric shape of a circle. For example, the relationship between circles and polygons helped you develop a method to find the area and circumference of a circle, while geometric relationships of intersecting circles helped you develop constructions of shapes such as a rhombus and a kite.

However, how can circles be represented *algebraically* or *graphically*? And how can you use these representations to learn more about circles? Today your team will develop the equation of a circle.

12-1.   EQUATION OF A CIRCLE

You know equations for lines and parabolas, but what type of equation could represent a circle? On a piece of graph paper, draw a set of *xy*-axes. Then use a compass to construct a circle with radius of length 10 units centered at the origin $(0, 0)$.

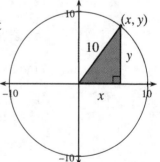

a.   What do all of the points on this circle have in common? That is, what is true about each point on the circle?

b.   Find all of the points on the circle where $x = 6$. For each point, what is the *y*-value? Use a right triangle (like the one shown at right) to justify your answer.

c.   What if $x = 3$? For each point on the circle where $x = 3$, find the corresponding *y*-value. Use a right triangle to justify your answer.

d.   Mia picked a random point on the circle and labeled it (x, y). Unfortunately, she does not know the value of *x* or *y*! Help her write an equation that relates x, y, and 10 based on her diagram above.

e.   Does your equation from part (d) work for the points $(10, 0)$ and $(0, 10)$? What about $(-8, -6)$? Explain.

12-2.   In problem 12-1, you wrote an equation of a circle with radius of length 10 units and center at $(0, 0)$.

   a.   What if the radius were instead 4 units long? Discuss this with your team and write an equation of this circle.

   b.   Write the equation of a circle centered at $(0, 0)$ with radius r.

   c.   On graph paper, sketch the graph of $x^2 + y^2 = 36$. Can you graph it without a table? Explain your method.

   d.   Describe the graph of the circle $x^2 + y^2 = 0$.

12-3.   What if the center of the circle is not at $(0, 0)$? On graph paper, construct a circle with a center $A(3, 1)$ and radius of length 5 units.

   a.   On the diagram at right, point P represents a point on the circle with no special characteristics. Add a point P to your diagram and then draw a right triangle like $\triangle ABC$ in the circle at right.

   b.   What is the length of $\overline{PB}$? Write an expression to represent this length. Likewise, what is the length of $\overline{AB}$?

   c.   Use your expressions for AB and BP, along with the fact that the length of the radius of the circle is 5 units, to write an equation for this circle. (Note: You do not need to worry about multiplying any binomials.)

   d.   Find the equation of each circle represented below.

      (1) The circle with center $(2, 7)$ (2)
            and radius of length 1 unit.

      (3) The circle for which $(6, 0)$ and
            $(-6, 0)$ are the endpoints of a
            diameter.

12-4.   On graph paper, graph and shade the solutions for the inequalities below. Then find the area of each shaded region.

   a. $x^2 + y^2 \leq 49$ b. $(x-3)^2 + (y-2)^2 \leq 4$

Core Connections Geometry

12-5.   LEARNING LOG

In a Learning Log entry, describe what you learned in this lesson about the equation of a circle. What connections did you make to other areas of algebra or geometry? Be sure to include an example of how to find the equation of a circle given its center and the length of its radius. Title this entry "Equation of a Circle" and include today's date.

12-6.   Examine the graph of the circle at right.

a.   Find the equation of the circle.

b.   On graph paper, sketch the graph of the equation $x^2 + y^2 = 49$. What is the radius?

12-7.   Find the volume of each shape below. Assume that all corners in part (b) are right angles.

a.   cone

b.

12-8.   Before there were radios and satellite communication systems, ships would communicate with each other by using a string of colored flags. With four blue flags and two red flags, how many six flag signals are possible?

12-9.   A credit union offers a long-term account that pays 6% interest compounded monthly and your college fund currently contains $8500.

   a.   What is the *monthly* multiplier?

   b.   Write a function of the form $f(t) = ab^t$ that represents the monthly situation.

   c.   At the current rate, what will be the value of the account in 5 years?

12-10.   Examine the diagram at right.

   a.   Write an equation using the geometric relationships in the diagram. Then solve your equation for x.

   b.   Find the measures of the acute angles of the triangle. What tool(s) did you use?

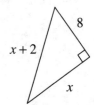

12-11.   Use the diagram of $\odot C$ at right to answer the questions below.

   a.   If $m\angle x = 28°$, what is $m\widehat{AD}$?

   b.   If $AD = 5$ and $BD = 5\sqrt{3}$, what is the area of $\odot C$?

   c.   If the radius of $\odot C$ is 8 and if $m\widehat{BD} = 100°$, what is BD?

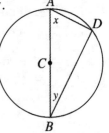

12-12.   **Multiple Choice:** Based on the markings in the diagrams at right, which statement is true?

   a. $\triangle ABC \cong \triangle XYZ$

   b. $\triangle ABC \cong \triangle YXZ$

   c. $\triangle ABC \cong \triangle ZXY$

   d. $\triangle ABC \cong \triangle ZYX$

   e.   None of these

Core Connections Geometry

12.1.2 How can I graph a circle from its equation?

Completing the Square for Equations of Circles

In this lesson, you will use the technique of completing the square to rewrite the equation of a circle so that it is easier to graph.

12-13. Katelyn is a student assistant in the Musketeers Math Lab. She helps fellow students with their math homework.

Becky and Diego are working on their algebra I homework. They have been asked to make a quick sketch of the equation $y = (x - 2)^2 - 25$.

a. Becky started by making an $x \rightarrow y$ table as shown below. Will her approach work?

x	–10	–8	–6	–4	–2	0	2	4	6	8	10
y	119	75	39	11	–9	–21					

b. Diego started by rewriting the quadratic equation as $y = x^2 - 4x - 21$, then factoring to find $y = (x + 3)(x - 7)$, because he thought he could find the x-intercepts easier. Will his approach work mathematically?

c. Katelyn complimented Becky and Diego on their mathematical thinking. Then she went on to say that they were both working too hard if their goal was just to make a quick sketch. What did she mean? Be prepared to share your team's thinking with the rest of the class.

12-14. The **standard form** for a quadratic function is $y = ax^2 + bx + c$. But when the equation is rewritten in **graphing form**, $y = a(x - h)^2 + k$, the parabola is easier to graph. In graphing form, the vertex is at the point (h, k), and finding the x-intercept(s) is often easier from the graphing form than from the standard form.

a. Discuss with your team how you would make a quick sketch of $y = x^2 - 6x + 4$. Explain in detail how to find the x- and y-intercept(s) and the vertex. You do not actually have to make the computations or sketch the function.

b. Discuss with your team how you would make a quick sketch of the same equation written in graphing form, $y = (x - 3)^2 - 5$. Again, explain in detail how to find the x- and y-intercept(s) and the vertex, but you do not actually have to make the computations or sketch the function.

12-15.   You may have learned the technique of **completing the square** in a previous course. It helps you rewrite a quadratic function that is given in standard form, $y = ax^2 + bx + c$, into graphing form, $y = a(x - h)^2 + k$.

Rewrite $y = x^2 + 8x + 10$ in graphing form and make a quick sketch of the function.

Further Guidance

12-16.   Diego was at the Musketeers Math Lab struggling with his Algebra I homework. He was supposed to **complete the square** to change $y = x^2 + 8x + 10$ to graphing form. Katelyn, the math lab assistant, brought over the algebra tiles. Katelyn explained, "$x^2 + 8x + 10$ *would look like this.*"

"*Yes*," said Diego, a little testily. "*We've been using tiles all year, you know.*"

Katelyn patiently continued, "*Now, take the x and x^2 tiles and start making them into a square.*"

"*OK*," said Diego. He arranged the one x^2-tile and the eight x-tiles as shown below.

"*So, to make a complete square*," said Katelyn, "*you need 16 small unit tiles to fill in the corner.*"

"*Oh, I get it!*" said Diego. "*The complete square is* $(x + 4)^2$."

"*Yes, that's right*," Katelyn continued. "*With the x and x^2 tiles, you can almost make* $(x + 4)^2$, *but you are 16 unit tiles short. Therefore,* $x^2 + 8x$ *is equal to* $(x + 4)^2 - 16$."

Diego was excited. "*Wait! Stop! I totally get it! I can change* $y = x^2 + 8x + 10$ *into graphing form now. Look!*" Diego wrote the following on his paper:

$$y = x^2 + 8x \quad\quad + 10$$
$$y = (x + 4)^2 - 16 \ + 10$$
$$y = (x + 4)^2 - 6$$

Problem continues on next page →

Core Connections Geometry

12-16.   *Problem continued from previous page.*

"*Yes, exactly!*" said Katelyn.

"*Cool. And next time I don't think I even need
tiles,*" said Diego. "*Instead, I can just start with a
generic rectangle like this:*"

	x	$+4$
x	x^2	$4x$
$+4$	$4x$	16

Help Diego with a new problem. He needs to complete the square to write
$y = x^2 + 4x + 9$ in graphing form. Draw a generic rectangle to help him figure
out how to make the x and x^2 part into a square, and then write his equation in
graphing form.

12-17.   How could you complete the square to change $f(x) = x^2 + 5x + 2$ into graphing
form? How would you split the five x-tiles into two equal parts?

Diego decided to use brute force. He cut one x-tile in half, as shown below.

a.   How much is needed to complete the square?

b.   Write the graphing form of the equation.

―――――   *Further Guidance*   ―――――
section ends here.

12-18.   Rewrite $y = x^2 + 3x + 4$ in graphing form. Then use either equation to find the
x-intercepts algebraically. What happens? Why?

12-19.   Equations of circles also have two forms.

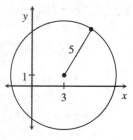

    a.   Write the equation of the circle graphed at right in **graphing form**, $(x-h)^2 + (y-k)^2 = r^2$, like you did in the previous lesson. What do h, k, and r represent in the graphing form of the equation of a circle?

    b.   Now, rewrite the equation of the circle from part (a) in **general form**, $ax^2 + ay^2 + bx + cy + d = 0$.

    c.   How can this process be done backwards? For example, if you are given an equation like $x^2 - 10x + y^2 - 4y = 7$, how can you change it to graphing form? Discuss with your team and be ready to share your strategy with the class.

12-20.   Use what you have learned in this lesson to write $x^2 + y^2 - 8x + 6y + 9 = 0$ in a form that allows you to make a quick sketch of the circle.

12-21.   A silo (a structure designed to store grain) is designed as a cylinder with a cone on top, as shown in the diagram at right.

    a.   If a farmer wants to paint the silo, how much surface area must be painted?

    b.   What is the volume of the silo? That is, how many cubic meters of grain can the silo hold?

12-22.   The figure at right is a **pentagram**. A pentagram is a 5-pointed star that has congruent angles at each of its outer vertices.

    a.   Use the fact that all pentagrams can be inscribed in a circle to find the measure of angle a at right.

    b.   Find the measure of angles b, c, and d.

12-23.   In Chapter 7, you discovered that the midsegment of a triangle is not only parallel to the third side, but also half its length. But what about the midsegment of a trapezoid?

The diagram at right shows a midsegment of a trapezoid. That is, $\overline{EF}$ is a midsegment because points E and F are both midpoints of the non-base sides of trapezoid $ABCD$.

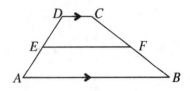

a.   If $A(0,0)$, $B(9,0)$, $C(5,6)$, and $D(2,6)$, find the coordinates of points E and F. Then compare the lengths of the bases ($\overline{AB}$ and $\overline{CD}$) with the length of the midsegment $\overline{EF}$. What seems to be the relationship?

b.   See if the relationship you observed in part (a) holds if $A(-4,0)$, $B(2,0)$, $C(0,2)$, and $D(-2,2)$.

c.   Write a conjecture about the midsegment of a trapezoid.

12-24.   Describe each circle by finding the center and radius. You need to "complete the square" to rewrite the equation in part (b) in graphing form.

a. $(x-2)^2+(y+3)^2=25$ b. $x^2+2x+y^2+6y-6=0$

12-25.   For each diagram below, solve for x. Show all work.

a.   b.   c.

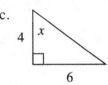

12-26.   For each relationship below, write and solve an equation for x. Justify your method.

a.   b.   c.

12-27.   **Multiple Choice:** The graph of $x^2 + y^2 = 4$ is:

    a.   A parabola with y-intercept $(0, 4)$.

    b.   A circle with radius 4 and center $(0, 0)$.

    c.   A parabola with x-intercepts $(-2, 0)$ and $(2, 0)$.

    d.   A circle with radius 2 and center $(0, 0)$.

    e.   None of these.

12-28.   Find the surface area of the solids below. Assume that the solid in part (a) is a prism with a regular octagonal base and the pyramid in part (b) is a square-based pyramid. Show all work.

    a. 16 m

        4 m

    b. 13 ft

        $\longleftarrow$10 ft$\longrightarrow$

12-29.   Solve each equation below for the given variable. Check your solution by verifying that your solution makes the original equation true.

    a. $\frac{2}{3}(15u - 6) = 14u$ b. $(5 - x)(3x + 8) = 0$

    c. $2(k - 5)^2 = 32$ d. $2p^2 + 7p - 9 = 0$

12-30.   Examine the diagram at right.

    a.   Explain why $y = \sin\theta$ and $x = \cos\theta$.

    b.   According to this diagram, what is $(\sin\theta)^2 + (\cos\theta)^2$? Explain how you know.

    c.   Does this relationship appear true for all angles? Use your calculator to find $(\sin 23°)^2 + (\cos 23°)^2$ and $(\sin 81°)^2 + (\cos 81°)^2$. Write down your findings.

12-31.   On graph paper, graph a circle with center $(4, 2)$ and radius 3 units.

      a.   Write its equation.

      b.   Find two points on the circle that are on opposite sides of the circle, that is they are 180° from one another. Prove that these two points are exactly one diameter in distance from each other.

12-32.   Solve the following problems:

      a.   How many numbers less than 500 can you make using the digits $0, 2, 4, 6,$ 8? Digits can be used over. A number cannot start with a zero.

      b.   How many numbers less than 500 are there if the digits $0, 2, 4, 6, 8$ cannot be repeated? The lead digit cannot be zero.

12-33.   Use all your circle relationships to solve for the variables in each of the diagrams below.

      a. $\overline{AB}$ and $\overline{CD}$ intersect at E.

      b.   The area of $\odot C$ is 25π sq. units

12-34.   **Multiple Choice:** What is the measure of each interior angle of a regular octagon?

      a.   135°   b.   120°   c.   180°   d.   1080°

12.1.3 What is the cross-section?

··

Introduction to Conic Sections

In Chapter 11 you learned about cross-sections of solids. (Refer to the Math Notes box in Lesson 11.1.3.) In this lesson you and your team will discover the various cross-sections of a cone. As you explore, look for connections with other mathematical concepts that you have studied previously.

12-35.   CONIC SECTIONS

Obtain the Lesson 12.1.3 Resource Page from your teacher and construct a cone. Then, with your team, explore the different cross-sections of a cone, which are called **conic sections**. Imagine slicing a cone as many different ways as you can. Draw and describe the shape of each cross-section on your paper. Do you know the names for any of these shapes?

12-36.   When mathematicians talk about conic sections, they are referring to the cross-sections that can be created from a *double* cone, a shape created with two cones placed in opposite directions with vertices together, as shown at right. The cone continues infinitely in both directions.

a.   Can a single point be a conic section? Explain.

b.   How you can slice the cone so that the cross-section is a line?

c.   What other conic sections are there? You should have seven all together.

Core Connections Geometry

12-37.   One of the conic sections that you have discovered
         can be constructed with perpendicular bisectors
         using tracing paper.

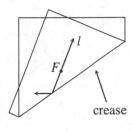

   a.   In your notebook, draw a line *l*, and a point *F* not on
        the line. Imagine (or sketch) all the segments
        connecting *F* with all the points on line *l*. What
        conic section do you think would appear if you drew
        all the perpendicular bisectors of those segments?

   b.   Now try it. On tracing paper, draw a line *l*, and a point *F* not on the line.
        Fold and crease the tracing paper so that line *l* passes through point *F* as
        shown in the figure above. This crease represents the perpendicular
        bisector of one of the segments connecting *F* with a point on line *l*.

        Unfold the tracing paper and fold it again at a different point on line *l* so
        that line *l* still passes through point *F*. Continue this process until you
        have at least 20 creased lines. What conic section appeared?

   c.   Describe where the conic section lies in relationship with the original point
        F and line *l*. Do these relationships seem to hold for the figures
        constructed by your teammates?

12-38.   FOCUS AND DIRECTRIX OF A PARABOLA

         Since the point and line help to determine the parabola, there are special names
         that are used to refer to them. The point is called the **focus** of the parabola,
         while the line is called the **directrix**.

   a.   Together, the focus and the directrix determine the
        parabola. For example, can you visualize the
        parabola formed by the focus and directrix shown at
        right? Trace the point and line on your paper and
        sketch the parabola.

   b.   What is the relationship between the points on the parabola and its focus
        and directrix? Carefully sketch the parabola that formed on your tracing
        paper from problem 12-37. Mark a point on the parabola and label it *P*.
        Notice the segment between *F* and *P*, and compare it to the segment that is
        perpendicular to the directrix *l* and goes to *P*. What do you notice? Does
        this relationship seem to hold for all points on the parabola? Explain.

   c.   How does the distance between the focus (the point) and the
        directrix (the line) affect the shape of the parabola? Explore
        this using a dynamic geometry tool, if possible. If a dynamic
        tool is not available, use tracing paper to test several different
        distances between the focus and directrix. Explain the result.

12-39.   LEARNING LOG

Write an entry in your Learning Log describing what you
learned during this lesson. Include information about the
cross-sections of a cone and the geometric relationships in
a parabola. What questions do you have about the other
conic sections? Title this entry "Conic Sections" and include today's date.

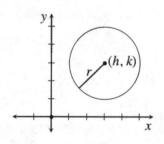

METHODS AND MEANINGS

MATH NOTES

Equation of a Circle

The equation of a circle can be
given in graphing form by the equation
$(x-h)^2 + (y-k)^2 = r^2$, where (h, k) are the
coordinates of the center of the circle, and
r is the radius. Note that the equation of a
circle does not describe a function,
because there are two y-values for most
x-values.

Alternatively, the equation of a circle can be written in general form as
$ax^2 + ay^2 + bx + cy + d = 0$ by multiplying the binomials. To rewrite the
equation of a circle in general form to one in graphing form, the
technique of completing the square can be used.

12-40.   Cawker City, Kansas, claims to have the
world's largest ball of twine. Started in 1953
by Frank Stoeber, this ball has been created
by wrapping more than 1300 miles of twine.
In fact, this giant ball has a circumference of
40 feet. Assuming the ball of twine is a
sphere, find the surface area and volume of
the ball of twine.

12-41.   The equations below are the types of equations that you will need to be able to solve automatically in a later course. Try to solve these in 10 minutes or less. The solutions are provided after problem 12-46 for you to check your answers.

a. $2x - 5 = 7$ b. $x^2 = 16$ c. $2(x - 1) = 6$

d. $\frac{x}{5} = 6$ e. $2x^2 + 5 = x^2 + 14$ f $(x - 3)(x + 5) = 0$

12-42.   Examine the pen or pencil that you are using right now. Imagine slicing it in different directions. On your paper, draw at least three different cross-sections of the pen or pencil.

12-43.   On graph paper, graph $x^2 + y^2 = 9$.

a.   Consider the inequality $x^2 + y^2 \le 9$. Does the point $(0, 0)$ make this inequality true? What is the graph of $x^2 + y^2 \le 9$? Explain.

b.   Now consider the inequality $x^2 + y^2 > 9$. Does the point $(0, 0)$ make this inequality true? What region is shaded? Describe the graph of this inequality.

12-44.   Consider the sample space for flipping a coin 10 times in a row. In how many sequences of heads and tails will 5 of the 10 coins show heads?

12-45.   Consider the circle that is centered at the origin and contains the point $(0, 3)$.

a.   Use geometry and the definition of a circle, but not the algebraic equation for a circle, to prove or disprove that the point $(1, \sqrt{5})$ lies on this circle.

b.   Find at least one value of x so that the point $(x, \sqrt{5})$ lies on the circle.

c.   Name 3 other points on this same circle.

12-46.   **Multiple Choice:** In the diagram at right, the value of x is:

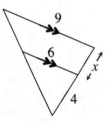

a.   1   b.   2   c.   3

d.   4   e.   None of these

Solutions to problem 12-41:

a: $x = 6$, b: $x = 4$ or -4, c: $x = 4$, d: $x = 30$, e: $x = 3$ or -3, f: $x = 3$ or -5

12.1.4 How can I graph it?

Graphing a Parabola Using The Focus and Directrix

Over the centuries, cones were sliced and the resulting conic sections were described geometrically long before conic sections were described with algebraic equations. For example parabolas were geometrically described as the figure resulting from all the points that are equidistant from the focus and the directrix. A circle is the figure resulting from all the points equidistant from a center point.

You already know how to describe a circle both geometrically and with an algebraic equation, $(x-h)^2 + (x-y)^2 = r^2$. Today you will make an informal connection between the algebraic equation for a parabola, $y = ax^2 + bx + c$, and the geometric description of the focus and directrix of a parabola.

Making a connection between the equation of a cone, and the equations of its parabolas (and other conic sections) is also possible, but that is reserved for a future course.

12-47.   GRAPHING WITH A FOCUS AND DIRECTRIX

In the past, you have graphed conics, such as circles and parabolas, using rectangular graph paper and an equation. However, another way to graph conic sections is to use **focus-directrix graph paper**, that is designed with lines and concentric circles like the example shown in Figure A at right.

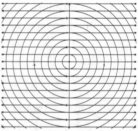

Figure A:
Focus-directrix paper

How can you graph parabolas using this paper? Obtain at least two sheets of focus-directrix paper (Lesson 12.1.4 Resource Page) from your teacher and follow the directions below.

Figure B:
Point R on grid

a.   In problem 12-38, you discovered that each point on a parabola is an equal distance from the focus and the directrix. To graph a parabola, use a colored pen or pencil to mark the center of the concentric circles on your focus-directrix grid. This will be the focus of the parabola. Then draw a colored line that is 2 units away from the focus, as shown in Figure B at right.

Problem continues on next page →

Core Connections Geometry

12-47.   *Problem continued from previous page.*

    b.   Examine point *R* on the focus-directrix grid in Figure B. Notice that the circles help you count the distance between point *R* and the focus (the center of the circles). Explain how you know that the point *R* is 3 units from the focus and 3 units from the directrix.

    c.   Use the circles and lines to plot a point that is 1 unit away from the focus and the directrix. Is there another point that is also 1 unit away from both the focus and directrix?

    d.   Likewise, find two points that are 2 units away from both the focus and the directrix. Continue plotting points that are equidistant from the focus and the directrix until the parabola appears. Compare your parabola with those of your teammates to double-check for accuracy.

12-48.   The graphs of points that are equidistant from the focus and directrix *look* like parabolas. However, Tom wants to know how he can know for sure that they *are* parabolas. He wonders, "*If math is about making sense of ideas and not taking someone else's word for it, then there must be a way to figure out if these points really make a parabola.*" Tom decided to think about this with his teammates.

    a.   Tom says, "*What if we try to find an equation to represent the points of the graph from problem 12-47 on a coordinate grid? I remember that parabolas have an equation in the form* $y = ax^2 + bx + c$. *If these points have that type of equation, then the graph is a parabola.*"

        Joan added, "*Yes, we could let the focus for the graph in problem 12-47 be at (0, 2) on a rectangular coordinate grid, and the directrix be the x-axis.*" On graph paper, graph this point and line.

    b.   "*Look, I know that the point (0, 1) will be on my graph because it is equidistant from the line and point. But what about the other points?*" Tom asked. Sofia answered, "*It might make sense to start with a simple case. What if we find the coordinates of the points that are equally distant from the focus and directrix when y = 5?*"

        The team thought about this and came up with the equation $x^2 + 3^2 = 5^2$. Where did this equation come from? Discuss this with your team.

Problem continues on next page →

12-48.   *Problem continued from previous page.*

c.   Sofia added, *"The solutions to that equation are $x = 4$ and $x = -4$."* Joan added, *"So now we know three points on our parabola that has focus at (0, 2) and directrix on the x-axis."* Justify Sofia's statement. What three coordinate points is Joan talking about?

d.   Tom asked, *"What about all of the other points? This will take us forever if we do them one by one!"* Joan replied, *"What if we just do the same thing except call the y-value 'y' to represent all of the possible y-values?"*

   On your graph, label a point (x,y) and use the same strategy from parts (b) and (c) to generate an equation that relates x and y. Remember the point (x,y) is equally distant from the focus and the directrix.

e.   Demonstrate that the equation in part (d) is equivalent to $y = \frac{1}{4}x^2 + 1$. What does this show about the set of points graphed in problem 12-47 and in this problem?

12-49.   MORE CROSS-SECTIONS

Find at least three different shapes that can be cross-sections of a cylinder, like the one at right. For each one, draw the resulting cross-section and explain how you sliced the cylinder. Then find as many cross-sections of a sphere as you can. Finally, find as many cross-sections of a cube that you can.

Review & Preview

12-50.   A solid with volume 820 cm³ is reduced proportionally with a linear scale factor of $\frac{1}{2}$. What is the volume of the resulting solid?

12-51.   On graph paper, graph the equations below. For each one, name the center and radius.

a. $x^2 + y^2 = 4.5^2$

b. $x^2 + y^2 = 75$

c. $(x - 3)^2 + y^2 = 1$

d. $x^2 - 4x + y^2 - 2y = 14$

12-52. Use the relationships in each diagram below to solve for the given variables.

a.

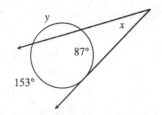

b. The area of $\odot K$ is 36π sq. units.

c. The diameter of $\odot C$ is 13 units. w is the length of $\overline{AB}$.

d.

12-53. In the triangle at right, $\overline{DE}$ is a midsegment of $\triangle ABC$ and $\overline{FG}$ is a midsegment of $\triangle ADE$.

a. If $DE = 7$ cm, find BC and FG.

b. If the area of $\triangle AFG$ is 3 cm², what is the area of $DECB$?

12-54. Find the volume and lateral surface area of a cone if the circumference of the base is 28π inches and the height is 18 inches.

12-55. A jar contains five red, four white, and three blue balls. If three balls are randomly selected, find the probability of choosing:

a. Three white balls.

b. Two red balls and one white ball.

c. Three balls of the same color.

12-56. **Multiple Choice:** Carol was shopping for a spring picnic. She spent $2.00 for each liter of soda and $3.50 for each bag of chips. In all, she bought 18 items for a total of $43.50. Assuming she only bought chips and soda, how many bags of chips did she buy?

a. 9   b. 5   c. 15   d. 3

12.2.1 What is the shape?

Using Coordinate Geometry and Constructions to Explore Shapes

In today's activity, you will learn more about quadrilaterals as you review what you know about coordinate geometry, construction, and proof.

12-57. Review what you have learned about the midsegment of a triangle as you answer the questions below. Assume that $\overline{DE}$ is a midsegment of $\triangle ABC$.

a. What is the relationship between $\overline{DE}$ and AB?

b. What is the relationship between $\angle CDE$ and $\angle DAB$? How do you know?

c. What is the relationship between $\triangle ABC$ and $\triangle DEC$? Justify your conclusion.

d. If $DE = 4x + 7$ units and $AB = 34$ units, what is x?

12-58. QUIRKY QUADRILATERALS

Quinn decided to experiment with the midpoints of the sides of a quadrilateral one afternoon. With a compass, he located the midpoint of each side of a quadrilateral. He then connected the four midpoints together to create a new quadrilateral inside his original quadrilateral.

a. Without knowing anything about Quinn's original quadrilateral and without trying the construction yourself, visualize the result. What can you predict about Quinn's resulting quadrilateral? Share your ideas with your team.

b. Use a compass and straightedge to repeat Quinn's experiment on an unlined piece of paper. Make sure each member of your team starts with a differently-shaped quadrilateral. Describe your results. Did the results of you and your teammates match your prediction from part (a)?

c. Does it matter if your starting quadrilateral is convex or not? Start with a non-convex quadrilateral, like the one shown at right, and repeat Quinn's experiment. On your paper, describe your results.

12-59.   Quinn decided to graph his quadrilateral on a set of coordinate axes and prove
         that his inner quadrilateral is, in fact, a parallelogram. His quadrilateral $ABCD$
         uses the points $A(-3, -2)$, $B(-5, 4)$, $C(5, 6)$, and $D(1, -4)$.

         a.   On graph paper, graph the quadrilateral $ABCD$.

         b.   If the midpoint of $\overline{AB}$ is E, the midpoint of $\overline{BC}$ is F, the midpoint of $\overline{CD}$
               is G, and the midpoint of $\overline{DA}$ is H, find and label points E, F, G, and H on
               $ABCD$.

         c.   Connect the midpoints of the sides you found in part (b). Then find the
               slope of each side of quadrilateral $EFGH$ and use these slopes to prove that
               Quinn's inner quadrilateral is a parallelogram.

         d.   Quinn wondered if his parallelogram is also a rhombus. Find EF and FG,
               and then decide if $EFGH$ is a rhombus. Show all work.

12-60.   PROVING THE RESULT FOR ALL QUADRILATERALS

         In problem 12-59, you proved that Quinn's inner
         quadrilateral was a parallelogram when $A(-3, -2)$,
         $B(-5, 4)$, $C(5, 6)$, and $D(1, -4)$. However, what
         about other, random quadrilaterals?

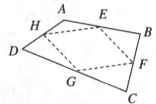

         To prove this works for all quadrilaterals, start with a diagram of a generic
         quadrilateral, like the one above. Assume that the midpoint of $\overline{AB}$ is E, the
         midpoint of $\overline{BC}$ is F, the midpoint of $\overline{CD}$ is G, and the midpoint of $\overline{DA}$ is H.
         Prove that $EFGH$ is a parallelogram by proving that its opposite sides are
         parallel. It may help you to draw diagonal $\overline{AC}$ and consider what you know
         about $\triangle ABC$ and $\triangle ACD$. Use any format of proof.

12-61.   In $\triangle PQR$ at right, what is $m\angle Q$? Explain how you
         found your answer.

12-62.   The United State Department of Defense is located in a building called the
         Pentagon because it is in the shape of a regular pentagon. Known as "the largest
         office building in the world," its exterior edges measure 921 feet. Find the area
         of land enclosed by the outer walls of the Pentagon building.

Core Connections Geometry

12-63.   Examine the triangles below. Decide if each one is a right triangle. If the triangle is a right triangle, justify your conclusion. Assume that the diagrams are not drawn to scale.

a.

12

12

12

b.

5

12

13

12-64.   On graph paper, graph the equation $x^2 + (y-3)^2 = 25$. State the x- and y-intercepts.

12-65.   For each equation below, decide if the equation has any real number for the given variable. For each problem, explain how you know.

a. $4(x-3) = 11$

b. $x^2 = -10$

c. $3x^2 - 18 = 0$

d. $-7 = |x-6|$

12-66.   Using focus-directrix graph paper, create a parabola that has a horizontal directrix that is six units below the focus. You can get focus-directrix paper on the Lesson 12.1.4 Resource Page available at www.cpm.org.

12-67.   **Multiple Choice:** Which number below could be the length of the third side of a triangle with sides of length 29 and 51?

a.   10   b.   18   c.   23   d.   81

12.2.2 What is the pattern?

Euler's Formula for Polyhedra

Throughout this course, you have developed your skills of
exploring a pattern, forming a conjecture, and then proving
your conjecture. Today, with the assistance of materials such
as toothpicks and gumdrops, you will review what you know
about basic polyhedra (with no holes) as you look for a
relationship between the number faces, edges, and vertices
each basic polyhedron has. Once you have written a
conjecture, your class will discuss how to prove that it
must be true.

As you work today, consider the following questions:

Which types of basic polyhedra have I not tested yet?

What relationship can I find between the number of edges, faces,
and vertices of a basic polyhedron?

Does this relationship always hold true?

12-68.   POLYHEDRA PATTERNS

Does a basic polyhedron (with no holes) usually have more faces, edges, or
vertices? And if you know the number of faces and vertices of a basic
polyhedron, can you predict the number of edges? Today you will answer these
questions and more as you investigate polyhedra.

Your Task: Obtain the necessary building materials from your teacher, such as
toothpicks (for edges) and gumdrops (for vertices). Your team should build *at
least* six distinctly different polyhedra and each person in your team is
responsible for building *at least* one polyhedron. Be sure to build some regular
polyhedra (such as a tetrahedron and an octahedron), basic prisms, pyramids,
and unnamed polyhedra.

Create a table like the
one at right to hold your
data. Once you have
recorded the number of
vertices, edges, and

Polyhedron	Faces (*F*)	Vertices (*V*)	Edges (*E*)

faces for your team's polyhedra, look for a relationship between the numbers in
each row of the table. Try adding, subtracting (or both) the numbers to find a
pattern. Write a conjecture (equation) using the variables F, V, and E.

12-69.   EULER'S FORMULA FOR POLYHEDRA

The relationship you discovered in problem 12-68 between the number of faces, vertices, and edges of a basic polyhedron is referred to as **Euler's Formula for Polyhedra**, after Leonhard Euler (pronounced "oiler"), one of the greatest mathematicians in history. While it is widely believed that Euler independently discovered this relationship, it has been recorded that René Descartes (pronounced "DAY-cart"), the mathematician who invented coordinate geometry, found the relationship over 100 years earlier. This relationship states that if V is the number of vertices, E is the number of edges, and F is the number of faces of a basic polyhedron, then $V - E + F = 2$.

Use Euler's Formula to answer the following questions about basic polyhedra.

a.   If a polyhedron has 5 faces and 6 vertices, how many edges must it have?

b.   What if a polyhedron has 36 edges and 14 faces? How many vertices must it have?

c.   Could a polyhedron have 10 faces, 3 vertices, and 11 edges? Explain why or why not.

12-70.   If V represents the number of vertices, E represents the number of edges, and F represents the number of faces of a basic polyhedron, how can you prove that $V - E + F = 2$? First think about this on your own. Then, as a class, prove Euler's Formula.

12-71.   For each situation below, decide if *a* is greater, *b* is greater, if they are the same value, or if not enough information is given.

   a.   *a* is the measure of a central angle of an equilateral triangle; *b* is the measure of an interior angle of a regular pentagon.

   b.

   c.

   d. $a = b + 3$

   e.

12-72.   In the diagram at right, *ABCD ~ DCFE*. Solve for *x* and *y*. Show all work.

12-73.   On graph paper, make a table and graph the function $f(x) = -2(x-1)^2 + 8$.

   a.   Label the *x*- and *y*-intercepts and state their coordinates.

   b.   Name the vertex.

   c.   Find $f(100)$ and $f(-15)$.

12-74.   Find the area of the graph of the solution region of $x^2 + y^2 \le 49$.

12-75.   In how many ways can five different French books and three different Spanish books be arranged on a shelf if all of the books of each language must remain together?

12-76.   Find the volume and surface area of the box formed by the shaded net at right.

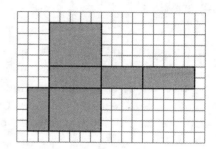

12-77.   **Multiple Choice:** The radius of the front wheel of Gavin's tricycle is 8 inches. If Gavin rode his tricycle for 1 mile in a parade, approximately how many rotations did his front wheel make? (Note: 1 mile = 5280 feet).

   a.   50   b.   1260   c.   660   d.   42,240

12.2.3   What is special about this ratio?

....

The Golden Ratio

In Chapter 8, you investigated an important irrational number: π. Pi (π) is the ratio of any circle's circumference to its diameter. Today you will discover another special ratio represented by the Greek letter phi (ϕ), pronounced "fee." Phi is also an irrational number. It appears not only in geometry, but also in nature. You will examine several different contexts in which this number appears.

12-78.   While doodling one day, Cyrus drew squares inside of rectangles like the ones below.

He noticed that if he chose the original rectangle carefully, the rectangle created inside was the same shape as the original rectangle. That is, the two rectangles were similar, as shown below.

Cyrus' teammate, Alex, wondered what the ratio of the sides of the original rectangle had to be to create a similar rectangle inside. So Alex drew and labeled the following rectangle.

What does x need to be so that the larger rectangle and the smaller rectangle are similar?

12-79.   GOLDEN RECTANGLES

Alex explored his special rectangle further.

a.   What is the scale factor from the smaller rectangle to the larger rectangle?

b.   What is the ratio of the longer side to the shorter side of either of the two rectangles? Express your answer both in exact form and as a decimal approximation.

c.   The ratio you found in part (b) has a special name: the **golden ratio**. It is often represented by the Greek letter lowercase phi, pronounced "fee" and written ϕ or φ. Rectangles whose side lengths are in the proportion ϕ are called **golden rectangles**. Historically many artists and architects have found rectangles whose sides are in the proportion phi to be aesthetically pleasing. Sometimes people see golden rectangles in the shape of the ancient Greek building the Parthenon (447 BC), or in the proportions of the face of the Renaissance painting Mona Lisa (1503 AD), or in the Great Pyramid of Giza (2560 BC).

Surrealist painter Salvador Dali intentionally used the golden rectangle for one of his most famous paintings. The canvas is 267 cm wide. If Dali intended the canvas to be a perfect golden rectangle, what height canvas should he have used?

12-80.   One way to construct golden rectangles is to start from a square and then extend parallel lines as shown at right.

Draw a line from the midpoint of the bottom side of the square to the right upper vertex of the square. Then use this segment as a radius to draw an arc to the bottom line as shown middle right.

Show that the rectangle you can now draw (shown below right) is a golden rectangle.

12-81.　GOLDEN SPIRALS

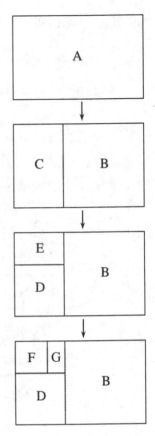

There is no stopping Alex! He continued doodling by making squares inside of a golden rectangle. First, he drew golden rectangle A. Then he drew square B inside the rectangle, creating rectangle C. Then square D was drawn inside of rectangle C creating square F and rectangle G, and so on as shown at right.

a.　In problem 12-78, Alex determined the ratios needed to draw rectangle A so that it is similar to rectangle C. Is rectangle C also a golden rectangle?

b.　Is rectangle E a golden rectangle?

c.　The non-square rectangles in Alex's diagrams from problem 12-81 are all golden rectangles because in each of them the ratio of the longer length to the shorter length is ϕ, the golden ratio. Alex's process of subdividing each golden rectangle into a square and smaller golden rectangle can be **iterated** (repeated over and over) creating an infinite series of similar golden rectangles.

When connected arcs are placed in each of the squares, a spiral forms, like the one shown at right.

Golden spiral

Use a compass to draw a golden spiral on the Lesson 12.2.3 Resource Page provided by your teacher. One place people sometimes see a golden spiral is the shape of the human ear, as shown at right. Where else in nature or art might you have seen a spiral like this?

12-82.   Alex wonders where else in mathematics the number phi (ϕ) shows up. Look for phi (ϕ) as you analyze the following situations.

a.   Examine the regular decagon at right. If the side length is 1 unit, find the radius of the decagon. What do you notice?

b.   Each central triangle in the regular decagon from part (a) is called a **golden triangle** because the ratio of the congruent sides to the base of each triangle is phi (ϕ). What are the angles of a golden triangle?

c.   Fifteenth century artist and scientist Leonardo da Vinci drew illustrations that he believed showed parts of the human body as golden ratios. Sixteenth century philosopher Heinrich Agrippa illustrated a human on a **star polygon** as shown at right, implying golden ratio proportions in humans. A **star polygon** is created by equally spacing points on the circumference of a circle, and then connecting the points. The star polygon at right is commonly called a **pentagram**. Note that all the corresponding lengths and angles are equal to each other.

With your team investigate the connection between a pentagram and the golden ratio in the diagram that follows. What is the ratio of length AC to length BC? What is the ratio of length AB to length BD?

d.   In problem 12-81, you learned about nested golden rectangles (where each golden rectangle is subdivided into a square and a smaller golden rectangle). But what about nested expressions?

Consider either one of the expressions at right. The "..." signifies that the pattern within the expression continues infinitely. With your team, find a way to approximate the value of the expression you chose. Try to find the most accurate approximation that you can. What do you notice?

$$\sqrt{1+\sqrt{1+\sqrt{1+\sqrt{1+\sqrt{1+...}}}}}$$

$$1+\cfrac{1}{1+\cfrac{1}{1+\cfrac{1}{1+...}}}$$

e.   The number ϕ has some interesting properties. What is $\frac{1}{\phi}$? What is ϕ^2? What do you notice? Is this true for other irrational numbers?

f.   Graph $y = x^2 - 1$ and $y = x$ for x-values from -3 to 3. Algebraically find the points of intersection. What do you notice?

12-83.   **FIBONNACI SPIRALS**

You may have seen the Fibonacci sequence in a previous course. Each term in
the sequence is created by adding the previous two terms:

$$1, 1, 2, 3, 5, 8, 13, 21, \ldots$$

Fibonacci spirals are created in the same manner that Alex used, but the side-
lengths of the starting rectangle are two consecutive Fibonacci numbers. For
example, you could start with an 8×13 rectangle.

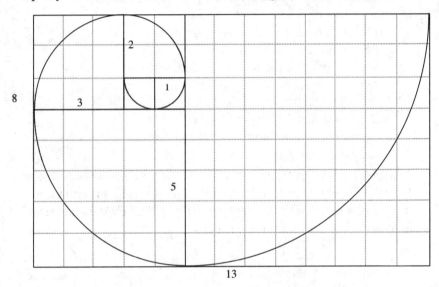

a.   Is a Fibonacci spiral also a golden spiral? How do you know?

b.   Mathematicians say that as a Fibonacci spiral gets larger and larger, it
approximates a golden spiral better and better. Why?

12-84.   What if three golden rectangles intersect
perpendicularly so that their centers coincide, as
shown at right? If each vertex of the golden
rectangles is connected with the five closest
vertices, what three-dimensional shape appears?
First visualize the result. Then, if you have a
model available, test your idea with string.

Core Connections Geometry

12-85.   If $\triangle ABC$ is equilateral, and if $A(3, 2)$ and $B(7, 2)$, find all possible coordinates of vertex C. Justify your answer.

12-86.   Find the area of the shaded region of the regular pentagon at right. Show all work.

4

12-87.   On graph paper, graph the system of equations at right. Then list all points of intersection in the form (x, y).

$$x^2 + y^2 = 25$$
$$y = x + 1$$

12-88.   Jamila solved the quadratic $x^2 + 3x - 10 = 8$ (see her work below). When she checked her solutions, they did not make the equation true. However, Jamila cannot find her mistake. Explain her error and then solve the quadratic correctly.

$$x^2 + 3x - 10 = 8$$
$$(x + 5)(x - 2) = 8$$
$$x + 5 = 8 \quad \text{or} \quad x - 2 = 8$$
$$x = 3 \quad \text{or} \quad x = 10$$

12-89.   If the sum of the interior angles of a regular polygon is $2160°$, how many sides must it have?

12-90.   From the 13 spades in a deck of cards, four are selected. Find the probability that:

   a.   Exactly one card is a "face" card (Jack, Queen, or King).

   b.   The cards form a consecutive sequence (count both A, 2, 3, 4 and J, Q, K, A as consecutive sequences).

12-91.   **Multiple Choice:** Assume that $A(6, 2)$, $B(3, 4)$, and $C(4, -1)$. If $\triangle ABC$ is rotated $90°$ counterclockwise ($\circlearrowleft$) to form $\triangle A'B'C'$, and then $\triangle A'B'C'$ is reflected across the x-axis to form $\triangle A''B''C''$, then the coordinates of C'' are:

   a. $(1, 4)$ b. $(-4, 1)$ c. $(1, -4)$ d. $(4, 1)$

12-92.   Find the area and perimeter of the shape at right. Assume that any non-straight portions of the shape are part of a circle. Show all work.

125°

4

12-93.   Examine the diagrams below. For each one, use the geometric relationships to solve for the given variable.

a. $\overrightarrow{PR}$ is tangent to $\odot C$ at P and $m\overset{\frown}{PMQ} = 314°$. Find QR.

314°

b.   Radius = 7 cm

x

102°

12-94.   Examine the net at right.

a.   Describe the solid that is formed by this net. What are its dimensions?

b.   Find the surface area and volume of the solid formed by this net.

c.   If all the dimensions of this solid are multiplied by 3, what is the SA of the resulting solid? What is the volume?

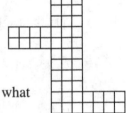

12-95.   Solve for y in terms of x. That is, rewrite each equation so that it starts "$y =$ ".

a. $6x + 5y = 20$

b. $4x - 8y = 16$

12-96.   Using focus-directrix graph paper, create a parabola that has a horizontal directrix that is four units above the focus. You can get focus-directrix paper on the Lesson 12.1.4 Resource Page available at www.cpm.org.

12-97.   **Multiple Choice:** Dillon starts to randomly select cards out of a normal deck of 52 playing cards. After selecting a card, he does not return it to the deck. So far, he has selected a 3 of clubs, an ace of spades, a 4 of clubs, and a 10 of diamonds. Find the probability that his fifth card is an ace.

a. $\frac{1}{16}$

b. $\frac{3}{52}$

c. $\frac{1}{13}$

d. $\frac{1}{52}$

12.2.4 What is the probability?

Using Geometry to Find Probabilities

In this final activity, you will connect and apply much of your knowledge from throughout the course to solve a challenging problem.

12-98. ZOE AND THE POISON WEED

Dimitri is getting his prize sheep, Zoe, ready for the county fair. He keeps Zoe in the pasture beside the barn and shed. What he does not know is that there is a single locoweed in this pasture, which will make Zoe too sick to go to the fair if she eats it, and she can eat it in one bite.

The layout of the field and building is provided at left and on the Lesson 12.2.4 Resource Page provided by your teacher. Assume that the entire field (the unshaded region) has plants growing on it. Also assume that each corner of the barn and field is a right angle.

Dimitri is worried that Zoe will get into trouble unless she is tethered with a rope to the building. He has decided to tether Zoe at point *A* with a 20-foot rope. Zoe is unable to enter the barn or shed while on her tether.

Your Task: Assuming that Zoe will eat all the plants in her tethered region, what is the probability that Zoe will get sick from the poisonous weed?

Discussion Points

What is the problem asking you to find?

What does Zoe's grazing region look like?

What do you need to figure out in order to find the probability?

12-99.   To help find the probability that Zoe will eat the single locoweed, first consider the grazing region if she is tethered to point *A* with a 20-foot rope.

   a.   On your Lesson 12.2.4 Resource Page, draw and label the region that Zoe can roam. Then find the area of that region.

   b.   What is the probability that the single locoweed is in her region? Find the area of the entire field (the total area region that the locoweed is possibly located) to help you find your answer. Be prepared to explain your answer to the class.

*Further Guidance
section ends here.*

12-100.   FAMILY DISCUSSION

When Dimitri discussed his idea with his family, he received many suggestions. Analyze each of the ideas given below and then report back to Dimitri about which of them, if any, he should choose. Assume that Zoe needs at least 500 square feet of grazing area between now and the fair. Your analysis should include:

   •   A diagram of each proposed region on the Lesson 12.2.4 Resource Page (or use the figure in problem 12-98).

   •   All calculations that help you determine the probability that Zoe will eat the poisoned weed for each proposed region.

   a.   **Dimitri's Father:** *"Dimitri! Why do you need to waste rope? All you need is to tether your sheep with a 10-foot rope attached at point A. Take it from me: Less area to roam means there is less chance that the sheep will eat the terrible locoweed!"*

   b.   **Dimitri's Sister:** *"I don't agree. I think you should consider using a 30-foot rope attached to point B. The longer rope will give Zoe more freedom."*

   c.   **Dimitri's Mother:** *"Both of those regions really restrict Zoe to the north-eastern part of the field. That means she won't be able to take advantage of the grass grown in the southern section of the field that is rich in nutrients because of better sunlight. I recommend that you use a 30-foot rope attached to point C. You won't be disappointed!"*

Core Connections Geometry

12-101. Find the area of each quadrilateral below. Show all work.

a. Kite

8

15

b. Rhombus

7

74°

12-102. Perry threw a tennis ball up into the air from the edge of a cliff. The height of the ball was $y = -16x^2 + 64x + 80$, where y represents the height in feet of the ball above ground at the bottom of the cliff, and x represents the time in seconds after the ball is thrown.

a. How high was the ball when it was thrown? How do you know?

b. What was the height of the ball 3 seconds after it was thrown? What was its height $\frac{1}{2}$ a second after it was thrown? Show all work.

c. When did the ball hit the ground? Write and solve an equation that represents this situation.

12-103. Examine the triangles below. Which, if any, are similar? Which are congruent? For each pair that must be similar, state how you know. Remember that the diagrams are not drawn to scale.

a.

60°

30°

16

b.

20

$10\sqrt{3}$

10

c.

30°

90°

8

d.

5

10

12-104.   Examine the mat plan of a three-dimensional solid at right.

mat plan

a.   On your paper, draw the front, right, and top views of this solid.

b.   Find the volume of the solid.

c.   If each edge of the solid is multiplied by 5, what will the new volume be? Show how you got your answer.

12-105.   Describe each circle by finding the center and radius. You need to "complete the square" to rewrite the equation in part (b) in graphing form.

a. $(x+5)^2 + y^2 = 10$

b. $x^2 - 6x + y^2 - 2y - 5 = 0$

12-106.   Remember that the absolute value function finds the distance on a number line between a number and zero. For example, the absolute value of –6 (written $|-6|$) equals 6, while $|2| = 2$.

On graph paper, copy and complete the table below and graph the function $y = |x| + 2$.

x	–4	–3	–2	–1	0	1	2	3	4
y	6				2				

12-107.   **Multiple Choice:** A square based pyramid has a slant height of 10 units and a base edge of 10 units. What is the height of the pyramid?

a.   5   b. $5\sqrt{3}$ c.   6   d.   8

Core Connections Geometry

Chapter 12 Closure   What have I learned?

Reflection and Synthesis

The activities below offer you a chance to reflect about what you have learned during this chapter. As you work, look for concepts that you feel very comfortable with, ideas that you would like to learn more about, and topics you need more help with. Look for connections between ideas as well as connections with material you learned previously.

① TEAM BRAINSTORM

What have you studied in this chapter? What ideas were important in what you learned? With your team, brainstorm a list. Be as detailed as you can. To help get you started, lists of Learning Log entries and Math Notes boxes are below.

What topics, ideas, and words that you learned *before* this chapter are connected to the new ideas in this chapter? Again, be as detailed as you can.

How long can you make your list? Challenge yourselves. Be prepared to share your team's ideas with the class.

Learning Log Entries
- Lesson 12.1.1 – Equation of a Circle
- Lesson 12.1.3 – Conic Sections

Math Notes
- Lesson 12.1.3 – Equation of a Circle
- Lesson 12.1.4 – Conic Sections

MAKING CONNECTIONS

Below is a list of the vocabulary used in this chapter. Make sure that you are familiar with all of these words and know what they mean. Refer to the glossary or index for any words that you do not yet understand.

circle	cone	conic section
cross-section	directrix	equidistant
Euler's Formula	focus	focus-directrix graph paper
golden ratio	golden spiral	parabola
phi (ϕ)		

Make a concept map showing all of the connections you can find among the key words and ideas listed above. To show a connection between two words, draw a line between them and explain the connection. A word can be connected to any other word as long as you can justify the connection.

While you are making your map, your team may think of related words or ideas that are not listed here. Be sure to include these ideas on your concept map.

③ PORTFOLIO: EVIDENCE OF MATHEMATICAL PROFICIENCY

Choose one or two of the activities from Lessons 12.2.1 through Lesson 12.2.5 that you feel best exhibits your growth in mathematical understanding this course. Copy your work from that activity, modifying and expanding it if needed. Make sure your explanation is clear and detailed. Remember, you are not only exhibiting your understanding of the mathematics, but you are also exhibiting your ability to communicate your justifications.

WHAT HAVE I LEARNED?

Most of the problems in this section represent typical problems found in this chapter. They serve as a gauge for you. You can use them to determine which types of problems you can do well and which types of problems require further study and practice. Even if your teacher does not assign this section, it is a good idea to try these problems and find out for yourself what you know and what you still need to work on.

Solve each problem as completely as you can. The table at the end of the closure section has answers to these problems. It also tells you where you can find additional help and practice with problems like these.

CL 12-108.   A coin is flipped 10 times in a row.

    a.   How many sequences of heads and tails are in the sample space?

    b.   How many ways can 10 heads come up?

    c.   In how many sequences can 0, 1, 2, or 3 heads show, with the rest tails? Hint: You may wish to refer back to problem 12-44.

    d.   Calculate the probability that 0, 1, 2, or 3 heads show up.

    e.   What is the probability that at least 4 heads come up?

CL 12-109.   "Complete the square" to rewrite the equation into graphing form. If the equation represents a circle, give the center and radius. If the equation represents a parabola, give the vertex.

    a. $x^2 + 6x + y^2 + 4y = -9$

    b. $x^2 - 4x - y = 1$

    c. $x^2 - 2x + y^2 - 10y = -16$

CL 12-110. Draw a mat plan for each of the following cube stacks and use the mat plan to find the volume of each stack. First find the area of the top of each stack.

a.

b.

c.

d.

CL 12-111. Write an equation for the graph at right.

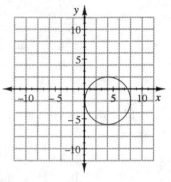

CL 12-112. When considering new plans for a covered baseball stadium, Smallville looked into a design that used a cylinder with a dome in the shape of a hemisphere. The radius of the proposed cylinder is 200 feet and the height is 150 feet. See a diagram of this at right below.

a. One of the concerns for the citizens of Smallville is the cost of heating the space inside the stadium for the fans. What is the volume of this stadium? Show all work.

b. The citizens of Smallville are also interested in having the outside of the new stadium painted in green. What is the surface area of the stadium? Do not include the base of the cylinder.

CL 12-113. An ice-cream cone is filled with ice cream. It also has ice-cream on top that is in the shape of a cylinder. It turns out that the volume of ice cream inside the cone equals the volume of the scoop on top. If the height of the cone is 6 inches and the radius of the scoop of ice cream is 1.5 inches, find the height of the extra scoop on top. Ignore the thickness of the cone.

CL 12-114. Use the diagram at right to prove the following statement. Use the proof format, two-column or flowchart, that you prefer.

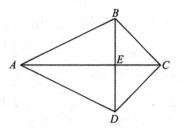

If $\overline{AB} \cong \overline{AD}$ and $\overline{BC} \cong \overline{DC}$, then $\overline{AC} \perp \overline{BD}$.

CL 12-115. Examine the diagrams below. For each one, use geometric relationships to solve for desired information.

a.

b.

c.

d.

CL 12-116. Using focus-directrix graph paper, create a parabola that has a horizontal directrix that is five units below the focus. Focus-directrix paper is on the Lesson 12.1.4 Resource Page, available at www.cpm.org.

CL 12-117. Check your answers using the table at the end of this section. Which problems do you feel confident about? Which problems were hard? Have you worked on problems like these in math classes you have taken before? Use the table to make a list of topics you need help on and a list of topics you need to practice more.

Answers and Support for Closure Activity #4
What Have I Learned?

Note: MN = Math Note, LL = Learning Log

Problem	Solution	Need Help?	More Practice
CL 12-108.	a. $2^{10} = 1024$ b. 1 c. 0 heads shows up only one way. The others are anagrams of Hs and Ts. $1 + \frac{10!}{9!} + \frac{10!}{8!2!} + \frac{10!}{7!3!} = 176$ d. $\frac{176}{1024} \approx 17.2\%$ e. This is the complement of part (d). $1 - \frac{176}{1024} \approx 82.8\%$	Section 10.2 MN: 10.2.1 and 10.2.3 LL: 10.2.1 and 10.2.3	Problems CL 11-129, 12-44, 12-55, 12-90, and 12-97
CL 12-109.	a. $(x+3)^2 + (y+2)^2 = 4$; circle; $(-3, -2)$ $r = 2$ b. $y = (x-2)^2 - 5$; parabola; $(2, -5)$ c. $(x-1)^2 + (y-5)^2 = 10$; circle; $(1, 5)$ $r = \sqrt{10}$	Lesson 12.1.2 MN: 12.1.4	Problems 12-6, 12-24, 12-51(d), and 12-105
CL 12-110.	a. $A = 4$ sq. units $V = 8$ cu. units	Lessons 9.1.1 and 9.1.2 MN: 9.1.3 LL: 9.1.1	Problems CL 9-111, CL 10-191, and 12-104

a. mat plan (RIGHT / FRONT):

	2
2	2
	2

FRONT, RIGHT

b. $A = 5$ sq. units $V = 15$ cu. units

0	3	0
3	3	3
0	3	0

FRONT, RIGHT

c. $A = 8$ sq. units $V = 16$ cu. units

2	2	2
2	0	2
2	2	2

FRONT, RIGHT

d. $A = 16$ sq. units $V = 48$ cu. units

0	3	0	3	0
3	3	3	3	3
0	3	0	3	0
3	3	3	3	3
0	3	0	3	0

FRONT, RIGHT

Problem	Solution	Need Help?	More Practice
CL 12-111.	$(x-4)^2 + (y+2)^2 = 16$	Lesson 12.1.1 MN: 12.1.3	Problems 12-6, 12-31, 12-51, 12-64, and 12-87
CL 12-112.	a. Volume of the cylinder is $6{,}000{,}000\pi$ cubic feet, volume of the dome is half of $\frac{2}{3}$ of the corresponding cylinder $\frac{1}{2} \cdot \frac{2}{3} \cdot \pi(200)^2 \cdot 400 = \frac{16{,}000{,}000}{3}\pi$ cubic feet, so total volume is approximately 35,600,000 cubic feet. b. Lateral area of cylinder is $2\pi(200)(150) = 60{,}000\pi$ sq. feet, surface area of hemisphere is $2\pi(200)^2 = 80{,}000\pi$ sq. feet. So total surface to be painted is approximately 440,000 sq. feet.	Lessons 9.1.3 and 11.1.5 MN: 9.1.3 and 11.2.2 Three-Dimensional Solids Toolkit	Problems 11-72, CL 11-132, 12-21, and 12-40
CL 12-113.	Volume of the cone is $\frac{1}{3}\pi(1.5)^2(6) = 4.5\pi$ cubic inches. Therefore, $\pi(1.5)^2(x) = 4.5\pi$ and $x = 2$ inches.	Lessons 11.1.4 and 11.1.5 MN: 11.1.5 Three-Dimensional Solids Toolkit	Problems 11-75, 12-21, and 12-54
CL 12-114.	Condensed proof 1. $\triangle ABC \cong \triangle ADC$; SSS $\cong$ 2. $\angle BCA \cong \angle DCA$; corresponding parts of congruent triangles 3. $\triangle BCE \cong \triangle DCE$; SAS $\cong$ 4. $\angle BEC \cong \angle DEC$; corresponding parts or congruent triangles 5. $m\angle BCA = 90°$; $\angle BEC$ and $\angle BEC$ are supplementary and congruent 6. $\overline{AC} \perp \overline{BD}$; definition of perpendicular	Section 7-2. MN: 6.1.4, 7.1.3 LL: 7.2.5	Problems CL 7-148, and CL 9-117

Problem	Solution	Need Help?	More Practice
CL 12-115.	a. $a = 240°$, $b = 60°$, $c = 5\sqrt{3}$ b. $x = 78°$, $y = 21$ c. $x = 22.5$ d. $x = \sqrt{30}$	Section 10.1 and Lessons 11.2.2 and 11.2.3 MN: 10.1.4 LL: 11.2.2	Problems CL 10-186, 11-110, 11-117, CL 11-124, 12-33, 12-52, and 12-93
CL 12-116.		Lesson 12.1.4	Problems 12-66 and 12-96

Core Connections Geometry
Checkpoint Materials

Notes to Students (and their Teachers)

Students master different skills at different speeds. No two students learn exactly the same way at the same time. At some point you will be expected to perform certain skills accurately. Most of the Checkpoint problems incorporate skills that you should have developed in previous courses. If you have not mastered these skills yet it does not mean that you will not be successful in this class. However, you may need to do some work outside of class to get caught up on them.

Starting in Chapter 1 and finishing in Chapter 11, there are 13 problems designed as Checkpoint problems. Each one is marked with an icon like the one above and numbered according to the chapter that it is in. After you do each of the Checkpoint problems, check your answers by referring to this section. If your answers are incorrect, you may need some extra practice to develop that skill. The practice sets are keyed to each of the Checkpoint problems in the textbook. Each has the topic clearly labeled, followed by the answers to the corresponding Checkpoint problem and then some completed examples. Next, the complete solution to the Checkpoint problem from the text is given, and there are more problems for you to practice with answers included.

Remember, looking is not the same as doing! You will never become good at any sport by just watching it, and in the same way, reading through the worked examples and understanding the steps is not the same as being able to do the problems yourself. How many of the extra practice problems do you need to try? That is really up to you. Remember that your goal is to be able to do similar problems on your own confidently and accurately. This is your responsibility. You should not expect your teacher to spend time in class going over the solutions to the Checkpoint problem sets. If you are not confident after reading the examples and trying the problems, you should get help outside of class time or talk to your teacher about working with a tutor.

Another source for help with the Checkpoint problems and other topics in *Core Connections Geometry* is the *Parent Guide with Extra Practice*. This resource is available for download free of charge at www.cpm.org.

Checkpoint Topics, Volume 2

Checkpoint 7
Problem 7-136
Solving with Trigonometric Ratios and the Pythagorean Theorem

Answers to problem 7-136: a. 23.83 ft, b. $x \approx 7$ yds, c. $x \approx 66.42°$, d. ≈ 334.57 ft

Three trigonometric ratios and the Pythagorean Theorem can used to solve for the missing side lengths and angle measurements in any right triangle.

In the triangle below, when the sides are described relative to the angle θ, the opposite leg is y and the adjacent leg is x. The hypotenuse is h regardless of which acute angle is used.

$$\tan \theta = \frac{\text{opposite leg}}{\text{adjacent leg}} = \frac{y}{x}$$

$$\sin \theta = \frac{\text{opposite leg}}{\text{hypotenuse}} = \frac{y}{h}$$

$$\cos \theta = \frac{\text{adjacent leg}}{\text{hypotenuse}} = \frac{x}{h}$$

Also for the triangle above, from the Pythagorean Theorem: $h^2 = x^2 + y^2$.

Example 1: A rectangle has a diagonal of 16 cm and one side of 11 cm. What is the length of the other side?

Solution: The diagonal represents the hypotenuse of a right triangle and the one given side represents one of the legs. Using the Pythagorean Theorem:

$$h^2 = x^2 + y^2 \Rightarrow 16^2 = 11^2 + y^2 \Rightarrow 256 = 121 + y^2$$
$$135 = y^2 \Rightarrow y = \sqrt{135} \approx 11.62 \text{ cm}$$

Example 2: Solve for x in the triangle at right.

Solution: Based on the 40° angle, 11 is the adjacent side and x is the hypotenuse. Use the cosine ratio to solve.

$$\cos 40° = \frac{11}{x}$$
$$x \cos 40° = 11 \Rightarrow x = \frac{11}{\cos 40°} \approx 14.36 \text{ units}$$

Example 3: A ten-foot ladder is leaning against the side of a house. If the top of the ladder touches the house nine feet above the ground, what is the angle made by the ladder and the ground?

Solution: Make a diagram of the situation similar to the one at right. The ladder (10) is the hypotenuse and the house (9) is the opposite leg. Using the sine ratio, $\sin\theta = \frac{9}{10}$ To find θ, "undo" the sine function with inverse sine function ($\sin^{-1}x$) as follows:

the

$$\sin\theta = \frac{9}{10}$$
$$\sin^{-1}(\sin\theta) = \sin^{-1}(\tfrac{9}{10})$$
$$\theta = \sin^{-1}\frac{9}{10}$$
$$\theta \approx 64.2°$$

Now we can go back and solve the original problems.

a. Separate the trapezoid into a rectangle and a triangle as shown below:

The legs of the triangle are 5 and 3. The hypotenuse or unlabeled side of the trapezoid is found by $h^2 = 5^2 + 3^2 = 34$. So $h = \sqrt{34} \approx 5.83$. The perimeter is:
$5 + 5 + 8 + 5.83 = 23.83\,\text{feet}$

b. $\tan 35° = \frac{x}{10}$

$x = 10\tan 35° \approx 7.0\text{ yds}$

c. $\cos x = \frac{60}{150}$

$\cos^{-1}(\cos x) = \cos^{-1}(\tfrac{60}{150})$

$x = \cos^{-1}(\tfrac{60}{150})$

$x \approx 66.4°$

d. Using the possible diagram below,

$\sin 42° = \frac{x}{500}$

$x = 500\sin 42° \approx 335\text{ ft}$

Here are some more to try. Use the right triangle trigonometric ratios or the Pythagorean Theorem to solve for the variable(s).

1.

2.

3.

4.

5.

6.

7.

8.

9.

10.

11.

12.

13. 14.

15. 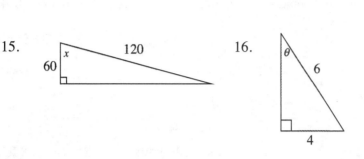 16.

Draw a diagram and solve each of the following problems.

17. The base of a 12-foot ladder is six feet from the wall. How high on the wall does the ladder touch?

18. A garden gate has a six-foot by four-foot rectangular frame that is strengthened by a diagonal brace. How long is the brace?

19. What is the distance between (–6, –6) and (–3, 2)?

20. What is the length of the hypotenuse of the right triangle with coordinates: (–2, –1), (–6, 5), and (4, 3)?

21. From the takeoff point, the launch crew of a hot air balloon can see the balloon in the sky at an elevation of 13°. The pilot tells the crew that the passenger basket is now 1200 feet above the ground. What is the current ground distance from the crew to the balloon?

22. Federal standards require the angle ramp for wheel chairs to be less than 5°. If the length of a ramp is 20 feet and the vertical rise is 15 inches, does it meet federal standards?

23. If an eight-foot stop sign casts a 10-foot shadow, what is the angle of elevation to the top of the sign?

24. Mayfield High School's flagpole is 15 feet high. Using a clinometer, Tamara measures and angle of 11.3° to the top of the pole. Tamara is 62 inches tall. How far from the flagpole is Tamara standing?

Answers:

1. 5 units

2. ≈ 50.7 units

3. ≈ 10.4 units

4. 5 units

5. $\sqrt{40} \approx 6.32$ units

6. 3 units

7. $a = 8, b = \sqrt{39} \approx 6.24$ units

8. $\approx 48.2°$

9. $6\sqrt{2} \approx 8.48$ units

10. $\approx 66.0°$

11. ≈ 6.37 units

12. ≈ 3.86 units

13. ≈ 12.2 units

14. ≈ 34.3 units

15. $60°$

16. $\approx 41.8°$

17. $\sqrt{108} \approx 10.4$ ft

18. $\sqrt{52} \approx 7.2$ ft

19. $\sqrt{73} \approx 8.5$ units

20. $\sqrt{104} \approx 10.2$ units

21. ≈ 5198 ft

22. $3.6°$, yes

23. $\approx 38.7°$

24. ≈ 590.5 in. or 49.2 ft

Checkpoint 8
Problem 8-124
Angle Relationships in Triangles and Lines

Answers to problem 8-124: a. supplementary angles sum to $180°$; $x = 26$,
b. alternate exterior angles are congruent; $x = 5$,
c. Triangle Sum Theorem; $x = 15$,
d. exterior angle equals sum of remote interior angles; $x = 35$

Illustrated below are several common relationships between angles in triangles and lines.

Parallel lines   Triangles

                              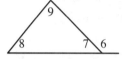

- corresponding angles are   • $m\angle 7 + m\angle 8 + m\angle 9 = 180°$
  equal: $m\angle 1 = m\angle 3$
                                                  • $m\angle 6 = m\angle 8 + m\angle 9$
- alternate interior angles are   (exterior angle = sum remote interior
  equal: $m\angle 2 = m\angle 3$ angles)

- $m\angle 2 + m\angle 4 = 180°$

Also shown in the above figures: • vertical angles are equal: $m\angle 1 = m\angle 2$

• linear pairs are supplementary: $m\angle 3 + m\angle 4 = 180°$
and $m\angle 6 + m\angle 7 = 180°$

In addition, an isosceles triangle, $\triangle ABC$, has
$\overline{BA} = \overline{BC}$ and $m\angle A = m\angle C$. An equilateral triangle,
$\triangle GFH$, has $\overline{GF} = \overline{FH} = \overline{HG}$ and
$m\angle G = m\angle F = m\angle H = 60°$.

Example 1: Solve for x.

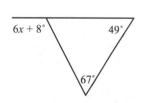

Solution: Use the Exterior Angle Theorem:

$6x + 8° = 49° + 67°$

$6x° = 108° \implies x = \dfrac{108°}{6} \implies x = 18°$

Example 2: Solve for x.

Solution: There are a number of relationships in this diagram. First, $\angle 1$ and the 127° angle are supplementary, so we know that $m\angle 1+127°=180°$ so $m\angle 1=53°$. Using the same idea, $m\angle 2=47°$. Next, $m\angle 3+53°+47°=180°$, so $m\angle 3=80°$. Because angle 3 forms a vertical pair with the angle marked $7x+3°$, $80°=7x+3°$, so $x=11°$.

Example 3: Find the measure of the acute alternate interior angles.

Solution: Parallel lines mean that alternate interior angles are equal, so $5x+28°=2x+46° \Rightarrow 3x=18° \Rightarrow x=6°$. Use either algebraic angle measure: $2(6°)+46°=58°$ for the measure of the acute angle.

Now we can go back and solve the original problems.

a. Supplementary angles sum to 180°

$$4x-3+3x+1=180°$$
$$7x-2=180°$$
$$7x=182°$$
$$x=26°$$

b. Alt. exterior angles are congruent

$$5x+6=2x+21$$
$$3x=15$$
$$x=5$$

c. Triangle Sum Theorem

$$4x+28+x+19+3x+13=180$$
$$8x+60=180$$
$$8x=120$$
$$x=15$$

d. Ext. angle = sum of remote int. angles

$$4x-10=40+90$$
$$4x=140$$
$$x=35$$

Here are some more to try. For each diagram, name the relationship used and solve for the variable.

1.

2.

3.

4.

5.

6.

7.

8.

9.

10.

11.

12.

13.

14. $\triangle ABC$ below is equilateral.

15.

16.

17.

18.

19.

20.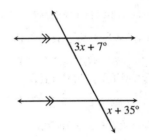

Answers: (explanations may vary)

1. congruent base angles in isosceles triangle; $x = 4$
2. supplementary same side interior angles; $y = 57$
3. exterior angle sum; $z = 67$
4. supplementary angles; $x = 42\frac{1}{3}$
5. congruent alternating interior angles; $x = 1\frac{2}{3}$
6. triangle angle sum; $x = 10$
7. isosceles triangle and exterior angle sum; $x = 55$
8. complementary angles; $x = 20$
9. supplementary angles and congruent alternating interior angles; $y = 43, x = 23$
10. triangle angle sum; $m = 42\frac{1}{4}$
11. isosceles triangle; $x = 5\frac{1}{2}$
12. congruent corresponding angles and exterior angle sum; $x = 30$
13. congruent vertical angles; $k = 6$
14. congruent sides on equilateral triangle; $n = 9$
15. two pairs of same side interior angles; $t = 9$
16. isosceles triangle; $k = 5$
17. congruent angles and angle sum; $m = 14$
18. congruent vertical angles, supplementary same side interior; $x = 18.5, y = 22$
19. isosceles triangle and exterior angle sum; $x = 63$
20. congruent corresponding angles; $x = 14$

Checkpoint 9A
Problem 9-73
Probabilities with Unions, Intersections, and Complements

Answers to problem 9-73:

   a. See tree diagram below.

   b. {WSM, WSP, WTM, WHM, GSM, GSP, GTM, GHM},

   $\frac{2}{18} + \frac{1}{18} + \frac{2}{36} + \frac{2}{36} + \frac{4}{18} + \frac{2}{18} + \frac{4}{36} + \frac{4}{36} = \frac{30}{36} \approx 83.3\%$

   c. {WTP, WHP, GTP, GHP},

   $\frac{2}{36} + \frac{2}{36} + \frac{1}{36} + \frac{1}{36} = \frac{6}{36} \approx 16.7\%$

   d. $100\% - 83.3\% = 16.7\%$

   e. {WSM, GSM}

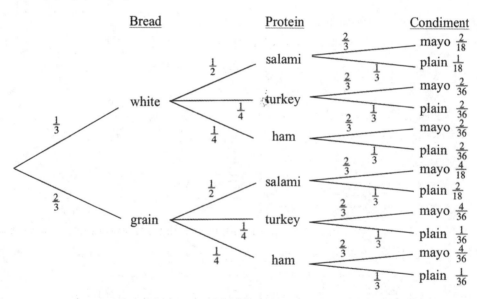

See the Lesson 1.2.1 Math Notes box for definitions of probability terms. There are several models for listing all of the outcomes of a probabilistic situation and showing their probabilities, such as, systematic lists, area models, and tree diagrams. See the Lesson 4.3.1 Math Notes box for an explanation of some of these probability models. An area model is best used when the situation involves exactly two events and the events are independent. See the Lesson 4.1.5 Math Notes box for more information about independent events.

Outcomes from probabilistic situations are called events. Several events can be combined using unions or intersections. See the Lesson 4.2.4 Math Notes box for more information about unions and intersections.

Example 1: Howard can never remember what kind of drink he is supposed to get for his wife from the coffee cart on the street. The coffee cart has 5 different hot coffee drinks, 2 different hot tea drinks, and a frozen coffee slush. Harold decides to randomly choose two drinks. When he sees his wife, he learns that she wanted a hot coffee drink. What is the probability (as a percent) that Harold chose at least one hot coffee drink? Make an area model or a tree diagram to justify your solution.

Solution: An area model can be used since there are exactly two events that are independent. The two events are picking the first drink, and picking the second drink. We are only concerned with the events that include a hot coffee drink.

	First Drink		
	hot coffee $\frac{5}{8}$	hot tea $\frac{2}{8}$	frozen coffee slush $\frac{1}{8}$
hot coffee $\frac{5}{8}$	$\frac{25}{64}$	$\frac{10}{64}$	$\frac{1}{64}$
hot tea $\frac{2}{8}$	$\frac{10}{64}$		
frozen coffee slush $\frac{1}{8}$	$\frac{1}{64}$		

Second Drink (row labels at left)

A tree diagram could have also been used.

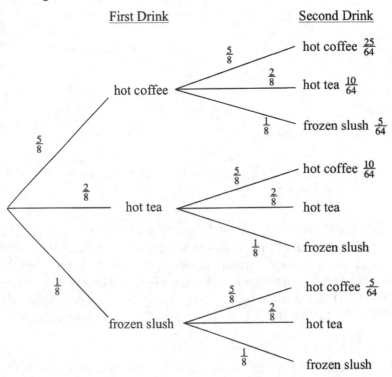

P(at least one hot coffee drink) = $\frac{25}{64} + \frac{10}{64} + \frac{5}{64} + \frac{10}{64} + \frac{5}{64} = \frac{55}{64} \approx 85.9\%$

There is an 85.9% chance that Howard chose at least one hot coffee drink.

Example 2: Denise is also at the coffee cart from Example 1. In addition to one drink, she chooses a bagel. The cart has 8 plain bagels and 5 blueberry bagels. She can top her bagel with cream cheese or butter. If she randomly chooses a drink, a bagel, and a topping, what are all the possible combinations in the sample space? Use the abbreviation C, T or F for the drink, and P or B for the bagel, and Cr or Bu for the topping.

Denise likes hot tea and blueberry bagels. Which outcomes are in the union of the events {hot tea} and {blueberry bagel}? Which outcomes are in the event {hot tea and blueberry bagel}. Are these two events the same? Explain why or why not.

Solution: An area model cannot be used since there are three events (drink, bagel, and topping). The following tree diagram can be used to represent the sample space of all possible outcomes:

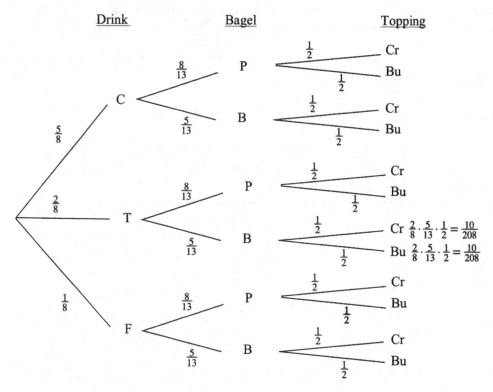

The union of {hot tea} and {blueberry bagel} is any outcome in the sample space above that contains T *or* B or both: {CBCr, CBBu, TPCr, TPBu, TBCr, TBBu, FBCr, FBBu}.

The event {hot tea and blueberry bagel} is different. {hot tea and blueberry bagel} is the *intersection* of {hot tea} and {blueberry bagel} and contains any combination with both T *and* B. Thus, {hot tea and blueberry bagel} = {TBCr, TBBu}.

Example 3: Denise is randomly handed a drink-bagel-topping combination by the coffee cart owner. Use a complement to find the probability that Denise was not handed a hot tea with a blueberry bagel.

Solution: P(hot tea and blueberry bagel) = $\frac{10}{208} + \frac{10}{208} = \frac{20}{208} \approx 9.6\%$ from the tree diagram in Example 2. The complement is the probability that Denise does not get a hot tea and blueberry bagel: P(not hot tea and blueberry bagel) = $100\% - 9.6\% = 90.4\%$.

There is a 90.4% chance that Denise was not handed a hot tea with a blueberry bagel.

Example 4: Zoey's grandfather has purchased a kit of 75 assorted pieces of sea life for her. The kit contains equal numbers of gastropod seashells, bivalve seashells, sand dollars, sea fans, and starfish. Each type of sea life is divided into equal numbers of large, medium, and small objects. Zoey is creating a piece of display art with the sea life.

To start the artwork, Zoey selects a random piece of sea life. What is the probability that she picks a small seashell?

Solution: There are 5 small gastropod seashells and 5 small bivalve seashells.

$$P(\text{small seashell}) = \frac{\text{number of successful outcomes}}{\text{total number of possible outcomes}} = \frac{10}{75} = \frac{2}{15} \approx 13.3\%$$

Alternatively, an area model, like the one below, could be used.

	gastropod seashells $\frac{1}{5}$	bivalve seashells $\frac{1}{5}$	sand dollar $\frac{1}{5}$	sea fans $\frac{1}{5}$	starfish $\frac{1}{5}$
small $\frac{1}{3}$	$\frac{1}{15}$	$\frac{1}{15}$			
medium $\frac{1}{3}$					
large $\frac{1}{3}$					

P(small seashell) = $\frac{1}{15} + \frac{1}{15} = \frac{2}{15} \approx 13.3\%$

What is the probability that she does *not* pick a small seashell?

Solution: The probability she does *not* pick a small seashell is the complement of the probability that Zoey *does* pick a small seashell.

P(not small seashell) = 1 – P(small seashell)
= $1 - \frac{2}{15} = \frac{13}{15} \approx 86.7\%$ OR $100\% - 13.3\% = 86.7\%$

What is the probability she picks a large piece *or* a seashell?

Solution: Use an area model, as shown below, or a tree diagram.

	gastropod seashells $\frac{1}{5}$	bivalve seashells $\frac{1}{5}$	sand dollar $\frac{1}{5}$	sea fans $\frac{1}{5}$	starfish $\frac{1}{5}$
small $\frac{1}{3}$	$\frac{1}{15}$	$\frac{1}{15}$			
medium $\frac{1}{3}$	$\frac{1}{15}$	$\frac{1}{15}$			
large $\frac{1}{3}$	$\frac{1}{15}$	$\frac{1}{15}$	$\frac{1}{15}$	$\frac{1}{15}$	$\frac{1}{15}$

P(large piece or seashell) = $9(\frac{1}{15}) = \frac{9}{15} = 60\%$

Alternatively, the Addition Rule could be used:

P(large piece or seashell) = P(large piece) + P(seashell) − P(large piece and seashell)

P(large piece or seashell) = $\frac{1}{3}$ + $\frac{2}{5}$ − $\frac{2}{15}$

$= \frac{9}{15} = 60\%$

Now we can go back and solve the original problems.

a. There are three probabilistic situations, or events, in this situation: choosing a bread (white or grain), choosing a protein (salami, turkey, or ham), and choosing a condiment (mayonnaise or plain). Area models are best used when there are two events, so an area model is not a good choice in this situation. See the answer for part (b) for the tree diagram.

b. The following sandwiches have salami or mayonnaise (or both) on them: {WSM, WSP, WTM, WHM, GSM, GSP, GTM, GHM}.

To find the probability of any of the sandwiches above, probabilities are added to each branch of the tree diagram, as shown in the part (b) answer above. For example, since 12 of the 36 sandwiches are made with white bread, the probability of randomly selecting a sandwich with white bread is $\frac{12}{36} = \frac{1}{3}$. Once white bread is chosen, the probability of choosing salami is $\frac{1}{2}$. The remaining half of the white-bread sandwiches are split evenly between turkey and ham, so the probability of choosing turkey is $\frac{1}{4}$ and the probability of choosing ham is $\frac{1}{4}$. In this manner, the remainder of the probabilities can be added to the remaining branches. *Note that the sum of the probabilities for any set of branches is always 1.* For example, for white bread, the probabilities of the branches for salami, turkey, and ham add to 1: $\frac{1}{2} + \frac{1}{4} + \frac{1}{4} = 1$.

Solution continues on next page →

Solution continued from previous page.

To find the probability of any one outcome (any one sandwich), multiply the probabilities across all the branches. For example the probability of white-salami-mayonnaise, or WSM, is $\frac{1}{3} \cdot \frac{1}{2} \cdot \frac{2}{3} = \frac{2}{18}$. The probabilities for individual outcomes are indicated in the far right column of the tree diagram.

The probability that Wade randomly picks a sandwich he likes is the sum of the probability of all the outcomes that are successes for Wade:

$$\frac{2}{18} + \frac{1}{18} + \frac{2}{36} + \frac{2}{36} + \frac{4}{18} + \frac{2}{18} + \frac{4}{36} + \frac{4}{36} = \frac{30}{36} \approx 83.3\%$$

c. Successes for Madison are any sandwich that has neither salami nor mayonnaise. That is, {WTP, WHP, GTP, GHP}. Using the tree diagram from part (b) above, the probability of each of these individual outcomes can be found. For example, P(WTP) = $\frac{1}{3} \cdot \frac{1}{4} \cdot \frac{1}{3} = \frac{1}{36}$.

The probability Madison picks a sandwich she likes is the sum of the probabilities of the sandwiches she considers a success:

$$\frac{2}{36} + \frac{2}{36} + \frac{1}{36} + \frac{1}{36} = \frac{6}{36} \approx 16.7\%$$

d. The sum of the probabilities of all the outcomes in any probabilistic situation is 1 or 100%. Madison likes any sandwich that Wade does not like. Since the probability of all the outcomes is 100%, and the probability of the outcomes that are success for Wade are about 83.3%, the probability for Madison's success must be 100% − 83.3% = 16.7%.

e. Intersections are the set of outcomes in which both the first *and* the second event must occur. The outcomes in which both {salami} and {mayonnaise} occur are {WSM, GSM}.

Unions, on the other hand, are the set of outcomes in which either the first *or* the second event must occur. Wade's favorite sandwiches in part (b) were the union of {salami} or {mayonnaise}.

Here are some more to try.

1.   As you open the ice chest during your family picnic you find that there are 10 bottles of fruit juice and 10 sandwiches. Unfortunately the bottle labels came off and the sandwiches are not labeled. Your mother says that there are 5 strawberry, 3 grape, and 2 raspberry juices. There are 4 turkey, 3 roast beef, and 3 tuna sandwiches. You are not really picky, but you are hungry and you really do not want grape juice and tuna together.

       a.   Draw a diagram to show the sample space for this situation.

       b.   What is the probability of picking a grape juice and tuna combination?

       c.   What is the probability of picking a lunch with strawberry juice or turkey?

2.   A carnival game has a spinner like the one at right. The sections are all the same size.

       R = red   B = blue   G = green

       a.   Draw a diagram to show the sample space for spinning twice.

       b.   What is the probability of spinning the same color twice?

3.   There is a 25% chance that you will have to work tonight and cannot study for the big math test. If you study, then you have an 80% chance of earning a good grade. If you do not study, you only have a 30% chance of earning a good grade.

       a.   Draw a diagram to represent this situation.

       b.   Calculate the probability of earning a good grade on the math test.

4.   For the spinners at right, assume that sections of spinner #1 are all the same size and the R and B sections of spinner #2 are each half the size of section G.

       R = red   B = blue   G = green

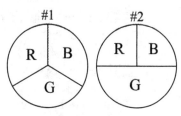

       a.   Draw a diagram for the sample space for spinning both spinners.

       b.   What is the probability of spinning green on both spinners?

       c.   What is the probability of spinning the same color on both spinners?

       d.   What is the probability of *not* spinning green on both spinners?

5.   Judy's pencil box contains two red, one blue, and three yellow pencils and one yellow and two red erasers. If she randomly picks out one pencil and one eraser, find the following probabilities.

    a.   Getting a yellow pencil and red eraser.

    b.   Getting a yellow pencil or a red eraser.

    c.   Not getting the yellow pencil and red eraser combination.

6.   A baseball player gets a hit 40% of the time if the weather is good but only 20% of the time if it is cold or windy. The weather forecast is 70% chance of nice weather, 20% chance of cold weather, and 10% chance of windy. What is the probability of the player getting a hit?

7.   The State Fair has the following carnival game.

Pay $5 to spin the wheel at right. Assume that sections B and G are each half the size of section R.

R = red   B = blue   G = green

• If red comes up on the first spin, you win a stuffed animal.

• If blue comes up on the first spin, you spin again. If blue comes up again you win $20. Otherwise you win nothing.

• If green comes up on the first spin, you spin again. If green comes up a second time, you spin again. If green comes up a third time you win $150. Otherwise you win nothing.

    a.   Draw a diagram to represent this situation.

    b.   What is the probability of winning something in the game?

8.   Evan gets up at 4 a.m. each day to deliver newspapers. He does not want to wake up his brother so he gets dressed in the dark and cannot see what clothes he is choosing. In his closet there are three pairs of shoes – one pair of dress shoes and two pairs of tennis shoes. There are also five pairs of pants – three pairs of jeans and two pairs of slacks. In the dresser are eight school shirts – three are blue, two are green and three are Hawaiian. If Evan randomly chooses a pair of shoes, a pair of pants, and a shirt, compute the following probabilities.

    a.   Evan wears tennis shoes, jeans, and a Hawaiian shirt.

    b.   Evan wears tennis shoes and jeans or tennis shoes and a Hawaiian shirt.

    c.   Evan does not wear a dress shoes, slacks, blue shirt combination.

Core Connections Geometry

Answers:

1. a.

	Sandwich		
	TY(0.4)	RB(0.3)	TU(0.3)
S(0.5)	0.20	0.15	0.15
G(0.3)	0.12	0.09	0.09
R(0.2)	0.08	0.06	0.06

(Drink — row label)

   b. $0.9 = 90\%$

   c. $0.08 + 0.12 + 0.20 + 0.15 + 0.15 = 0.70 = 70\%$

$\frac{1}{2}$ R $\frac{1}{2}$ R $= \frac{1}{4}$, $\frac{1}{3}$ B $= \frac{1}{6}$, $\frac{1}{6}$ G $= \frac{1}{12}$

$\frac{1}{3}$ B $\frac{1}{2}$ R $= \frac{1}{6}$, $\frac{1}{3}$ B $= \frac{1}{9}$, $\frac{1}{6}$ G $= \frac{1}{18}$

$\frac{1}{6}$ G $\frac{1}{2}$ R $= \frac{1}{12}$, $\frac{1}{3}$ B $= \frac{1}{18}$, $\frac{1}{6}$ G $= \frac{1}{36}$

2. a. See tree diagram at right.

   b. $\{RR\} + \{BB\} + \{GG\} = \frac{1}{4} + \frac{1}{9} + \frac{1}{36} = \frac{7}{18}$

3. a.

	good grade (0.3)	bad grade (0.7)
work (not study) (0.25)	0.075	0.175
no work (study) (0.75)	0.6	0.15
	good grade (0.8)	bad grade (0.2)

   b. $0.075 + 0.60 = 0.675 = 67.5\%$

4. a.

#2

	R$\left(\frac{1}{4}\right)$	B$\left(\frac{1}{4}\right)$	G$\left(\frac{1}{2}\right)$
R$\left(\frac{1}{3}\right)$	$\frac{1}{12}$	$\frac{1}{12}$	$\frac{1}{6}$
B$\left(\frac{1}{3}\right)$	$\frac{1}{12}$	$\frac{1}{12}$	$\frac{1}{6}$
G$\left(\frac{1}{3}\right)$	$\frac{1}{12}$	$\frac{1}{12}$	$\frac{1}{6}$

(#1 — row label)

   b. $\frac{1}{6}$

   c. $\frac{1}{12} + \frac{1}{12} + \frac{1}{6} = \frac{1}{3}$

   d. $1 - \frac{1}{6} = \frac{5}{6}$

5. a. $\frac{1}{2} \cdot \frac{2}{3} = \frac{1}{3}$

   b. $\frac{2}{9} + \frac{2}{18} + \frac{1}{6} + \frac{1}{3} = \frac{5}{6}$

   c. $1 - \frac{1}{3} = \frac{2}{3}$

6. $(0.7)(0.4) + (0.2)(0.2) + (0.2)(0.1) = 0.28 + 0.04 + 0.02 = 0.34$

7. a. See tree diagram at right.

    b. $\frac{1}{2} + \frac{1}{16} + \frac{1}{64} = \frac{37}{64} \approx 57.8\%$

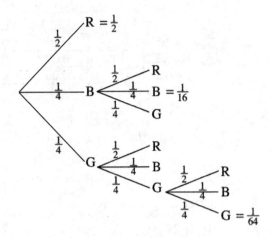

8. a. $\frac{3}{20}$

    b. $\frac{2}{3} \cdot \frac{3}{5} + \frac{2}{3} \cdot \frac{3}{8} \cdot \frac{2}{5} = \frac{2}{5} + \frac{2}{20} = \frac{1}{2}$

    c. $1 - \frac{1}{3} \cdot \frac{2}{5} \cdot \frac{3}{8} = \frac{19}{20}$

Checkpoint 9B
Problem 9·107
Exponential Functions

Answers to problem 9-107: a. See graph at right.

b. $f(x) = 10(2.3)^x$

c. $y = 42,000(0.75)^5 = 9967$

d. $60 = 25(b)^{10}$, $b = 1.09$, 9% increase

An exponential function is an equation of the form $y = ab^x$ (with $b \geq 0$).

In many cases a represents a starting or initial value, b represents the multiplier or growth/decay factor, and x represents the time. If something is increasing by a percent then the multiplier b is always found by adding the percent increase (as a decimal) to the number 1. If something is decreasing by a percent then the multiplier b is always found by subtracting the percent from the number 1. From a table, the multiplier can be calculated using the ratio of the y-values corresponding to one integer x-value divided by the preceding x-value.

Example 1: Graph $y = 3 \cdot 2^x$.

Solution:
First, make a table of values.

x	−1	0	1	2	3
y	1.5	3	6	12	24

This is called an increasing exponential curve.

Then, plot the points and connect them to form a smooth curve

Example 2: The ticket prices at African Safari Land have increased annually according to the table at right. Write an equation that represents the cost over various years.

Year	Price
0	$50
1	$55
2	$60.50
3	$66.55

Solution: The initial value is $a = 50$. The multiplier is the ratio of one y-value divided by the previous one:
$b = \frac{55}{50} = \frac{60.50}{55} = \frac{66.55}{60.50} = 1.1$. The prices are increasing by 10% each year. The equation is $y = 50(1.1)^x$.

Example 3: A house that was worth \$200,000 in 2005 was only worth \$150,000 in 2010. Write an equation to represent the value since 2005 and tell the percent of decrease.

Solution: The equation to use is $y = ab^x$. The given initial value is $a = 200,000$. The other given value is $y = 150,000$ when $x = 5$. Substituting these into the equation and solving for b we get:

$$150,000 = 200,000b^5$$
$$0.75 = b^5$$
$$b = \sqrt[5]{0.75} \approx 0.944$$

The equation is $y = 200000(0.944)^x$. $1 - 0.944 = 0.056 = 5.6\%$ decrease.

Now we can go back and solve the original problems.

a. Make a table of values. Plot the points and connect them to form a smooth curve. See table below and graph at right.

x	−1	0	1	2	3
y	2.7	2	1.5	1.1	0.8

b. The multiplier $b = \frac{52.9}{23} = 2.3$. The starting value for $x = 0$ can be determined by working backwards from the value of $x = 1$. $a = \frac{23}{2.3} = 10$. The equation represented by the table is: $f(x) = 10(2.3)^x$.

c. $y = ab^x$ $a = 42,000, b = 1 - 0.25 = 0.75, x = 5$
    $y = 42,000(0.75)^x \implies 42,000(0.75)^5 \approx 9967$

d. $y = ab^x$ $a = 25, y = 60, x = 10$
    $60 = 25b^{10} \implies \frac{60}{25} = b^{10} \implies b = \sqrt[10]{\frac{60}{25}} \approx 1.09$ That is a 9% increase.
    $y = 25(1.09)^x$

Here are some more to try. Make a table of values and draw a graph of each exponential function.

1. $y = 4(0.5)^x$ 2. $y = 2(3)^x$

3. $f(x) = 5(1.2)^x$ 4. $f(x) = 10\left(\frac{2}{3}\right)^x$

Write an equation to represent the information in each table.

5.

x	f(x)
0	1600
1	2000
2	2500
3	3125

6.

x	y
1	40
2	32
3	25.6

7.

x	f(x)
0	1.8
1	5.76
2	18.432

8.

x	y
0	5
1	35
2	245

Write a possible context based on each equation.

9. $y = 32,500(0.85)^x$

10. $f(x) = 2.75(1.025)^x$

Write and use an exponential equation to solve each problem.

11. A powerful computer is purchased for $1500, but on the average loses 20% of its value each year. How much will it be worth 4 years from now?

12. If a gallon of milk costs $3 now and the price is increasing 10% per year, how long before milk costs $10 a gallon? (Note that guess and check will be required to solve the equation after it is written.)

13. Dinner at your grandfather's favorite restaurant now costs $25.25 and has been increasing steadily at 4% per year. How much did it cost 35 *years ago* when he was courting your grandmother?

14. The number of bacteria present in a colony is 280 at 12 noon and the bacteria grows at a rate of 18% per hour. How many will be present at 10 p.m.?

15. A house purchased for $226,000 has lost 4% of its value each year for the past five years. What is it worth now?

16. A 1970 comic book has appreciated 10% per year and originally sold for $0.35. What will it be worth in 2020?

17. A compact car depreciates at 15% per year. Six year ago it was purchased for $21,000. What is it worth now?

18. Inflation is at a rate of 7% per year. Today Janelle's favorite bread costs $4.79. What would it have cost ten years ago?

19. Ryan's motorcycle is now worth $2500. It has decreased in value 12% each year since it was purchased. If he bought it four years ago, what did it cost new?

20. The cost of a High Definition television now averages $900, but the cost is decreasing about 12% per year. In how many years will the cost be under $400?

21. A two-bedroom house in Nashville is worth $110,000. If it appreciates at 2.5% per year, when will it be worth $200,000?

22. Last year the principal's car was worth $28,000. Next year it will be worth $25,270. What is the annual rate of depreciation? What is the car worth now?

23. A concert has been sold out for weeks, and as the date of the concert draws closer, the price of the ticket increases. The cost of a pair of tickets was $150 yesterday and is $162 today. Assume that the cost continues to increase at this rate exponentially.

    a. What is the daily rate of increase? What is the multiplier?

    b. What will be the ticket cost one week from now, the day before the concert?

    c. What was the cost two weeks ago?

Answers:

1.
x	−1	0	1	2	3
y	8	4	2	1	0.5

2.
x	−1	0	1	2	3
y	2/3	2	6	18	54

3.
x	−1	0	1	2	3
y	4.17	5	6	7.2	8.64

4.
x	−1	0	1	2	3
y	15	10	6.67	4.44	2.96

5. $1600(1.25)^x$ 6. $40(0.8)^x$ 7. $1.8(3.2)^x$ 8. $5 \cdot 7^x$

9. Possible answer: If a \$32,500 boat loses 15% of its value each year, what will it be worth x years from now?

10. Possible answer: A soda at the movies now costs \$2.75. If the cost is increasing 2.5% per year, what will it cost x years from now?

11. \$614.40   12. $\approx$ 12-13 years

13. \$6.40 (Note that answers of \$6.05 used $b = 0.96$ which is incorrect.)

14. $\approx$ 1465   15. \$184,274   16. \$41.09

17. $\approx$ \$7920   18. $\approx$ \$2.43   19. $\approx$ \$4169

20. $\approx$ 6-7 years   21. $\approx$ 24-25 years   22. 5%, $\approx$ \$26,600

23. a.   8%, 1.08   b. $\approx$ \$277.64   c. $\approx$ \$55.15

Checkpoint 10
Problem 10-156
Finding Angles in and Areas of Regular Polygons

Answers to problem 10-156: a. 162°; b. 16 sides; c. ≈ 120.8 cm²

The sum of the measures of a polygon with n sides is $(n-2)180°$ and therefore each angle in a regular polygon with n sides measures $\frac{(n-2)180°}{n}$.

The sum of the exterior angles of any polygon is 360°.

To find the area of a regular polygon, use the angles and side length of one the identical triangles that make up the polygon to find the area of the triangle. Then multiply by the number of identical triangles to determine the area of the polygon.

Example 1: What is the measure of each interior angle of a regular 10-gon?

Solution: Using $n = 10$ in the formula given above $\frac{(n-2)180°}{n} = \frac{8 \cdot 180°}{10} = 144°$

Example 2: If the regular 10-gon in Example 1 has a side length of 6 inches, what is the area of the polygon?

Solution: The regular 10-gon is made is made up of 10 identical isosceles triangles like the one at right. From Example 1, each interior angle is 144°. The base angle in the triangle is half of the interior angle so $m\angle 1 = 72°$. We can use the tangent ratio to find the height of the triangle:
$\tan 72° = \frac{h}{3} \Rightarrow h = 3\tan 72° \approx 9.23$. The area of the triangle is $\frac{1}{2} \cdot 6 \cdot 9.23 \approx 27.69$.

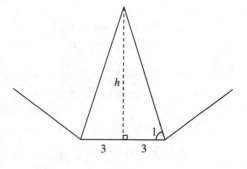

Therefore the area of the 10-gon is $10(27.69) \approx 276.9 \text{ in.}^2$.

Now we can go back and solve the original problems.

a. $\frac{(n-2)180°}{n} = \frac{18 \cdot 180°}{20} = 162°$

b.   Method 1 (using the formula): $157.5° = \frac{(n-2)180°}{n} \Rightarrow 157.5° \, n = (n-2)180°$

       $\Rightarrow 157.5° \, n = 180° \, n - 360° \Rightarrow -22.5° \, n = -360° \Rightarrow n = 16$

Method 2 (using the exterior angle): If the interior angle is 157.5° then the exterior angle is 180°-157.5° = 22.5°. Since the sum of the exterior angles of a polygon is 360°, 360° ÷ 22.5° = 16 sides.

c.　The octagon is made up of 8 identical triangles. Each interior angle of the polygon measures $\frac{6\cdot180°}{8} = 135°$. Using a diagram as in example 2 above, $m\angle 1 = \frac{135°}{2} = 67.5°$. The base of the small triangle is 2.5 cm. To find the height, $\tan 67.5° = \frac{h}{2.5} \Rightarrow h = 2.5 \tan 67.5° \approx 6.04$. The area of the large triangle is $\frac{1}{2} \cdot 5 \cdot 6.04 \approx 15.1$. Eight of these triangles make up the octagon so the area of the octagon is $8 \cdot 15.1 \approx 120.8$ cm^2.

Here are some more to try. Find the measure of the angle of each regular polygon.

1.　Interior angle, 12 sides

2.　Interior angle, 15 sides

3.　Interior angle, 7 sides

4.　Interior angle, 60 sides

5.　Exterior angle, 10 sides

6.　Exterior angle, 20 sides

Answer each of the following questions.

7.　What is the measure of each interior angle of a regular polygon with 16 sides?

8.　What is the measure of each exterior angle of a regular polygon with 16 sides?

9.　What is the area of a regular polygon with 16 sides and side length 4 inches?

10.　Each interior angle of a regular polygon measures 156°. How many sides does it have?

11.　What is the area of a regular pentagon with side length 10 feet?

12.　Each exterior angle of a regular polygon measures 15°. How many sides does it have?

13.　Each interior angle of a regular polygon measures 165.6°. How many sides does it have?

14.　What is the area of a regular octagon with side length 1 meter?

15.　Each exterior angle of a regular polygon measures $13\frac{1}{3}°$. How many sides does it have?

16.　What is the area of a regular polygon with 15 sides and a side length of 4 inches?

Answers:

1. $150°$ 2. $156°$ 3. $128\frac{4}{7}°$

4. $174°$ 5. $36°$ 6. $18°$

7. $157.5°$ 8. $22.5°$ 9. ≈ 321.7 in.^{2}

10. 15 sides 11. ≈ 344.1 ft^2 12. 24 sides

13. 25 sides 14. ≈ 4.83 m^2 15. 27 sides

16. ≈ 282.3 in.^{2}

Checkpoint 11
Problem 11-102
Volumes and Surface Areas of Prisms and Cylinders

Answers to problem 11-102: a. $V = 2100$ units^3, $SA \approx 1007.34$ units^2
b. $V = 1000\pi \approx 3141.59$ cm^3, $SA = \frac{1100\pi}{3} + 240 \approx 1391.92$ cm^2
c. $V = 60$ in.^{3}, $SA = 144$ in.^{2}

The volume (in cubic units) of a prism or cylinder is found by multiplying the area of the base by the height: $V = Bh$.

The surface area (in square units) of either of these solids is found by adding the areas of the bases and the area of the lateral faces (sides).

Example 1: Find the volume and surface area of the cylinder at right.

Solution: To find the volume we need to calculate the area of the base, which in this case is a circle with radius 5 m.
$$B = \pi r^2 = \pi(5)^2 = 25\pi$$
$$V = Bh = (25\pi)(2) = 50\pi \approx 157.08 \text{ m}^3$$

To find the surface area we need to add the area of the two bases and the area of the side. The unrolled side is a rectangle with a base length equal to the circumference of the circle and a height equal to the height of the cylinder.

2(area of the base) + area of the side
$$2(\pi r^2) + \pi 2r(h)$$
$$2\pi \cdot 25 + \pi \cdot 10 \cdot 2 = 70\pi \approx 219.91 \text{ m}^2$$

Example 2: Find the volume and surface area of the prism at right.

Solution: To find the volume we need to calculate the area of the base, which in this case is a triangle. First use the Pythagorean theorem to find the second leg of the right triangular base. Since $3^2 + \text{leg}^2 = 5^2$, leg = 4.
$$B = \tfrac{1}{2}bh = \tfrac{1}{2}(3)(4) = 6 \qquad V = Bh = (6)(8) = 48 \text{ units}^3$$

To find the surface area we must add together the area of the two bases and the area of the three rectangular sides. The three rectangular sides all have a height of 8 units and the three bases are the lengths of the sides of the triangle.

2(area of the base) + area of side #1 + area of side #2 + area of side #3
$$2(\tfrac{1}{2} \cdot 3 \cdot 4) \quad + \quad 5 \cdot 8 \quad + \quad 3 \cdot 8 \quad + \quad 4 \cdot 8 = 108 \text{ units}^2$$

Now we can go back and solve the original problems.

a. The bases are a trapezoid. $B = \frac{1}{2}h(b_1 + b_2) = \frac{1}{2} \cdot 15(8 + 12) = 150$.

To calculate the volume: $V = Bh = 150 \cdot 14 = 2100$ units^3

To find the surface area we must add together the area of the two bases and the area of the four rectangular sides. The four rectangular sides all have a height of 14 units and the four bases are the lengths of the sides of the trapezoid. To find the missing length of the trapezoid we need to use the Pythagorean Theorem.

Use the triangular part of the trapezoid:
$(12 - 8)^2 + 15^2 = \text{hypotenuse}^2 \Rightarrow 241 = \text{hypotenuse}^2$

The length of the unlabeled side $= \sqrt{241}$.

2(area of the base) + area of side #1 + area of side #2 + area of side #3 + area of side #4

$2(\frac{1}{2} \cdot 15(8 + 12)) + 12 \cdot 14 + 15 \cdot 14 + 8 \cdot 14 + \sqrt{241} \cdot 14 \approx 1007.34$ units^2

b. The base is $\frac{300°}{360°} = \frac{5}{6}$ of a circle. $B = \frac{5}{6}\pi r^2 = \frac{5}{6}\pi \cdot 10^2 = \frac{500\pi}{6}$

To find the volume: $V = Bh = (\frac{500\pi}{6})(12) = 1000\pi \approx 3141.59$ cm^3

To find the surface area we must add together the area of the two bases and the area of the three rectangular sides. The three rectangular sides all have a height of 12 cm and the three bases are two radii and $\frac{5}{6}$ the circumference of the circle.

2(area of the base) + area of side #1 + area of side #2 + area of side #3

$2(\frac{5}{6}\pi \cdot 10^2) + 10 \cdot 12 + 10 \cdot 12 + \frac{5}{6}\pi \cdot 20 \cdot 12 = \frac{1100\pi}{3} + 240 \approx 1391.92$ cm^2

c. The base is a square with a square cut out. $B = 4^2 - 2^2 = 12$
To find the volume: $V = Bh = 12 \cdot 5 = 60$ in.^{3}

To find the surface area we must add together the area of the two bases and the area of the four identical external rectangular sides and the four identical internal rectangular sides.

2(area of the base) + 4(area of external side) + 4(area of internal side)

$2(4^2 - 2^2) + 4(4 \cdot 5) + 4(2 \cdot 5) = 144$ in.^{2}

Here are some more to try. Compute the volume and surface area of each solid.

1.

2.

3.

4.

5.

6.

7.

8.

9.

10.

11.

12.

Answers:

1. $V = 200\pi \approx 628.32 \text{ ft}^3$; $SA = 130\pi \approx 408.41 \text{ ft}^2$

2. $V = 48 \text{ m}^3$; $SA = 80 \text{ m}^2$

3. $V = 540 \text{ cm}^3$; $SA = 468 \text{ cm}^2$

4. $V \approx 1508.75 \text{ m}^3$; $SA \approx 728.35 \text{ m}^2$

5. $V = 126 \text{ ft}^3$; $SA \approx 165.19 \text{ ft}^2$

6. $V \approx 332.6 \text{ cm}^3$; $SA \approx 275.14 \text{ cm}^2$

7. $V \approx 9.42 \text{ m}^3$; $SA \approx 7.85 \text{ m}^2$

8. $V \approx 163.65 \text{ cm}^3$; $SA \approx 191.65 \text{ cm}^2$

9. $V = 81 \text{ in.}^3$; $SA = 126 \text{ in.}^2$

10. $V = 75 \text{ ft}^3$; $SA \approx 122.08 \text{ ft}^2$

11. $V \approx 28.27 \text{ cm}^3$; $SA \approx 64.27 \text{ cm}^2$

12. $V \approx 65.72 \text{ cm}^3$; $SA \approx 126.28 \text{ cm}^2$

Glossary

30°-60°-90° triangle   A special right triangle with acute angle measures of 30° and 60°. The side lengths are always in the ratio of $1:\sqrt{3}:2$. See the diagram at right.

45°-45°-90° triangle   A special right triangle with acute angle measures of 45°. The side lengths are always in the ratio of $1:1:\sqrt{2}$. See the diagram at right.

AA ~ (Triangle Similarity)   If two angles of one triangle are congruent to the two corresponding angles of another triangle, then the triangles are similar. For example, given $\triangle ABC$ and $\triangle A'B'C'$ with $\angle A \cong \angle A'$ and $\angle B \cong \angle B'$, then $\triangle ABC \sim \triangle A'B'C'$. You can also show that two triangles are similar by showing that *three* pairs of corresponding angles are congruent (which would be called AAA ~), but two pairs of angles are sufficient to demonstrate similarity.

AAS ≅ (Triangle Congruence)   If two angles and a non-included side of one triangle are congruent to the corresponding two angles and non-included side of another triangle, the two triangles are congruent. Note that AAS ≅ is equivalent to ASA ≅.

absolute value   The absolute value of a number is the distance of that number from zero. Since absolute value represents a distance, without regard to direction, it is always non-negative. Thus the absolute value of a negative number is its opposite, while the absolute value of a non-negative number is just the number itself. The absolute value of x is usually written $|x|$. For example, $|-5| = 5$ and $|22| = 22$.

acute angle   An angle with measure greater than 0° and less than 90°. One example is shown at right. See also *obtuse angle*.

Addition Rule for Probability   For any two events {A} and {B}, P(A or B) = P(A) + P(B) – P(A and B). See also *Multiplication Rule for Probability*.

adjacent angles   For two angles to be adjacent, they must satisfy these three conditions: (1) The two angles must have a common side; (2) They must have a common vertex; and (3) They can have no interior points in common. This means that the common side must be between the two angles; no overlap between the angles is permitted. In the example at right, $\angle ABC$ and $\angle CBD$ are adjacent angles.

adjacent leg   In a right triangle, the leg adjacent to an acute angle is the side of the angle that is not the hypotenuse. For example, in $\triangle ABC$ shown at right, $\overline{AB}$ is the leg adjacent to $\angle A$.

alpha (α)   A Greek letter that is often used to represent the measure of an angle. Other Greek letters used to represent the measure of an angle include theta (θ) and beta (β).

alternate interior angles   Angles between a pair of lines that switch sides of a third intersecting line (called a transversal). For example, in the diagram at right the shaded angles are alternate interior angles. If the lines intersected by the transversal are parallel, then the alternate interior angles are congruent. Conversely, if the alternate interior angles are congruent, then the two lines intersected by the transversal are parallel. See also *same-side interior angles* and *corresponding angles*.

altitude   See *height*.

ambiguous   Information is ambiguous when it has more than one interpretation or conclusion.

anagram   A word game in which different arrangements of the letters of a word are created, using all the letters in the original word, one time each. The term anagram is also informally used in this course to refer to permutations in which there are duplicates of some items. For example, finding the number of ways to arrange one red, two blue, and three yellow flags in a row is the same as the number of ways to arrange the "word" RBBYYY. To compute this, find the number of permutations, and divide by the numbers of ways to arrange the repeated items, for example, $\frac{5!}{2!3!}$ for the flags.

angle   In general, an angle is formed by two rays joined at a common endpoint. Angles in geometric figures are usually formed by two segments, with a common endpoint (such as the angle shaded in the figure at right).

angle bisector   A line segment or ray with an endpoint at the vertex of the angle that divides the angle into two equal pieces.

angle measure   See *measurement*.

angle of depression   When an object (*B*) is below the horizontal line of sight of the observer (*A*), the angle of depression is the angle formed by the line of sight to the object and the horizontal line of sight.

angle of elevation   When an object (*B*) is above the horizontal line of sight of the observer (*A*), the angle of elevation is the angle formed by the line of sight to the object and the horizontal line of sight.

apex   In a cone or pyramid, the apex is the point that is the farthest away from the flat surface (plane) that contains the base. In a pyramid, the apex is also the point at which the lateral faces meet. An apex is also sometimes called the vertex of a pyramid or cone.

Core Connections Geometry

apothem A segment that connects the center of a regular polygon to a point on one of its sides, and is perpendicular to that side.

arc A connected part of a circle. Because a circle does not contain its interior, an arc is more like a portion of a bicycle tire than a slice of pizza. See also *major arc* and *minor arc* and *sector*.

arc length The length of an arc (in inches, centimeters, feet, etc.) is the distance from one of the arc's endpoints to the arc's other endpoint, measured around the circle. Note that arc length is different from arc measure. Arcs of two different circles may have the same arc measure (like 90°), but have different arc lengths if one circle has a larger radius than the other one.

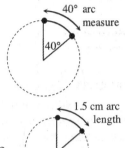

arc measure The measure in degrees of an arc's central angle. Note that arc measure is measured in degrees and is different from arc length.

arccosine, arcsine, and arctangent. Other names for *inverse cosine* ($\cos^{-1} x$), *inverse sine* ($\sin^{-1} x$), and *inverse tangent* ($\tan^{-1} x$).

area On a flat surface (plane), the number of non-overlapping square units needed to cover the region. See also *surface area*.

area model A model that uses the area of rectangles to represent the probabilities of possible outcomes when considering two *independent* events. For example, suppose you are going to randomly select a student from a classroom. If the probability of selecting a female student from the room is $\frac{2}{3}$ and the probability of selecting a 9th grader from the room is $\frac{1}{4}$, the area of the shaded rectangle at right represents the probability that a randomly selected student is a female 9th grader ($\frac{2}{3} \cdot \frac{1}{4} = \frac{1}{6}$). A "generic" area model enables you to find the probabilities of outcomes without drawing a diagram to scale. See also *tree diagram*.

	male $\frac{1}{3}$	female $\frac{2}{3}$
9th grader $\frac{1}{4}$	$\frac{1}{12}$	$\frac{1}{6}$
not 9th grader $\frac{3}{4}$	$\frac{1}{4}$	$\frac{1}{2}$

Area model

arithmetic sequence An ordered sequence of mathematical terms in which a constant number is added to each term to determine the next term in the sequence. The number added to each term to get the next term is called the sequence generator or common difference. The equation for an arithmetic sequence is $t(n) = mn + b$ or $a_n = mn + a_0$, where n is the term number, m is the common difference, and b or a_0 is the zeroth (or initial) term of the sequence. Sequences are usually written starting with the first term, where $n = 1$. For example in the sequence, $4, 7, 10, 13, \ldots$, the common difference is 3, and the equation is $t(n) = 3n + 1$. See also *geometric sequence*.

arrow diagram   A pictorial representation of a conditional statement. The arrow points toward the conclusion of the conditional (the "then" part of the "If… then" statement). For example, the conditional statement *"If two lines cut by a transversal are parallel, then alternate interior angles are congruent"* can be represented by the arrow diagram below.

Lines cut by a transversal are parallel → *alternate interior angles are congruent.*

arrowheads   To indicate a line on a diagram, we draw a segment with arrowheads on its ends. The arrowheads show that our diagram indicates a line, which extends indefinitely, as opposed to a segment, which has endpoints. Marks on pairs of lines or segments such as ">>" and ">>>" indicate that the lines or segments are parallel. Both types of marks are used in the diagrams above.

ASA ≅ (Triangle Congruence)   If two angles and the included side of one triangle are congruent to the corresponding two angles and included side of another triangle, the triangles are congruent. Note that ASA ≅ is equivalent to AAS ≅.

association   A relationship between two (or more) variables. An association between *numerical* variables can be displayed on a scatterplot, and described by its form, direction, strength, and outliers. Possible association between two *categorical* variables can be studied in a two-way table.

auxiliary lines   Segments and lines added to existing figures. Auxiliary lines are usually added to a figure to allow us to prove something about the figure.

axioms   Statements accepted as true without proof. Also known as *postulates*.

base   (a) Triangle: Any side of a triangle to which a height is drawn. There are three possible bases in each triangle; (b) Trapezoid: the two parallel sides; (c) Parallelogram (and rectangle, rhombus, and square): Any side to which a height is drawn (there are four possible bases in each parallelogram); (d) Solid: See *cone, cylinder, prism,* and *pyramid.*

beta (β)   A Greek letter that is often used to represent the measure of an angle. Other Greek letters used to represent the measure of an angle include alpha (α) and theta (θ).

binomial   An expression that is the sum or difference of exactly two terms, each of which is a monomial. For example, $-2x + 3y^2$ is a binomial.

bisect   To bisect a geometric object is to divide it into two congruent parts.

Cavalieri's Principle   Two solids have the same volume if corresponding cross-sectional areas are the same. For example, an oblique solid has the same volume as the corresponding right solid with the same height, as long as all the cross-sections perpendicular to the base have the same area. See also *oblique prism (or cylinder)* and *oblique pyramid (or cone)*.

center of a circle   On a flat surface, the fixed point from which all points on the circle are equidistant. See also *circle*.

central angle   An angle with its vertex at the center of a circle.

centroid   The point at which the three medians of a triangle intersect. The centroid is also the center of balance of a triangle. The other points of concurrency studied in this course are the circumcenter and the incenter.

Centroid

Medians

chord   A line segment with its endpoints on a circle. A chord that passes through the center of a circle is called a diameter. See also *circle*.

circle   The set of all points on a flat surface that are the same distance from a fixed point. If the fixed point (center) is O, the symbol $\odot O$ represents a circle with center O. If r is the length of a circle's radius and d is the length of its diameter, the circumference of the circle is $C = 2\pi r$ or $C = \pi d$. The area of the circle is $A = \pi r^2$. The graphing form (also called "center-radius form" or standard form) of the equation of a circle with radius length r and center (h, k) is $(x - h)^2 + (y - k)^2 = r^2$. The general form (also called expanded form) is $ax^2 + ay^2 + bx + cy + d = 0$.

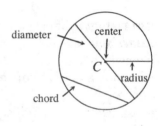

diameter   center

C

radius

chord

circular angle   An angle with a measure of 360°.

360°

circumcenter   The center of the circle that passes through the vertices of a triangle. It can be found by locating the point of intersection of the perpendicular bisectors of the sides of the triangle. The other points of concurrency studied in this course are the centroid and the incenter.

circumference   The perimeter of (distance around) a circle.

circumscribed circle   A circle circumscribes a polygon when it passes through all of the vertices of the polygon.

$C\bullet$

$\odot C$ circumscribes
the pentagon.

clinometer   A device used to measure angles of elevation and depression.

clockwise   Clockwise identifies the direction of rotation shown in the diagram at right. The word literally means "in the direction of the rotating hands of a clock." The opposite of clockwise is *counter-clockwise*.

combination   A combination is an arrangement of items that were selected without repeating items and without regard to order. The number of combinations that can be made by selecting r items from a set of n items can be found by dividing the total number of *permutations* by the number of arrangements of a single permutation, $_nC_r = \frac{_nP_r}{r!}$, which can be rewritten as $_nC_r = \frac{_nP_r}{r!} = \frac{n!}{r!(n-r)!}$. For instance, choosing a committee of 3 students from a group of 5 volunteers is a combination since the order in which committee members are selected does not matter: $_5C_3 = \frac{5!}{3!(5-3)!} = \frac{5 \cdot 4 \cdot 3 \cdot 2 \cdot 1}{3 \cdot 2 \cdot 1 \ \cdot \ 2 \cdot 1} = \frac{5 \cdot 4}{2} = 10$. See also *permutation*.

common difference   The difference between consecutive terms of an arithmetic sequence, also known as the sequence generator of an arithmetic sequence. When the common difference is positive the sequence increases; when it is negative the sequence decreases. In the sequence $3, 7, 11, ...$, the common difference is 4. See also *arithmetic sequence*.

common multiplier of a sequence   Another name for *common ratio of a sequence*.

common ratio of corresponding sides   Another name for the ratio of similarity. See *ratio of similarity*.

common ratio of a sequence   Common ratio is another name for the multiplier or sequence generator of a geometric sequence. It is the number to multiply one term by to get the next one. In the sequence: $96, 48, 24, ...$, the common ratio is $\frac{1}{2}$. See also *geometric sequence*.

compass   (a) A tool used to draw circles; (b) A tool used to navigate the Earth. A compass uses the Earth's magnetic field to determination which direction is north.

completing the square   A standard procedure for rewriting a quadratic equation from standard form into graphing form, or for rewriting the circle of an equation from general form into graphing form. For example, the first two terms in the equation $y = x^2 - 6x + 4$ look somewhat like $(x-3)^2$. But $(x-3)^2$ is 9 more than $x^2 - 6x$. That is, $x^2 - 6x = (x-3)^2 - 9$. We can rewrite $y = x^2 - 6x + 4$ in graphing form as follows:

$$y = x^2 - 6x \qquad + 4$$
$$y = (x-3)^2 - 9 \ \ + 4$$
$$y = (x-3)^2 - 5$$

complement of an event   The set of all the outcomes in the sample space that are not in the event. For example, if you randomly select one card from a deck of cards, the event {the card is a diamond} has a probability of $\frac{13}{52}$. The complement of the event is {the card is not a diamond}, or {the card is a heart, spade, or club}, and has a probability of $1 - \frac{13}{52}$.

complementary angles   Two angles whose measures add up to 90°. Angles T and V are complementary because $m\angle T + m\angle V = 90°$. Complementary angles may also be adjacent, like $\angle ABC$ and $\angle CBD$ in the diagram at far right.

concentric circles   Circles that have the same center. For example, the circles shown in the diagram at right are concentric.

concurrency (point of)   See *point of concurrency*.

conditional probability   The probability of outcome A occurring, given that outcome B has already happened, is called the conditional probability of A given B. One way to calculate the conditional probability of A given B is to use the Multiplication Rule, $P(A \text{ given } B) = \frac{P(A \text{ and } B)}{P(B)}$. In many situations it is possible to calculate the conditional probability directly from the data by counting the number of outcomes (or computing the probabilities) of A that are within the outcomes (probabilities) for B. See also *Multiplication Rule for Probabilities*.

conditional statement   A statement written in "If ..., then ..." form. For example, "*If a rectangle has four congruent sides, then it is a square*" is a conditional statement.

cone   A three-dimensional figure that consists of a circular face, called the base, a point called the apex, that is not in the flat surface (plane) of the base, and the lateral surface that connects the apex to each point on the circular boundary of the base. The slant height of a cone is the distance from the circular boundary to the apex. See also *right pyramid (or cone)* and *oblique pyramid (or cone)*.

congruence conditions   See *triangle congruence conditions*.

congruence statement   A statement indicating that two figures are congruent. The order of the letters in the names of the shapes indicates which sides and angles are congruent to each other. For example, if $\triangle ABC \cong \triangle DEF$, then $\angle A \cong \angle D$, $\angle B \cong \angle E$, $\angle C \cong \angle F$, $\overline{AB} \cong \overline{DE}$, $\overline{BC} \cong \overline{EF}$, and $\overline{AC} \cong \overline{DF}$.

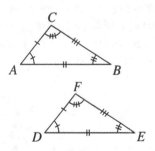

congruent   Two shapes are congruent if they have exactly the same shape and size. Congruent shapes are similar and have a scale factor of 1. The symbol for congruence is $\cong$.

conic section   A curve that is the intersection of a flat surface or plane with an infinite double cone. Conic sections include parabolas, ellipses, and hyperbolas. Circles, lines, and points are special cases of the conic sections.

conjecture   An educated guess. Conjectures often result from noticing a pattern during an investigation. Conjectures are also often written in conditional ("If…, then…") form. Once a conjecture is proven, it becomes a theorem.

consecutive angles of a polygon   The angles that occur at the two ends of any side of a polygon. For example, $\angle B$ and $\angle C$ are consecutive angles in the right trapezoid at right.

construction   The process of using a straightedge and compass to solve a problem and/or create a geometric diagram.

converse   The converse of a conditional statement can be found by switching the hypothesis (the "if" part) and the conclusion (the "then" part). For example, the converse of *"If P, then Q"* is *"If Q, then P."* Knowing that a conditional statement is true does not tell you whether its converse is true.

convex polygon   A polygon is convex if any pair of points inside the polygon can be connected by a segment without leaving the interior of the polygon. See also *non-convex polygon*.

coordinate geometry   The study of geometry on a coordinate graph.

coordinate graph   A method of specifying points (x, y) by their relationship to two perpendicular linear axes, often labeled the x-axis and y-axis. Also known as a rectangular coordinate graph or a Cartesian coordinate graph. See also *graph*.

corresponding angles   (a) When two lines are intersected by a third line (called a transversal), angles on the same side of the two lines and on the same side of the transversal are called corresponding angles. For example, the shaded angles in the diagram at right are corresponding angles. Note that if the two lines cut by the transversal are parallel, the corresponding angles are congruent. Conversely, if the corresponding angles are congruent, then the two lines intersected by the transversal are parallel; (b) Angles in two figures may also correspond, as shown in the figure in *corresponding parts*. See also *alternate interior angles* and *same-side interior angles*.

corresponding parts   Points, sides, edges, or angles in two or more figures that are images of each other with respect to a sequence of transformations. If two figures are congruent, their corresponding parts are congruent to each other.

cosine ratio In a right triangle, the cosine ratio of an acute angle, A, is $\cos A = \frac{\text{length of adjacent side}}{\text{length of hypotenuse}}$. In the triangle at right, $\cos A = \frac{AB}{AC} = \frac{4}{5}$. See also *sine ratio, tangent ratio*, and *inverse cosine*.

counter-clockwise Counter-clockwise identifies the direction of rotation shown in the diagram at right. The opposite of counter-clockwise is clockwise.

counterexample An example showing that a generalization has at least one exception; that is, a situation in which the statement is false. For example, the number 4 is a counterexample to the statement "*All even numbers are greater than 7.*"

cross-section The intersection of a three-dimensional solid and a plane. The cross-sections of an infinite double cone are called conic sections.

cube A polyhedron all of whose faces are squares.

cylinder (circular) A three-dimensional figure that consists of two parallel congruent circular regions (called bases) and a lateral surface containing segments connecting each point on the circular boundary of one base to the corresponding point on the circular boundary of the other. See also *oblique prism (or cylinder)* and *right cylinder*.

bases

decagon A polygon with ten sides.

decision chart A method for counting the number of outcomes (the size of the sample space) for a sequence of probabilistic situations, often in which the order of the items matters. A tree diagram could be used to count the number of outcomes, but if the number of outcomes is large a decision chart is more useful. For example, how many three-letter arrangements could be made by lining up any three blocks, chosen from a set of 26 alphabet blocks, if the first letter must be a vowel and the blocks are not reused? There are three decisions (three blocks to be chosen), with 5 choices for the first letter (a vowel), 25 for the second, and 24 for the third. According to the Fundamental Principle of Counting, the total number of possibilities is:

$$\underbrace{5}_{\text{1st decision}} \cdot \underbrace{25}_{\text{2nd decision}} \cdot \underbrace{24}_{\text{3rd decision}} = 3000 \ .$$

This decision chart is a short way to represent a tree with 5 branches for the first alphabet block, followed by 25 branches for each of those branches; each of those 125 branches would then have 24 branches representing the possibilities for the third alphabet block. See also *Fundamental Principle or Counting*.

deck of cards See *playing cards*.

degree One degree is an angle measure that is $\frac{1}{360}$ of a full circle.

delta (Δ)   A Greek letter that is often used to represent a difference. Its uses include Δx and Δy, which represent the lengths of the horizontal and vertical legs of a slope triangle, respectively.

Δy

Δx

density   The quantity of something per unit measure, especially length, area, or volume. For example, the density of birds on a power wire may be 7 birds/meter, the population density of Singapore is 7301 people per square meter, or the mass density of iron is $7.874 \frac{\text{g}}{\text{cm}^3}$.

diagonal   In a polygon, it is a segment that connects any two vertices of the polygon but is not a side of the polygon.

diagonal

diameter   A line segment drawn through the center of a circle with both endpoints on the circle. The length of a diameter is usually denoted d. Note that the length of a circle's diameter is twice the length of its radius. See also *circle*.

dilation   A transformation which produces a figure similar to the original by proportionally shrinking or stretching the figure. In a dilation, a shape is stretched (or compressed) proportionally from a point, called the point of dilation. See also *point of dilation*.

dimension   (a) Flat figures have two dimensions (which can be labeled base and height); (b) Solids have three dimensions (such as "width," "height," and "depth").

directrix   A line that, along with a point (called a focus), defines a conic section (such as a parabola). For any point on a parabola, the length of the segment between the focus and the point is equal to the length of the segment perpendicular from the directrix to point.

disjoint   Another name for *mutually exclusive*.

dissection   The process of dividing a flat shape or solid into parts that have no interior points in common.

dodecahedron   A polyhedron with twelve faces.

double cone   Two cones placed apex to apex so that their bases are parallel. Generally we think of double cones as extending to infinity beyond their bases.

double cone

edge   In three dimensions, a line segment formed by the intersection of two faces of a polyhedron.

edge

ellipse   A conic section created by slicing a cone with a plane. In a future course it will be defined using a focus and a directrix. A typical algebraic equation of an ellipse in graphing form is $\frac{(x-h)^2}{a^2} + \frac{(y-k)^2}{b^2} = 1$ and in general form it is $ax^2 + by^2 + cx + dy + e = 0$.

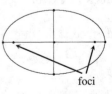

foci

endpoint   See *line segment* and *ray*.

equator   If we represent the Earth as a sphere, the equator is the great circle equally distant between the North and South poles. The equator divides the Earth into two halves called the Northern and Southern hemispheres. The equator also marks a latitude of 0°. See also *latitude*.

equilateral   A polygon is equilateral if all its sides have equal length. The word equilateral comes from *equi* (meaning equal) and *lateral* (meaning side). Equilateral triangles not only have sides of equal length, but also angles of equal measure. However, a polygon with more than three sides can be equilateral without having congruent angles. For example, see the rhombus at right.

evaluate (an expression)   Substitute one or more numbers for the variables in a mathematical expression. Compare evaluating an expression, in which you know the value of a variable and use it to rewrite an expression, to solving an equation, in which you determine the value of a variable. For example, to evaluate $x^2 + 3$ for $x = -4$ means to rewrite $x^2 + 3$ as $(-4)^2 + 3$ or 19. See also *solve (an equation)*.

event   The set of one or more outcomes (or results) of a probabilistic situation.

exact answer   An answer that is precisely accurate and not approximate. For example, if the length of a side of a triangle is exactly $\sqrt{10}$, the exact answer to the question "*How long is that side of the triangle?*" would be $\sqrt{10}$, while 3.162 would be a decimal approximation of the answer.

expected value   For this course, the expected value of a game is the average amount expected to be won or lost on each play of the game if the game is played many times. Expected value can be found by summing the probability of each outcome multiplied by its value. For example, if you play a game where you roll a die and win one point for every dot on the face that comes up, the expected value of this game is $(\frac{1}{6})1 + (\frac{1}{6})2 + (\frac{1}{6})3 + (\frac{1}{6})4 + (\frac{1}{6})5 + (\frac{1}{6})6 = 3.5$ points for each play. The expected value need not be a value that a player could actually win on a single play of the game.

experimental probability   The probability based on data collected in experiments. The experimental probability of an event is defined to be $\frac{\text{number of successful outcomes in the experiment}}{\text{total number of outcomes in the experiment}}$.

exterior angle (of a polygon)   When a side of a polygon is extended to form an angle with an adjacent side outside of the polygon, that angle is called an exterior angle. For example, the angles marked with letters in the diagram at right are exterior angles of the quadrilateral. Note that an exterior angle of a polygon is always adjacent and supplementary to an interior angle of that polygon. The sum of the exterior angles of a convex polygon is always 360°. See also *interior angle (of a polygon)*.

face of a polyhedron   One of the flat surfaces of a polyhedron, including the base(s).

factor   A factor of an expression is an integer or a polynomial, which when multiplied by one or more other factors, gives the expression. For example, $3, 6, (2x + 1)$, and $(4x+2)$ are each factors of $12x+6$, and factors of $x^2 + 3x + 2$ are $(x+1)$ and $(x+2)$.

factorial   A shorthand notation for the product of a list of consecutive positive integers from the given number down to 1: $n! = n(n-1)(n-2)(n-3) \cdot \ldots \cdot 3 \cdot 2 \cdot 1$. For example, $5! = 5 \cdot 4 \cdot 3 \cdot 2 \cdot 1 = 120$.

fair game   For the purposes of this course, a fair game has an expected value of 0 for all players. Therefore, over many plays, any player would expect to neither win nor lose points or money by playing a fair game.

flip   See *reflection*.

flowchart   A diagram showing an argument for a conclusion from certain evidence. A flowchart uses ovals connected by arrows to show the logical structure of the argument. When each oval has a reason stated next to it showing how the evidence leads to that conclusion, the flowchart represents a proof. See the example at right.

focus   A point that, along with a line (called a directrix), can be used to define a conic section (like a parabola). For any point on a parabola, the length of the segment between the focus and the point is equal to the length of the segment perpendicular from the directrix to point.

Fraction Buster   Fraction Busting is a method of simplifying equations involving fractions by using the Multiplicative Property of Equality to alter the equation so that no fractions remain. To use this method, multiply both sides of an equation by the common denominator of all the fractions in the equation. The result will be an equivalent equation with no fractions. For example, when given the equation $\frac{x}{7} + 2 = \frac{x}{3}$, we can multiply both sides by the Fraction Buster 21. The resulting equation, $3x + 42 = 7x$, is equivalent to the original but contains no fractions.

frequency table   A two-way table that contains entries that are counts (as opposed to fractions or percents). See also *two-way table*.

function   A relation in which for each input value there is one and only one output value. For example, the relation $f(x) = x + 4$ is a function; for each input value (x) there is exactly one output value. In terms of ordered pairs (x, y), no two ordered pairs of a function have the same first member (x). For example, a graph of a circle does not represent a function because for most x-values there are two y-values.

Fundamental Principle of Counting A method for counting the number of outcomes (the size of the sample space) of a probabilistic situation, often in which the order of the items matters. If event {A} has m outcomes, and event {B} has n outcomes after event {A} has occurred, then event {A} followed by event {B} has $m \cdot n$ outcomes. For a sequence of events, a tree diagram could be used to count the number of outcomes, but if the number of outcomes is large a decision chart is more useful. See also *decision chart*.

generic rectangle A type of diagram used to visualize multiplying expressions without algebra tiles. Each expression to be multiplied forms a side length of the rectangle, and the product is the sum of the areas of the sections of the rectangle. For example, the generic rectangle at right can be used to multiply $(2x+5)$ by $(x+3)$.

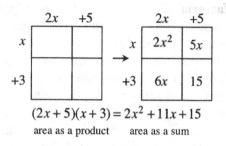

$$(2x+5)(x+3) = 2x^2 + 11x + 15$$

area as a product   area as a sum

geometric sequence An ordered sequence of mathematical terms in which each term is multiplied by a constant number to determine the next term in the sequence. The number each term is multiplied by to get the next term is called the multiplier, sequence generator, or common ratio. The equation for a geometric sequence is $t(n) = ab^n$ or $a_n = a_0 \cdot b^n$, where n is the term number, b is the multiplier, and a or a_0 is the zeroth (or initial) term of the sequence. Sequences are usually written starting with the first term, where $n = 1$. For example in the sequence, $5, 15, 45, \ldots$, the multiplier is 3, and the equation is $t(n) = \frac{5}{3} \cdot 3^n$. See also *arithmetic sequence*.

golden ratio The number $\frac{1+\sqrt{5}}{2}$, which is often labeled with the Greek letter phi (ϕ), pronounced "fee."

golden rectangle A rectangle whose side lengths are in the proportion of the golden ratio.

graph A graph represents numerical information spatially. The numbers may come from a table, situation (pattern), rule (equation or inequality), or figure. Most of the graphs in this course show points, lines, figures, and/or curves on a two-dimensional coordinate graph like the one below right.

A complete graph includes all the necessary information about a line or a curve. To be complete, a graph must have the following components: (1) the x-axis and y-axis labeled, clearly showing the scale; (2) the equation of the graph written near the line or curve; (3) the line or curve extended as far as possible on the graph with arrows if the line or curve continues beyond the axes; (4) the coordinates of all special points, such as x- and y-intercepts, shown in (x, y) form.

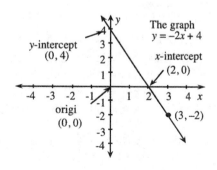

great circle A cross-section of a sphere that has the same radius as the sphere. If the Earth is represented with a sphere, the equator is an example of a great circle.

height (a) Triangle: the length of a segment that connects a vertex of the triangle to a line containing the opposite base (side) and is perpendicular to that line; (b) Trapezoid: the length of any segment that connects a point on one base of the trapezoid to the line containing the opposite base and is perpendicular to that line; (c) Parallelogram (includes rectangle, rhombus, and square): the length of any segment that connects a point on one base of the parallelogram to the line containing the opposite base and is perpendicular to that line; (d) Pyramid and cone: the length of the segment that connects the apex to a point in the plane containing the figure's base and is perpendicular to that plane; (e) Prism or cylinder: the length of a segment that connects one base of the figure to the plane containing the other base and is perpendicular to that plane. Some texts make a distinction between height and altitude, where the altitude is the segment described in the definition above and the height is its length.

hemisphere Half of a sphere. A great circle of a sphere divides it into two congruent parts, each of which is called a hemisphere. Hemispheres can also be created by slicing a sphere with a plane passing through the sphere's center. If the Earth is represented as a sphere, the Northern hemisphere is the portion of the Earth north of (and including) the equator. Likewise, the Southern hemisphere is the portion of the Earth south of (and including) the equator.

heptagon A polygon with seven sides.

heptahedron A polyhedron with seven faces.

hexagon A polygon with six sides.

hexahedron A polyhedron with six faces. A regular hexahedron is a cube.

HL ≅ (Triangle Shortcut) If the hypotenuse and one leg of one right triangle are congruent to the hypotenuse and corresponding leg of another right triangle, the two right triangles are congruent. Note that this congruence condition applies only to right triangles.

hyperbola A hyperbola looks like two curves (not parabolas) facing away from each other. A hyperbola is a conic section created by slicing a double cone with a plane. In a future course it will be defined using a focus and a directrix. A typical algebraic equation of a hyperbola is $\frac{(x-h)^2}{a^2} - \frac{(y-k)^2}{b^2} = 1$.

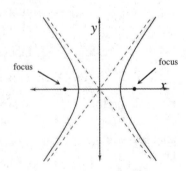

hypothesis A conjecture (or educated guess) in science.

hypotenuse   The side of a right triangle opposite the right angle. Note that legs of a right triangle are always shorter than its hypotenuse.   See also *legs*.

icosahedron   A polyhedron with twenty faces.

"If ..., then ..." statement   A statement written in the form "If ..., then ...."   Also known as a conditional statement.

image   The shape that results from a transformation, such as a translation, rotation, reflection, or dilation.

incenter   The center of the circle inscribed in a triangle. It can be found by locating the point at which the angle bisectors of a triangle intersect. The other points of concurrency studied in this course are the centroid and the circumcenter.

independent events   If the outcome of a probabilistic event does not affect the probability of another event, the events are independent. For example, assume you plan to roll a normal six-sided die twice and want to know the probability of rolling a 1 twice. The result of the first roll does not affect the probability of rolling a 1 on the second roll; the events are independent. If two events {A} and {B} are independent, then P(A given B) = P(A). The converse is also true. Alternatively, by rewriting the Multiplication Rule, if two events are independent, then P(A and B) = P(A) · P(B). Again, the converse is also true.

indirect proof   See *proof by contradiction*.

inequality symbols   The symbols < (less than), > (greater than), ≤ (less than or equal to), and ≥ (greater than or equal to).

inscribed angle   An angle with its vertex on the circle and sides intersecting the circle at two distinct points. In the figure at right ∠ABC is an inscribed angle.

Inscribed Angle Theorem   The measure of an inscribed angle is half the measure of its intercepted arc. Likewise, the measure of an intercepted arc is twice the measure of an inscribed angle whose sides pass through the endpoints of the arc. In the figure at right, if $m\overarc{AC} = 60°$, then $m∠ABC = 30°$.

inscribed circle   A circle is inscribed in a polygon if each side of the polygon intersects the circle at exactly one point.

inscribed polygon   A polygon is inscribed in a circle if each vertex of the polygon lies on the circle.

⊙B is inscribed in the pentagon.

The pentagon is inscribed in ⊙C.

integers The set of numbers $\{\,\ldots -3, -2, -1, 0, 1, 2, 3, \ldots\,\}$.

intercepted arc The arc of a circle bounded by the points where the two sides of an inscribed angle meet the circle. In the circle at right, $\angle ABC$ intercepts $\overset{\frown}{AC}$.

interior angle (of a polygon) An angle formed by two consecutive sides of the polygon. The vertex of the angle is a vertex (corner) of the polygon. The sum of the interior angles of a polygon with n-sides is $180°(n-2)$.

interior angle

intersection A point of intersection is a point that the graphs of two or more equations have in common. Graphs may intersect in one, two, several, many or no points. The set of coordinates of a point of intersection are a solution to the equation for each graph. The functions at right have two points of intersection.

intersection of two events The intersection of the two events {A} and {B} is a new event that includes all the outcomes in which both A *and* B will occur. For example, if event {A} is the thirteen diamond-suited cards in a deck of playing cards, and {B} is the four Aces, then the event {A intersection B} contains 1 outcome: {A♦}. See also *union of two events*.

inverse cosine ($\cos^{-1} x$)**, inverse sine** ($\sin^{-1} x$)**, and inverse tangent** ($\tan^{-1} x$)
The inverse of the cosine, sine, and tangent functions (the functions that "undo" cosine, sine, and tangent). When the ratio between the lengths of two sides of a right triangle is known, $\sin^{-1}$, $\cos^{-1}$, or $\tan^{-1}$ can be used to find the measure of one of the triangle's acute angles. For example, if $\cos\theta = \frac{\sqrt{3}}{2}$, to find θ, find the inverse cosine of both sides:

$$\cos\theta = \frac{\sqrt{3}}{2}$$
$$\cos^{-1}(\cos\theta) = \cos^{-1}\left(\frac{\sqrt{3}}{2}\right)$$
$$\theta = 30°$$

irrational numbers The set of numbers that cannot be expressed in the form $\frac{a}{b}$, where a and b are integers and $b \neq 0$. For example, π and $\sqrt{2}$ are irrational numbers.

isosceles trapezoid A trapezoid with a pair of equal base angles (from the same base). The base of a trapezoid is always one of the two parallel sides. Note that the non-parallel sides on an isosceles triangle are congruent.

isosceles triangle A triangle with two sides of equal length.

Isosceles Triangle Theorem If a triangle is isosceles, then the base angles (which are opposite the congruent sides) are congruent. For example, if $\triangle ABC$ is isosceles with $\overline{BA} \cong \overline{BC}$, then the angles opposite these sides are congruent; that is, $\angle A \cong \angle C$.

iteration   The act of repeating an action over and over.

justify   To give a logical reason supporting a statement or step in a proof.   More generally, to use facts, definitions, rules, and/or previously proven conjectures in an organized sequence to convincingly demonstrate that your claim (or your answer) is valid (true).

kite   A quadrilateral with two distinct pairs of consecutive congruent sides.

lateral edge   See *pyramid*.

lateral face   See *pyramid*.

lateral surface   (a) All the faces of a prism or pyramid, with the exception of the base(s); (b) On a cone, the surface not including the circular base.   The lateral surface connects the apex to each point on the circular boundary of the base.

lateral surface area   The sum of the areas of all the lateral surfaces of a polyhedron or solid.   See *lateral surface*.

latitude   An angular measure (in degrees) that indicates how far north or south of the equator a position on the Earth is.   All points on the equator have a latitude of 0°.   The North Pole has a latitude of 90°, while the South Pole has a latitude of –90°.

Law of Cosines   For any $\triangle ABC$ with sides $a, b,$ and c opposite $\angle A$, $\angle B$, and $\angle C$ respectively, it is always true that $c^2 = a^2 + b^2 - 2ab \cdot \cos(C)$, $b^2 = a^2 + c^2 - 2ac \cdot \cos(B)$, and $a^2 = b^2 + c^2 - 2bc \cdot \cos(A)$.

Law of Sines   For any $\triangle ABC$ with sides $a, b,$ and c opposite $\angle A$, $\angle B$, and $\angle C$ respectively, it is always true that $\frac{\sin A}{a} = \frac{\sin B}{b} = \frac{\sin C}{c}$.

legs   The two sides of a right triangle that form the right angle.   Note that the right triangle are always shorter than its hypotenuse.   See also *hypotenuse*.

line   A line is one-dimensional and extends without end in two directions.   It is made up of points and has no thickness.   A line can be named with a letter (such as *l*), but also can be labeled using two points on the line, such as $\overleftrightarrow{AB}$ below.   A line is a mathematically undefined term in geometry.   See also *ray* and *line segment*.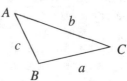

line of reflection   Same as the *line of symmetry*.

line of symmetry   A line that divides a shape into two congruent parts that are mirror images of each other. If you fold a shape over its line of symmetry, the shapes on both sides of the line will match each other perfectly. Some shapes have more than one line of symmetry, such as the example at right. Other shapes may only have one line of symmetry or no lines of symmetry.

line segment   The portion of a line between two points. A line segment is named using its endpoints. For example, the line segment at right can be named either $\overline{AB}$ or $\overline{BA}$. See also *line*.

A B

linear scale factor   Same as *ratio of similarity*.

logical argument   A logical sequence of statements and reasons that lead to a conclusion. A logical argument can be written in a paragraph, represented with a flowchart, or documented in a two-column proof.

longitude   An angular measure (in degrees) that indicates how far west or east of the prime meridian a position on the Earth is. Lines of longitude (which are actually circles) are all great circles that pass through the North and South Poles.

major arc   An arc with measure greater than 180°. Each major arc has a corresponding minor arc that has a measure that is less than 180°. A major arc is named with three letters on the arc. For example, the highlighted arc at right is the major arc $\overarc{ABC}$.

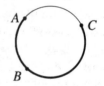

mapping   In general, the term mapping is synonymous with function, but in this course we restrict its meaning to refer to functions that take points on a line or in the plane, to other points on a line or in the plane.

mat plan   A top (or bottom) view of a multiple cube solid. The number in each square is the number of cubes in that stack. For example, the mat plan at right represents the solid at the far right.

3	0	2
1	0	1
0	1	0

FRONT

measurement   For the purposes of this course, a measurement is an indication of the size or magnitude of a geometric figure. For example, an appropriate measurement of a line segment would be its length. Appropriate measurements of a square would include not only the length of a side, but also its area and perimeter. The measure of an angle represents the number of degrees of rotation from one ray to the other about the vertex.

median   A line segment that connects a vertex of a triangle with the midpoint of side opposite to the vertex. For example, since D is a midpoint of $\overline{BC}$, then $\overline{AD}$ is a median of $\triangle ABC$. The three medians of a triangle intersect at a point called the centroid.

Core Connections Geometry

meridian   A line of longitude. See *longitude* and *prime meridian*.

midpoint   A point that divides a segment into two segments of equal length. For example, point D is the midpoint of $\overline{BC}$ in $\triangle ABC$ in the example for median.

midsegment   A segment joining the midpoints of two sides of a triangle.

minor arc   An arc with measure less than 180°. Each minor arc has a corresponding major arc that has a measure that is more than 180°. Minor arcs are named using the endpoints of the arc. For example, the highlighted arc at right is named $\overset{\frown}{AC}$.

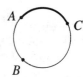

Möbius strip   A one-sided surface in a closed loop that can be formed by giving a rectangular strip of paper a half-twist and affixing its ends.

monomial   An expression with only one term. It can be a number, a variable, or the product of a number and one or more variables. For example, 7, $3x$, $-4ab$, and $3x^2y$ are each monomials.

Multiplication Rule for Probabilities   For two events, {A} and {B}, $P(A \text{ and } B) = P(A \text{ given } B) \cdot P(B)$, or equivalently, $P(A \text{ given } B) = \frac{P(A \text{ and } B)}{P(B)}$. When the two events are independent, then $P(A \text{ given } B) = P(A)$, and the Multiplication Rule can be rewritten as $P(A \text{ and } B) = P(A) \cdot P(B)$. See also *Addition Rule for Probability*.

multiplier in a geometric sequence   The number by which one term in a geometric sequence is multiplied to generate the next term. The multiplier is also known as the common ratio or the sequence generator. In the sequence $5, 15, 45, \ldots$, the multiplier is 3. See also *geometric sequence*.

mutually exclusive   Two events {A} and {B} are mutually exclusive if they have no outcomes in common. That is, $P(A \text{ and } B) = 0$. This situation is also called disjoint.

n-gon   A polygon with n sides. A polygon is often referred to as an n-gon when we do not yet know the value of n.

net   A diagram that, when folded, forms the surface of a three-dimensional solid. A net is essentially the faces of a solid laid flat. It is one of several ways to represent a three-dimensional diagram. The diagram at right is a representation of the solid at the far right. Note that the shaded region of the net indicates the (bottom) base of the solid.

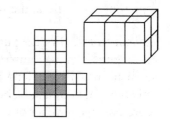

nonagon   A polygon with nine sides.

nonahedron   A polyhedron with nine faces.

non-convex polygon A polygon that is not convex. An example of a non-convex polygon is shown at right. See also *convex polygon*.

oblique prism (or cylinder) A prism (or cylinder) is oblique when its lateral surface(s) are not perpendicular to the base. See figure at right. See also *Cavalieri's Principle*.

oblique pyramid (or cone) A pyramid (or cone) is oblique when its apex is not directly above the center of the base.

obtuse angle Any angle that measures between (but not including) 90° and 180°.

octagon A polygon with eight sides.

octahedron A polyhedron with eight faces. In a regular octahedron, all of the faces are equilateral triangles.

opposite In a figure, opposite means "across from." For example, in a triangle, an opposite side is the side that is across from a particular angle and is not a side that makes the angle. For example, the side $\overline{AB}$ in $\triangle ABC$ at right is opposite $\angle C$, while $\overline{AC}$ is opposite the right angle.

opposite interior angles See *remote interior angles*.

orientation In this course, orientation refers to the placement and alignment of a figure in relation to others or an object of reference (such as coordinate axes). Unless it has rotation symmetry, the orientation of a figure changes when it is rotated (turned) less than 360°. Also, the orientation of a shape changes when it is reflected, except when reflected across a line of symmetry.

outcome The result of a probabilistic situation. The set of all possible outcomes of a probabilistic situation is called the sample space. See also *event*.

parabola A parabola is a conic section created by slicing a cone with a plane parallel to a lateral edge of the cone. Parabolas may also be generated geometrically: the set of all points that are equidistant from a single point (the focus) and a line (the directrix). The graph of a quadratic equation is a parabola. A quadratic equation can be given in standard form $y = ax^2 + bx + c$ or in graphing form $y = a(x-h)^2 + k$, with vertex at (h,k).

parallel lines Two lines on a flat surface are parallel if they never intersect. Two line segments on a flat surface are parallel if the lines they lie on never intersect. There is a constant distance between two parallel lines (or line segments). Identical arrow markings are used to note parallel lines or line segments as shown in the diagrams at right.

parallelogram A quadrilateral with two pairs of parallel sides.

pentagon A polygon with five sides.

pentagram A pentagram is created by connecting five equally-spaced points on the circumference of a circle. Note that all of the corresponding lengths and angles are equal to each other.

pentahedron A polyhedron with five faces.

perimeter The distance around the exterior of a figure on a flat surface. For a polygon, the perimeter is the sum of the lengths of its sides. The perimeter of a circle is also called the circumference.

permutation An arrangement of items in which items cannot be selected more than once and the order of selection matters. The number of permutations that can be made by selecting r items from a set of n total items can be represented with tree diagrams or decision charts, or calculated using the formula $_nP_r = \frac{n!}{(n-r)!}$. For example, if each of five letters, A, B, C, D, E, is printed on a card, the number of 3-letter sequences can you make by selecting three of the five cards is a permutation, $_5P_3 = \frac{5!}{2!} = \frac{5 \cdot 4 \cdot 3 \cdot 2 \cdot 1}{2 \cdot 1} = 5 \cdot 4 \cdot 3 = 60$. See also *combination*.

perpendicular Two rays, line segments, or lines that meet (intersect) to form a right angle (90°) are called perpendicular. A line and a flat surface can also be perpendicular if the line does not lie on the flat surface, but intersects it and forms a right angle with every line on the flat surface passing through the point of intersection. A small square at the point of intersection of two lines or segments indicates that the lines are perpendicular.

perpendicular bisector The perpendicular bisector of a line segment is a line segment perpendicular to the original segment, and passing through its midpoint.

phi (ϕ) A Greek letter, pronounced "fee," that represents the golden ratio. $\phi = \frac{1+\sqrt{5}}{2}$

pi (π) The ratio of the circumference (C) of the circle to its diameter (d). For every circle, $\pi = \frac{\text{circumference}}{\text{diameter}} = \frac{C}{d}$. Numbers such as 3.14, 3.14159, or $\frac{22}{7}$ are approximations of π.

plane A plane is an undefined term in geometry. It is a two-dimensional flat surface that extends without end. It is made up of points and has no thickness.

Platonic solid   A convex regular polyhedron. All faces of a platonic solid are congruent, regular polygons. There are only five possible Platonic solids: tetrahedron (with four faces of equilateral triangles), cube (with six faces of squares), octahedron (with eight faces of equilateral triangles), dodecahedron (with twelve faces of regular pentagons), and icosahedron (with twenty faces of equilateral triangles).

playing cards   A standard deck of playing cards contains the following 52 cards:
- 13 cards with red hearts (♥), numbered 2 through 10, Jack, Queen, King, and Ace
- 13 cards with red diamonds (♦), numbered 2 through 10, Jack, Queen, King, and Ace
- 13 cards with black spades (♠), numbered 2 through 10, Jack, Queen, King, and Ace
- 13 cards with black clubs (♣), numbered 2 through 10, Jack, Queen, King, and Ace

The face cards are the Jacks, Queens, and Kings (Aces are not considered face cards).

point of concurrency   The single point where two or more lines intersect on a plane. For the points of concurrency of a triangle, see *circumcenter, centroid,* and *incenter*.

point of dilation   The point from which a figure is stretched proportionally when the figure is dilated. For example, in the diagram at right, $\triangle ABC$ is dilated to form $\triangle A'B'C'$. Notice that while a dilation changes the size and location of the original figure, it does not rotate or reflect the original. While lengths can change, angles do not change under a dilation.

point of intersection   See *intersection*.

polygon   A two-dimensional closed figure of three or more line segments (sides) connected end to end. Each segment is a side and only intersects the endpoints of its two adjacent sides. Each point of intersection is a vertex. At right are two examples of polygons. See also *regular polygon*.

polyhedron (plural: polyhedra)   A three-dimensional object with no holes that is bounded by polygons. The polygons are joined at their sides, forming the edges of the polyhedron. Each polygon is a face of the polyhedron. See also *solid*.

polynomial   An algebraic expression that involves at most the operations of addition, subtraction, and/or multiplication. A polynomial in one variable is an expression that can be written as the sum of terms that have the form: (any number) $\cdot$ $x^{\text{(whole number)}}$.

postulates   Statements accepted as true without proof. Also known as axioms.

preimage   The original figure in a transformation.

prime meridian   The line of longitude on the Earth chosen to represent $0°$. It passes through Greenwich, England, on the eastern edge of London.

Core Connections Geometry

prism A three-dimensional figure that consists of two parallel congruent polygons (called bases) and a lateral surface containing segments connecting each point on each side of one base to the corresponding point on the other base. The lateral surface of a prism consists of parallelograms. See also *right prism* and *oblique prism*.

probabilistic situation A situation in which the outcomes are determined by random processes. See also *random*.

probability A number that represents how likely an event is to happen. When a event has a finite number of equally-likely outcomes, the probability that one of those outcomes, called *A*, will occur is expressed as a ratio and written as:

$$P(A) = \frac{\text{number of successful outcomes}}{\text{total number of possible outcomes}}.$$

For example, when flipping a coin, the probability of getting tails, P(tails), is $\frac{1}{2}$ because there is only one tail (successful outcome) out of the two possible equally-likely outcomes (a head and a tail). Probability can be written as a ratio, decimal, or percent. A probability of 0 (or 0%) indicates that it is impossible for the event to occur, while a probability of 1 (or 100%) indicates that the event must occur. Events that "might happen" will have values somewhere between 0 and 1 (or between 0% and 100%).

probability table Another name for *two-way table*.

proof A convincing logical argument that uses definitions and previously proven conjectures in an organized sequence to show that a conjecture is true. A proof can be written in a paragraph, represented with a flowchart, or documented in a formal two-column proof.

proof by contradiction A proof that begins by assuming that an assertion is true and then shows that this assumption leads to a contradiction of a known fact. This demonstrates that the assertion is false. Also known as an indirect proof.

proportional equation An equation stating that two ratios are equal. For example, the equation below is a proportion. A proportion is a useful type of equation to set up when solving problems involving proportional relationships.

$$\frac{68 \text{ votes for Mr. Mears}}{100 \text{ people surveyed}} = \frac{34 \text{ votes for Mr. Mears}}{50 \text{ people surveyed}}$$

protractor A geometric tool used for measuring the number of degrees in an angle.

pyramid   A polyhedron with a polygonal base formed by connecting each vertex of the base to a single point (the apex) that is above the flat surface containing the base. The lateral faces of a pyramid are the triangles formed by connecting consecutive vertices of the base to the apex. Lateral edges are two of the sides of these lateral triangular faces. The slant height is the height of a lateral triangular face. See also *right pyramid* and *oblique pyramid*.

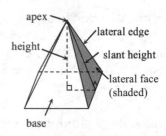

Pythagorean Theorem   The statement relating the lengths of the legs of a right triangle to the length of the hypotenuse: $(\text{leg \#1})^2 + (\text{leg \#2})^2 = \text{hypotenuse}^2$. The Pythagorean Theorem is powerful because if you know the lengths of any two sides of a right triangle, you can use this relationship to find the length of the third side.

Pythagorean Triple   Any three positive integers a, b, and c that make the relationship $a^2 + b^2 = c^2$ true. Commonly used Pythagorean Triples include $3, 4, 5$ and $5, 12, 13$.

quadratic function (equation)   An equation that can be written in the form $ax^2 + bx + c = 0$, where a, b, and c are real numbers and a is nonzero. A quadratic equation written in this form is said to be in standard form. For example, $3x^2 - 4x + 7.5 = 0$ is a quadratic equation in standard form. The graph of a quadratic function is a parabola.

Quadratic Formula   The Quadratic Formula states that if $ax^2 + bx + c = 0$ and $a \neq 0$, then $x = \frac{-b \pm \sqrt{b^2 - 4ac}}{2a}$. For example, if $5x^2 + 9x + 3 = 0$, then $x = \frac{-9 \pm \sqrt{9^2 - 4(5)(3)}}{2(5)} = \frac{-9 \pm \sqrt{21}}{10}$.

quadrilateral   A polygon with four sides.

radians   The ratio of the arc length to the radius for any sector of a circle. The ratio will be constant for a given central angle, regardless of the length of the radius of the circle. Along with degrees, radians are a very common method unit of measurement for the central angle of a circle.

radius (plural: radii)   (a) Of a circle: A line segment drawn from the center of a circle to a point on the circle. Note that the length of a circle's radius is half the length of the circle's diameter. See also *circle*. (b) Of a regular polygon: A line segment that connects the center of a regular polygon with a vertex. The length of a radius is usually denoted r.

random   An outcome is random if it happens by chance, that is, its result cannot be predicted from previous outcomes. A sequence of several random outcomes in a row will have no predictable order or pattern. For example, the outcome of rolling a die is random because the outcome cannot be predicted, and many rolls in a row will have no predictable pattern.

Core Connections Geometry

ratio A ratio compares two quantities by division. A ratio can be written using a colon, but is more often written as a fraction. For example, in the two similar triangles shown below, a ratio can be used to compare the length of $\overline{BC}$ in $\triangle ABC$ with the length of $\overline{EF}$ in $\triangle DEF$. This ratio can be written as 5:11 or as the fraction $\frac{5}{11}$.

ratios of similarity $r : r^2 : r^3$ (a) The ratio of any pair of corresponding sides of two similar figures. This means that once it is determined that two figures are similar, all of their pairs of corresponding sides have the same ratio. For example, for the similar triangles $\triangle ABC$ and $\triangle DEF$ above, the ratio of similarity is $\frac{5}{11}$. The ratio of similarity can also be called the linear scale factor. When the ratio is comparing a figure and its image after a dilation, this ratio can also be called the zoom factor.

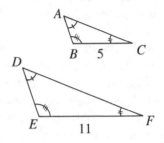

When a two-dimensional figure is enlarged (or reduced) proportionally, its lengths and area change. If the linear scale factor is r, then all lengths (such as sides, perimeter, and heights) of the original (preimage) figure is multiplied by a factor of r while the area is multiplied by a factor of r^2.

When a solid is enlarged (or reduced) proportionally, its lengths, surface area, and volume also change. If the linear scale factor is r, then the surface area is multiplied by a factor of r^2 and the volume is multiplied by a factor of r^3. Thus, if a solid is enlarged proportionally by a linear scale factor of r, then the new edge lengths, surface area, and volume can be found using the relationships below.

$$\text{New edge length} = r \cdot \text{(corresponding edge length of original polyhedron)}$$
$$\text{New surface area} = r^2 \cdot \text{(original surface area)}$$
$$\text{New volume} = r^3 \cdot \text{(original volume)}$$

rationalizing the denominator Rewriting a fractional expression that has radicals in the denominator, in order to eliminate the radicals from the denominator. For example, $\frac{2}{\sqrt{3}}$ can be rationalized as follows: $\frac{2}{\sqrt{3}} = \frac{2}{\sqrt{3}} \cdot \frac{\sqrt{3}}{\sqrt{3}} = \frac{2\sqrt{3}}{3}$.

ray A ray is part of a line that starts at one endpoint and extends without end in one direction. In the example at right, ray $\overrightarrow{AB}$ is part of $\overleftrightarrow{AB}$ that starts at A and contains all of the points of $\overleftrightarrow{AB}$ that are on the same side of A as point B, including A. Point A is the endpoint of $\overrightarrow{AB}$. See also *line*.

reasoning See *logical argument* and *proof*.

rectangle A quadrilateral with four right angles.

reflection   A transformation across a line that produces a mirror image of the original (preimage) shape. The reflection is called the image of the original figure. The line is called a line of symmetry. See the example at right. Note that a reflection is also sometimes referred to as a "flip."

original   image

line of reflection

Reflexive Property   The Reflexive Property states that any expression is always equal to itself. That is, $a = a$. This property is often useful when proving that two triangles that share a side or an angle are congruent. For example, in the diagram at right, since $\triangle ABD$ and $\triangle CBD$ share a side ($\overline{BD}$), the Reflexive Property justifies that $BD = BD$.

reflection symmetry   See *symmetry*.

regular polygon   A polygon is regular if it is a convex polygon with congruent angles and congruent sides. For example, the shape at right is a regular hexagon.

relation   An equation that relates two or more variables. For example, $y = 3x - 2$ and $x^2 + y^2 = 9$ are both relations. See also *function*.

relationship   For this course, a relationship is a way that two objects (such as two line segments or two triangles) are connected. When you know that the relationship holds between two objects, learning about one object can give you information about the other. Relationships can be described in two ways: a geometric relationship (such as a pair of vertical angles or two line segments that are parallel) and a relationship between the measures (such as two angles that are complementary or two sides of a triangle that have the same length). Common geometric relationships between two figures include being similar (when two figures have the shape, but not necessarily the same size) and being congruent (when two figures have the same shape and the same size).

relative frequency table   A two-way table that contains entries that are fractions or percents (as opposed to counts). See also *two-way table*.

remote interior angles   If a triangle has an exterior angle, the remote interior angles are the two angles not adjacent to the exterior angle. Also called opposite interior angles.

remote interior angles

exterior angle

Reuleaux curve   The curve created by drawing arcs between two consecutive vertices (with a center at the opposite vertex) on a regular polygon with an odd number of sides. As the curve is "rolled," the width of the figure is constant.

width

834

rhombus   A quadrilateral with four congruent sides.

right angle   An angle that measures 90°. A small square is used to note a right angle, as shown in the example at right.

right prism (or cylinder)   A prism (or cylinder) with lateral surface(s) that are perpendicular to the base. See the figure at right.

right pyramid (or cone)   A pyramid (or cone) with its apex directly above the center of the base.

right triangle   A triangle that has one right angle. The side of a right triangle opposite the right angle is called the hypotenuse, and the two sides adjacent to the right angle are called legs. Note that legs of a right triangle are always shorter than its hypotenuse.

rigid motions   See *rigid transformations*.

rigid transformations   Movements of figures that preserve their shape and size. Examples of rigid transformations are reflections, rotations, and translations. Also called rigid motions or "isometries." See also *similarity transformations*.

rotation   A transformation that turns all of the points in the original (preimage) figure the same number of degrees around a fixed center point (such as the origin on a graph). The result is called the image of the original figure. The point that the shape is rotated about is called the center of rotation. To define a rotation, you need to state the measure of turn (in degrees), the direction the shape is turned (such as clockwise or counter-clockwise), and the center of rotation. See the example at right. Note that a rotation is also sometimes referred to as a "turn."

rotation symmetry   See *symmetry*.

same-side interior angles   Two angles between two lines and on the same side of a third line that intersects them (called a transversal). The shaded angles in the diagram at right are an example of a pair of same-side interior angles. Note that if the two lines that are cut by the transversal are parallel, then the two angles are supplementary (add up to 180°). Conversely, if the two angles are supplementary, then the two lines that are cut by the transversal are parallel. See also *alternate interior angles* and *corresponding angles*.

sample space   The set of all possible outcomes of a probabilistic situation. The sample space for rolling a standard 6-sided die is the set $\{1, 2, 3, 4, 5, 6\}$ because those are all the possible outcomes.

SAS ≅ (Triangle Congruence)   Two triangles are congruent if two sides and their included angle of one triangle are congruent to the corresponding two sides and included angle of another triangle.

SAS ~ (Triangle Similarity)   If two triangles have two pairs of corresponding sides that are proportional and have congruent included angles, then the triangles are similar.

scale   The ratio between a length of the representation (such as a map, model, or diagram) and the corresponding length of the actual object. For example, the map of a city may use one inch to represent one mile.

scalene triangle   A triangle with no congruent sides.

scatterplot   A way of displaying two-variable numerical data where two measurements are taken for each subject (like height and forearm length, or surface area of cardboard and volume of cereal held in a cereal box). To create a scatterplot, the two values for each subject are written as coordinate pairs and graphed on a pair of coordinate axes (each axis representing a variable). See also *association*.

secant   A line that intersects a circle at two distinct points.

sector   A region formed by two radii of a central angle and the arc between their endpoints on the circle. You can think of it as a portion of a circle and its interior, resembling a piece of pizza.

segment   See *line segment*.

semicircle   In a circle, a semicircle is an arc with endpoints that are endpoints of any diameter of the circle. It is a half circle and has a measure of 180°.

sequence   An ordered sequence of mathematical terms. A sequence is a function in which the independent variable is a positive integer (sometimes called the term number). The dependent variable is the term value. A sequence is usually written as a list of numbers, starting with the first term where $n = 1$. See also *arithmetic sequence* and *geometric sequence*.

sequence generator   The generator of a sequence tells what you do to each term to get the next term. Note that this is different from the function for the nth term of the sequence. The generator only tells you how to find the following term, when you already know one term. In an arithmetic sequence the generator is the common difference; in a geometric sequence it is the multiplier or common ratio. See also *arithmetic sequence* and *geometric sequence*.

side of an angle   One of the two rays that form an angle.

side of a polygon   See *polygon*.

similar figures   Two shapes are similar if they have exactly the same shape but are not necessarily the same size. Similar polygons have congruent angles, but not congruent sides – the corresponding sides are proportional. The symbol for similar is ~ . See also *ratio of similarity*.

similarity conditions   See *triangle similarity conditions*.

similarity statement   A statement that indicates that two figures are similar. The order of the letters in the names of the shapes in the similarity statement indicates which sides and angles correspond to each other. For example, $\triangle ABC \sim \triangle DEF$ is a similarity statement. It indicates that $\angle A$ corresponds to $\angle D$, and $\overline{AB}$ corresponds to $\overline{DE}$.

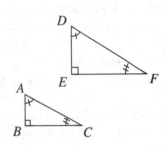

similarity transformations   Movements of figures that preserve their shape, but not necessarily their size. Examples of similarity transformations are reflections, rotations, translations, and dilations. See also *rigid transformations*.

sine ratio   In a right triangle, the sine ratio of an acute angle ($\angle A$) is $\sin A = \frac{\text{length of opposite side}}{\text{length of hypotenuse}}$. In the triangle at right, $\sin A = \frac{BC}{AC} = \frac{3}{5}$. See also *cosine ratio, tangent ratio,* and *inverse sine*.

skew lines   Lines that do not lie in the same flat surface (or plane).

slant height   See *pyramid* or *cone*.

slide   See *translation*.

slope   A ratio that describes how steep (or flat) a line is. Slope can be positive, negative, or even zero, but a straight line has only one slope. Slope is the ratio $\frac{\text{vertical change}}{\text{horizontal change}}$ or $\frac{\text{change in } y\text{-value}}{\text{change in } x\text{-value}}$, sometimes written $\frac{\Delta y}{\Delta x}$. When the equation of a line is written in $y = mx + b$ form, m is the slope of the line. A line has positive slope if it slopes upward from left to right on a graph, negative slope if it slopes downward from left to right, zero slope if it is horizontal, and undefined slope if it is vertical. Parallel lines have equal slopes, and the slopes of perpendicular lines are opposite reciprocals of each other (e.g., $\frac{3}{5}$ and $-\frac{5}{3}$).

slope angle   The angle a line forms with the *x*-axis on a coordinate graph. If the slope is of the line is positive, the angle will be acute (less than 90°). If the slope is negative, the angle will be obtuse (between 90° and 180°). See also *slope triangle*.

Slope-Intercept Form   A form of a linear equation: $y = mx + b$. In this form, m is the slope and the point $(0, b)$ is the *y*-intercept.

slope triangle   A right triangle with legs (parallel to the x- and y-axes) that meet the hypotenuse at two points on a given line or line segment. The lengths of the legs of the slope triangle can be used to find the slope of the line. The angle (θ) formed in a slope triangle by the hypotenuse and the horizontal leg is equivalent to the slope angle. See also *slope angle*.

solid   A closed three-dimensional shape and all of its interior points. Examples include regions bounded by pyramids, cylinders, and spheres.

solve (an equation)   To find all the solutions to an equation or an inequality (or a system of equations or inequalities). Compare evaluating an expression, in which you know the value of a variable and use it to rewrite an expression, to solving an equation, in which you determine the value of a variable. For example, solving the equation $x^2 = 9$ gives the solutions $x = 3$ and $x = -3$. The solution(s) may be number(s), variable(s), or an expression.

space   The set of all points in three-dimensions.

special right triangle   A right triangle with particular notable features that can be used to solve problems. Sometimes, these triangles can be recognized by the angles, such as the 45°- 45°- 90° triangle (also known as an isosceles right triangle) and a 30°- 60°- 90° triangle. Some people also categorize triangles for which the sides are Pythagorean Triples as special triangles.

sphere   The set of all points in space that are the same distance from a fixed point. The fixed point is the center of the sphere and the distance is its radius.

square   A quadrilateral with four right angles and four congruent sides.

square root   A number a is a square root of b if $a^2 = b$. For example, the number 9 has two square roots, 3 and –3. A negative number has no real square roots; a positive number has two; and zero has just one square root, namely, itself. In a geometric context, the principal square root of a number x (written $\sqrt{x}$) represents the length of a side of a square with area x. For example, $\sqrt{16} = 4$. Therefore if the side of a square has a length of 4 units, then its area is 16 square units.

SSS ≅ (Triangle Congruence)   Two triangles are congruent if all three pairs of corresponding sides are congruent.

SSS ~ (Triangle Similarity)   If two triangles have all three pairs of corresponding sides that are proportional (this means that the ratios of corresponding sides are equal), then the triangles are similar.

straight angle An angle that measures 180°. This occurs when the rays of the angle point in opposite directions, forming a line.

straightedge A tool used as a guide to draw lines, rays, and segments. A ruler has measurement markings while a straightedge does not.

star polygon A star polygon is created by connecting equally-spaced points on the circumference of a circle. The star polygon to the right is commonly called a pentagram.

statement A recording of fact to present evidence in a logical argument (proof).

stretch point See *point of dilation*.

Substitution Method A method for solving a system of equations by replacing one variable with an expression involving the remaining variable(s). For example, in the system of equations at right the first equation tells you that y is equal to $-3x+5$. We can substitute $-3x+5$ in for y in the second equation to get $2(-3x+5)+10x=18$, then solve this equation to find that $x = 2$. Once we have x, we substitute that value back into either of the original equations to find that $y = -1$.

$$y = -3x+5$$
$$2y + 10x = 18$$

Substitution Property The Substitution Property states that in an expression, one can replace a variable, number, or expression with something equal to it without altering the value of the whole. For example, if $x = 3$, then $5x - 7$ can be evaluated by replacing x with 3. This results in $5(3) - 7 = 8$.

supplementary angles Two angles a and b for which $a + b = 180°$. Each angle is called the supplement of the other. In the example at right, angles A and B are supplementary. Supplementary angles are often adjacent. For example, since $\angle LMN$ is a straight angle, then $\angle LMP$ and $\angle PMN$ are supplementary angles because $m\angle LMP + m\angle PMN = 180°$.

surface area The sum of all the area(s) of the surface(s) of a three-dimensional solid. For example, the surface area of a cylinder is the sum of the areas of its top base, its bottom base, and its lateral surface.

symmetry (a) Rotation symmetry: A shape has rotation symmetry when it can be rotated for less than 360° and it appears not to change. For example the hexagon at right appears not to change if it is rotated 60° clockwise (or counter-clockwise); (b) Reflection symmetry: A shape has reflection symmetry when it appears not to change after being reflected across a line. The regular hexagon at right also has reflection symmetry across any line drawn through opposite vertices, such as those shown in the diagram. See *reflection, rotation,* and *line of symmetry*.

system of equations A system of equations is a set of equations with the same variables. Solving a system of equations means finding one or more solutions that make each of the equations in the system true. A solution to a system of equations gives a point of intersection of the graphs of the equations in the system. There may be zero, one, or several solutions to a system of equations. For example, $(1.5, -3)$ is a solution to the system of linear equations at right; $x = 1.5$ and $y = -3$ makes both of the equations true. Also, $(1.5, -3)$ is a point of intersection of the graphs of these two equations.

$$y = 2x - 6$$
$$y = -2x$$

systematic list A list created by following a system (an orderly process).

tangent A line on the same flat surface as a circle that intersects the circle in exactly one point. A tangent of a circle is perpendicular to a radius of the circle at their point of intersection (also called the point of tangency).

tangent ratio In a right triangle, the tangent ratio of an acute $\angle A$ is $\tan A = \frac{\text{length of opposite side}}{\text{length of adjacent side}}$. In the triangle at right, $\tan A = \frac{BC}{AB} = \frac{3}{4}$. See also *cosine ratio, sine ratio,* and *inverse tangent.*

tetrahedron A polyhedron with four faces. The faces of a tetrahedron are triangles. In a regular tetrahedron, all of the faces are congruent equilateral triangles. Any of the faces of a tetrahedron can be considered the base.

theorem A conjecture that has been proven to be true. Some examples of theorems are the Pythagorean Theorem and the Triangle Angle Sum Theorem.

theoretical probability A calculated probability based on the possible outcomes when each outcome has the same chance of occurring: (number of successful outcomes)/(total number of possible outcomes).

theta (θ) A Greek letter that is often used to represent the measure of an angle. Other Greek letters used to represent the measure of an angle include alpha (α) and beta (β).

three-dimensional An the object that has length, width, and depth.

transformation This course studies four transformations: reflection, rotation, translation, and dilation. All of them preserve shape, and the first three preserve size. See each term for its particular definition.

translation A transformation that preserves the size, shape, and orientation of a figure while sliding (moving) it to a new location. The result is called the image of the original figure (preimage). Note that a translation is sometimes referred to as a "slide."

transversal   A line that intersects two or more other lines on a flat surface (plane). In this course, we often work with a transversal that intersects two parallel lines.

trapezoid   A quadrilateral with at least one pair of parallel sides.

tree diagram   A model used to organize the possible outcomes, and the respective probabilities, of two or more events. For an example of a tree diagram, see the Math Notes box *Probability Models* in Lesson 4.2.3.

triangle   A polygon with three sides.

Triangle Angle Sum Theorem   The sum of the measures of the interior angles in any triangle is 180°.

triangle congruence conditions   Conditions that use the minimum number of congruent corresponding parts to prove that two triangles are congruent. They are: SSS ≅, SAS ≅, AAS ≅, ASA ≅, and HL ≅.

Triangle Inequality   In a triangle with side lengths a, b, and c, c must be less than the sum of a and b and greater than the difference of a and b. In the example at right, a is greater than b (that is, $a > b$), so the possible values for c are all numbers such that $c > a - b$ and $c < a + b$.

Triangle Midsegment Theorem   The segment that connects the midpoints of any two sides of a triangle measures half the length of the third side is and parallel to that side.

triangle similarity conditions   Conditions that use the minimum number of congruent and/or proportional corresponding parts to prove that two triangles are similar. They are: SSS ~, SAS ~, and AA ~.

trigonometry   Literally, the "measure of triangles." In this course, this word is used to refer to the development of triangle tools such as trigonometric ratios (sine, cosine, and tangent) and the Laws of Sines and Cosines.

turn   See *rotation*.

two-column proof   A form of proof in which statements are written in one column as a list and the reasons for the statements are written next to them in a second column.

two-dimensional   A figure that that lies on a flat surface and that has length and width. See also *plane*.

two-way table   A way to display categorical two-variable data. The categories of one of the variables is the header of the rows, the other variable is the header of the columns. The entries in the table can be counts (frequencies) or percents (relative frequencies). See also *relative frequency table*.

union of two events   The union of the two events {A} and {B} is a new event that includes all the outcomes that either A will occur *or* B will occur. For example, if event {A} is the thirteen diamond-suited cards in a deck of playing cards, and {B} is the four Aces, then the event {A union B} contains 16 outcomes:
{all the diamonds (including the A♦), A♥, A♣, and A♠}. See also *intersection of two events*.

unit of measure   A standard quantity (such as a centimeter, second, square foot, or gallon) that is used to measure and describe an object. A single object can be measured using different units of measure, which will usually yield different results. For example, a pencil may be 80 mm long, meaning that it is 80 times as long as a unit of 1 mm. However, the same pencil is 8 cm long, so that it is the same length as 8 cm laid end-to-end. (This is because 1 cm is the same length as 10 mm.)

Venn diagram   A type of diagram used to classify objects. It is usually composed of two or more overlapping circles representing different conditions. An item is placed or represented in the Venn diagram in the appropriate position based on the conditions it meets. In the example of the Venn diagram at right, if an object meets one of two conditions, it is placed in region A or C but outside region B. If an object meets both conditions, it is placed in the intersection (B) of both circles. If an object does not meet either condition, it is placed outside of both circles (region D).

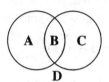

vertex (plural: vertices)   (a) For a two-dimensional geometric shape, a vertex is a point where two or more line segments or rays meet to form a "corner," such as in a polygon or angle. (b) For a three-dimensional polyhedron, a vertex is a point where the edges of the solid meet. See also *apex*. (c) On a graph, a vertex can be used to describe the highest or lowest point on the graph of a parabola or absolute value function (depending on the graph's orientation).

vertical angles   The two opposite (that is, non-adjacent) angles formed by two intersecting lines. "Vertical" is a relationship between pairs of angles, so one angle cannot be called vertical. Angles that form a vertical pair are always congruent.

volume   A measurement of the size of the three-dimensional region enclosed within an object. It is expressed as the number of $1 \times 1 \times 1$ unit cubes (or parts of cubes) that fit inside a solid.

x-intercept   A point where a graph crosses the *x*-axis. A graph may have several *x*-intercepts, no *x*-intercepts, or just one.

Core Connections Geometry

y-intercept   A point where a graph crosses the *y*-axis. A function has at most one *y*-intercept; a relation may have several.

Zero Product Property   The Zero Product Property states that when the product of two or more factors is zero, one of these factors must equal zero. That is, if $a \cdot b = 0$, then either $a = 0$ or $b = 0$ (or both). For example, if $(x + 4)(2x - 3) = 0$, then either $x + 4 = 0$ or $2x - 3 = 0$ (or both). The Zero Product Property can be used to solve factorable quadratic equations.

zoom factor   The amount each side of a figure is multiplied by when the figure is proportionally enlarged or reduced in size. It is written as the ratio of a length in the new figure (image) to a length in the original figure (preimage). For the triangles at right, the zoom factor is $\frac{8}{6}$ or $\frac{4}{3}$. See also *ratio of similarity*.

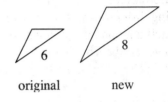

original   new

zero factorial   Zero factorial is 1, $0! = 1$.

Index
Student Version

Many of the pages referenced here contain a definition or an example of the topic listed, often within the body of a Math Notes box. Others contain problems that develop or demonstrate the topic. It may be necessary to read the text on several pages to fully understand the topic. Also, some problems listed here are good examples of the topic and may not offer any explanation. References to Math Notes boxes are bolded.

Dilation, 145, **148**
  creating with rubber bands, 145
  on a graph, 146
Dimensions, 107
  cubic units, **542**
  three, 403
  two, 403
Directrix, 743, 746
Disjoint, **610**
Distance, shortest, 407
Dual polyhedron, 675

E
Earth
  equator, 699
  great circle, 700
  hemisphere, 699
  latitude lines, 699
  longitude lines, 699, **700**
  prime meridian, 700
Edge, 403, 671
  lateral, **680**
Ellipse, **749**
Equation(s)
  of a circle, 731, 735
    general form, 738, **744**
    graphing form, **744**
  proportional, **158**
  quadratic, **238**
    Checkpoint 5A, 319
    graphing/vertex form, 735
    standard form, 735
  solving
    Checkpoint 1, 69
    linear, **21**
  writing linear
    Checkpoint 3, 197
Equator, 699
  great circle, 700
Equiangular, **416**
  polygon, **476**
Equilateral, **416**
  polygon, **476**
  triangle, 12, 24, **416**
Equivalent expressions, 118
Eratosthenes Remarkable Discovery, 586
Euler's Formula, 754, 755

Event, **31**, **255**
  complement, 251, 254, **255**
  disjoint, **610**
  independent, 225, **232**, 608, 621, **624**
    applications, 620
  intersection, 251, 253, **255**
  mutually exclusive, **610**
  union, 251, 252, **255**
Exact answer, **133**, 284, 296, 300
Expected value, 258, **304**
Experimental probability, **31**
Exploration, **11**
Exponential function, **426**
  Checkpoint 9B, 570
Expression, equivalent, 118
Exterior angle(s), 432, 477, 484
  sum of, **494**

F
Face, 403, 671
  lateral, 536, **537**, **680**
Facilitator, 5
Factorial, 630, **638**
  zero, 644, 650, **658**
Factoring, **238**
Fair game, **304**
Family Fortune, The, 191
Fibonnaci numbers, 762
Fibonnaci Spirals, 762
First term, **223**
Flip. *See* reflection
Flowchart, 173, **187**
  changing to a proof, 419
  congruence, 356
Focus, 743, 746
Focus-directrix graph paper, 746
Formula, quadratic, **238**
Function
  absolute value, 768
  exponential, **426**
    Checkpoint 9B, 570
Fundamental Principle of Counting, 627, 629, **631**

G
Generator, of a sequence, **223**
Game, fair, **304**
General form of a circle, 738, **744**

Rectangle, 6, **431**
  diagonals, **481**
  golden, 759
Rectangular prism, 540
Reflection, 28, 29, 35, **37**, **47**
  line of, 29, **37**, **47**
  of light, 93
  symmetry, 3, **6**, 54, 55
Reflexive Property of Equality, **421**
Regular
  decagon, **416**
  hexagon, 23, 54, 84, **416**
    constructing, 554
  octagon, **416**, 483
  pentagon, 25
  polygon, **52**, 414, **416**, **476**
    area, **506**
    central angle, 460
  polyhedron, 672
    dual, 675
Remote interior angles, 477
Repeated reasoning, 203, 465, 720
Resource Manager, 5
Reuleaux curves, 400
Rhombus, 84, **431**, **481**, **560**
  diagonals, **435**, **481**, **560**
  properties of, 423
Right
  angle, 24, **26**
  pyramid, 684
  trapezoid, 443
Right triangle, **128**
  hypotenuse, 126, **128**, 280
  leg, **128**
  Pythagorean Theorem, 131, 132, **133**
  Pythagorean Triple, 302, 303
  ratios, 211
  special, 296, **310**
    30°-60°-90°, 297
    45°-45°-90°, 297
Rigid transformation, **37**
  definitions, **47**
  reflection, **47**
  rotation, **47**
  to prove congruence, 352
  translation, **47**
Rock, Paper, Scissors, 246
Rotation, 34, 35, **37**, 45, **47**
  center of, **37**
  symmetry, 54, 56

S
Same-side interior angles, **100**
Sample space, **31**, 48, 234, 627
SAS~, **170**, **192**
SAS ≅, **358**
  proving, 352
Scale factor, **154**
Scalene triangle, 68
Secant, circle, 598, 709
Sector, 511, **512**
Segment, 46
Semicircle, 592
Sequence
  arithmetic
    Checkpoint 5B, 329
    equation, **223**
    first term form, **223**
  geometric
    Checkpoint 5B, 329
    equation, **223**
  term, first, **223**
Shapes
  congruent, **344**
  naming, **88**
Shape Bucket, The, 62
Shape Factory, The, 50, 127, 457
Shape Toolkit, 67
Shifty Shauna, 622
Similar figures, 146, 147, 150, **163**
  area, 13, 15, 497
  congruent, 152, **175**, **344**
  linear scale factor, **499**
  perimeter, 15
  proportional equation, **158**
  solids, 548
    volume of, 544
  triangles, 178
Similarity, 146, 147, 150
  AA~, **170**, **192**
  applications, 194
  conditions for, 166
  ratios of, 501, 548, **549**
  SAS~, **170**, **192**
  side length ratio, 152, **154**
  SSS~, **185**, **192**
  statement, **163**
  transformation, **163**
  triangle, 183
    conditions for, 189, **192**
  using ratio of, 156